S0-BNB-766

How your car works

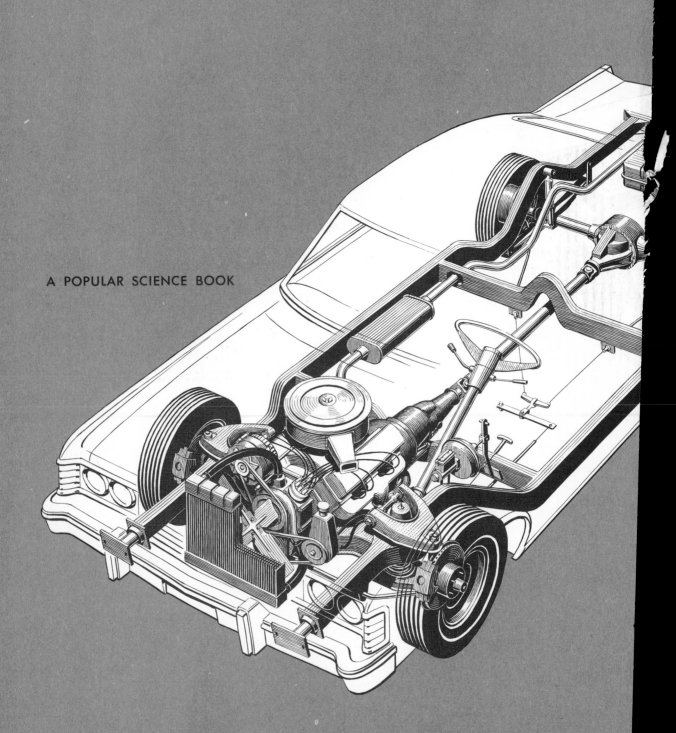

A POPULAR SCIENCE BOOK

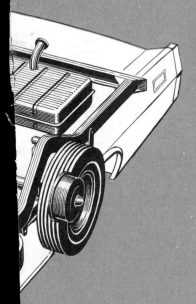

How your car works

by Sam Julty
Illustrated by Ray Pioch

POPULAR SCIENCE

HARPER & ROW
NEW YORK, EVANSTON, SAN FRANCISCO, LONDON

Library of Congress Catalog Number: 72-83028
SBN: 06-012224-2

Designed by Jeff Fitschen

Manufactured in the United States of America

CONTENTS

PREFACE

My training in auto-mechanic skills began several years after I finished high school. Not until I began to learn my new trade did I fully appreciate what they had tried to teach me back in those high school physics and chemistry classes. For me the car became the living proof and lucid example of the many laws, theorems, and formulas I had crammed into my head for end-term exams.

In school I had made the connection between the theoretical and the practical. So, as a mechanic, I was able to appreciate better the workings of the car, to understand why parts had to be designed a certain way, and to ponder how a design could be improved.

After many years as a practicing mechanic and some time as manager of a few large service shops, I left the "shop" to become a teacher of the trade. I used this opportunity to offer the theory/practice connection to my students. Class discussion, shop practice and exams always explored "why" something was happening in the car's mechanism as well as "what" was happening. This approach succeeded, and I look back at that stage of my career with pleasant memories.

The present-day automobile is a unique piece of machinery. Sitting there on its four wheels is a composite of most of what the scientific community has unearthed in the last 2,000 years. Yet, despite the fact that the automobile is so commonplace and has so affected our lives, the automobile is still a mystery to many of us and a frustration to those who want to know more about it. That is why my teacher's notes were among the many sources I used while writing this book. I hope that my use of the notes will succeed as well with you, the reader, as it has with my students.

Though this book is essentially about the workings of the automobile, there is a broader aspect I wish to share. My philosophy dictates that there is no such thing as "pure" study. Everything relates to something else. Studying how a car works relates to the ways cars affect us personally and socially, and this study also determines how we feel about cars. There is no question in my mind that the automobile has had some profound effects on our history—most of them good and some of them bad. It has given most of us individual transportation and a means of stretching our own horizons. No more are towns limited by their distance from rail lines. No more are people confined to local dirt roads and trails. The automobile has increased a mobility which has been an intrinsic part of our history from the very beginning. It strikes me as no coincidence that automotive production took an earnest turn at about the time the frontier closed in the early 1900s. The growth of the automotive industry has indeed reached a point where it now directly affects the lives of six out of every ten working people.

On the debit side, the unbridled growth of the number of automobiles has given us jammed downtown areas of cities. It has grossly affected the quality of the air in many of our major cities. It has been responsible for the endless paving of our countryside, the disruption of many communities and the razing of homes in the name of "better transportation." The automobile is now, with some justification, accused of putting a strain on what finite natural resources we have left. Clearly, I see as many profound changes occurring in this half-century as have already been wrought in the first half.

Which direction will these changes take? This is hard to say. My guess is that there will always be some means of personal transportation, more than likely with a more efficient power plant than the internal-combustion engine. I also feel that the most profound changes will first take place in the cities where the present chaos is a clear danger to life and commerce.

But what the future brings will have to be explained when it gets here. Now we have the car as we know it. And to know it better you have this book.

I feel particularly fortunate that this book includes the work of Ray Pioch who, as far as I am concerned, is the finest technical artist around. Without Pioch's illustrations, my text would have been shallow no matter how many ways I tried to explain something. Words of praise go also to Frank Schwarz, who assisted with finished renderings from Pioch sketches.

Of course, no writer can ever give birth to his best talent without the midwifery of an editor. My compliments to those who had the awesome and sometimes awful task of shaping this manuscript into its final form.

Finally, greetings to all my friends and contacts in the automotive service industry who shared their information, suggestions and reference sources.

Sam Julty
New York

How your car works

1
ENGINE

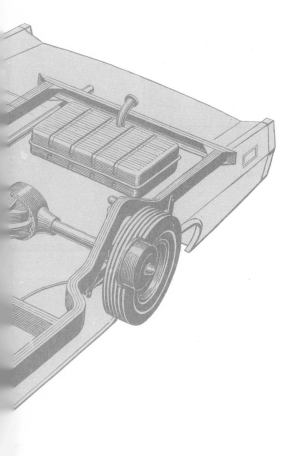

An engine is a source of power. Automobile and railroad engines turn wheels. Ship and airplane engines drive propellers. Crane engines operate pulleys. Lawn mower engines move cutters. The engine supplies energy to move the parts that do a job.

Where does the engine get the power it so freely gives away? Simply by unlocking and releasing power from yet another source—fuel. Therefore, to understand what an engine actually is, we must consider it a powerful conversion machine, a plant which changes chemical energy into mechanical energy—fuel into motion.

Fuel is for burning. And it is precisely through the process of combustion that the engine pries loose the hidden energy within the fuel. Just where the fuel is burned is a matter of engine design. One of the ways all engines are classified is by the location of the burning process. Combustion can take place outside the engine or inside the engine. The two main types of engines, then, are the *External Combus-*

1

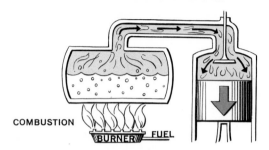

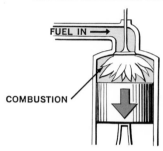

Two types of engines; two types of combustion. The piston in the engine at the left is driven by steam pressure—produced in a separate boiler, heated *outside* the engine. The piston at the right is driven by the expansion of air, produced by an explosion occurring *inside* the cylinder.

tion Engine (ECE) and the *Internal Combustion Engine* (ICE).

In the ECE the fuel is burned in a separate fire chamber, away from the active parts. The heat energy is then transmitted by some medium, usually steam pressure, to accomplish the work to be done. An excellent example of this type of engine is the steam locomotive.

The ICE has no outside fuel chamber. The fuel burns internally. The force of expansion created by the burned gases in a confined area is transformed into mechanical motion by the appropriately designed parts within the engine.

So far, this type of engine is still the standard power plant in automobiles (though its future is challenged at this point). Therefore, the ICE will be the engine receiving the fullest attention in this chapter.

THE INTERNAL COMBUSTION ENGINE

A wide variety of ICE engines are used in automobiles. Some have one cylinder, some four cylinders, some six or eight. In some the cylinders are in a straight line;

in others they are in the form of a V. Internal designs vary also, and these will be discussed later.

Despite the differences in design, all ICE engines function on the same principle. Therefore, if you understand the principle, you can recognize them all.

In order to get the proper perspective on how all the intricate parts are coordinated to produce a source of power for moving the car, we will quickly describe a typical V-8 engine, mentioning only the most basic parts and the role each plays. Later, we will explain each part in detail and show how it plays a role in providing power.

The *engine block* is the body of the engine. Basically, it is a large piece of iron or aluminum which is machined and bored with carefully drilled holes called *cylinders*. The size of each cylinder is carefully determined.

Bolted to the top of the engine block is the *cylinder head*. Its main function is to provide a lid for the cylinders. It has a hollowed-out area over each cylinder where the fuel is burned. This is called the *combustion chamber*. The cylinder head

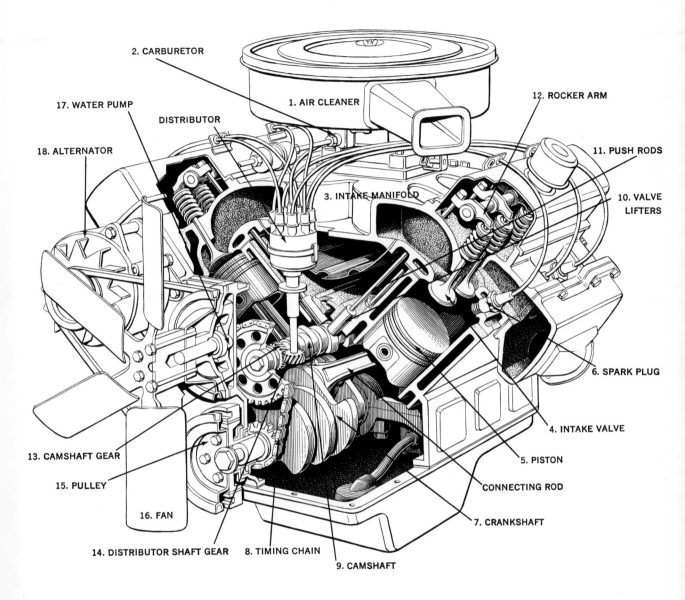

2. CARBURETOR

17. WATER PUMP

DISTRIBUTOR

1. AIR CLEANER

12. ROCKER ARM

18. ALTERNATOR

11. PUSH RODS

10. VALVE LIFTERS

3. INTAKE MANIFOLD

6. SPARK PLUG

4. INTAKE VALVE

5. PISTON

CONNECTING ROD

13. CAMSHAFT GEAR

15. PULLEY

7. CRANKSHAFT

16. FAN

14. DISTRIBUTOR SHAFT GEAR

8. TIMING CHAIN

9. CAMSHAFT

V-8 engine. Air enters cleaner (1), mixes with fuel in carburetor (2) and is drawn into cylinder via intake manifold (3). Intake valve (4) admits mixture when piston (5) goes down. On piston upstroke, valve closes, trapping mixture for compression. Spark plug (6) ignites mixture, forcing piston down. This turns crankshaft (7) which, through gears, eventually turns rear wheels. Crankshaft also has timing chain (8) that links crankshaft to camshaft (9). The turning camshaft activates valve lifters (10) and push rods (11) which are linked to valves via rocker arms (12). Camshaft gear (13) meshes with distributor shaft gear (14), causing distributor points to open and close. This rotates spark to each cylinder. Finally, belt at crankshaft pulley (15) operates fan (16), water pump (17), alternator (18) and other accessories.

3

has a threaded hole for installing the spark plug.

The *crankshaft* is the "backbone" of the engine. This is the component which turns as a result of the activity of all other components in the energy-conversion process.

Attached to each crank on the shaft is a short, rigid beam called the *connecting rod*. It serves as a link between the crankshaft and the *piston*.

The piston is a plunger which moves up and down in the cylinder to effect the combustion process. It resembles an inverted drinking glass with two holes in its side. The piston fits over the upper end of the connecting rod in such a manner that the piston holes line up with the hole in the rod. A steel tube, called the *piston pin* goes through all three holes and locks the two components together.

The other basic components get the fuel into the combustion chamber and discharge the spent exhaust gases. Each cylinder has a pair of valves. The *intake valve* allows the air-fuel mixture in; the *exhaust valve* allows exhaust gases out. The top of each valve is machined to fit snugly into a matching hole, either in the cylinder head or the engine block. The holes, called ports, are the ends of the line for two passageways. One comes from the base of the carburetor and is called the *intake manifold*. The other leads to the exhaust pipe and is called the *exhaust manifold*.

If we add a carburetor for fuel and an ignition system for spark, we have all the makings for a functioning engine.

The Cycle. To create power for any length of time an engine must accomplish a strict

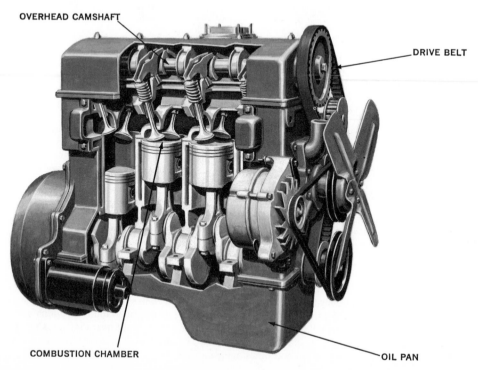

OVERHEAD CAMSHAFT

DRIVE BELT

COMBUSTION CHAMBER

OIL PAN

Inside view of an in-line 4-cylinder engine. In this Chevrolet Vega, the camshaft is on top. Hence, such an engine is called an overhead camshaft engine, or OHC.

order of events over and over again. This sequence of events is called a cycle. Engines are also classified by the number of events in each cycle. The present-day automobile is equipped with a four-stroke cycle engine, though there have been cars with two-stroke engines. Two-stroke en-

the bottom, the turning crank forces the piston upward. Both valves are now closed. Accumulated fuel and air have no place to go. The farther the piston rises in the cylinder, the greater is the compression of the mixture stuffed into the small combustion chamber.

INTAKE VALVE OPEN   **BOTH VALVES CLOSED**   **EXHAUST VALVE OPEN**

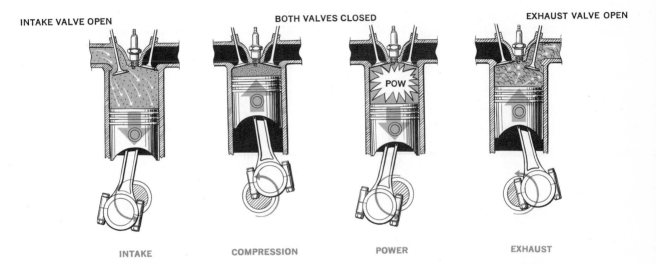

INTAKE   COMPRESSION   POWER   EXHAUST

The 4-stroke Otto cycle repeated in each cylinder. In this typical automotive engine, the cycle never occurs simultaneously in any two or more cylinders. Rather, the cycles are staggered to produce a smooth flow of power strokes. Naturally, the more pistons the engine has, the closer the time space between power strokes, and the smoother the operation.

gines are still used on many motorcycles, outboard motors and lawnmower motors.

The four-stroke engine is designed for a process called the Otto cycle, named after the German engineer who developed it, Nikolaus August Otto (1832–1891). The four strokes are called Intake, Compression, Power, and Exhaust.

Intake. The downward movement of the piston creates a very strong vacuum in the cylinder. The intake valve opens and permits fuel and air to be sucked into the cylinder from the intake manifold.

Compression. When the piston reaches

Power. When the piston just about reaches the top of the cylinder, all the fuel-air mixture is tightly compressed. The spark plug provides the final ingredient for an explosion. Then—blast! The piston is sent down with force, pushing on the connecting rod and crank, and rotating the crankshaft.

It is worthwhile to pause here to examine the nature of an explosion. An explosion is nothing more than rapid combustion, a first cousin of the bonfire. The only difference between the two is speed of combustion. The bonfire consumes fuel rather slowly; the explosion consumes it rapidly. The bonfire releases and expands the gases in the fuel in an almost imperceptible manner. The explosion heats and expands the gases with a great deal of force. The boom that is associated with explosion is actually air filling the void that is created by a sudden and rapid expansion of the burning fuel.

Exhaust. This is the final stroke in the cycle. Through the force of the explosion,

the piston is sent all the way down; the crank is brought around and the piston is forced upward. At this point, the exhaust valve opens and the spent gases are forced through the exhaust ports into the exhaust manifold and out through the muffler.

When the piston reaches the top, the cylinder is fully cleared, and the intake valve is already open. Then the piston starts downward, creating a suction. Thus another cycle begins with the intake stroke.

HOW ENGINES ARE CLASSIFIED

Though all four-stroke cycle engines work as just above described, and all internal-combustion engines have the basic makeup such as crankshaft, pistons, cylinder, etc., they are not always similarly designed. Throughout automotive history, engineers have varied the placement of these parts in the engine and have experimented with different fuels, cooling systems, and valve arrangements. Hence, automobile engines are classified in a number of different ways. It has already been established that the modern automobile is driven by an internal-combustion engine. There are at least a half-dozen more ways an engine is classified.

Cylinder Number. An auto engine can have any number of cylinders. Before 1900 one cylinder was quite common. After that the 4-cylinder engine became quite popular; then the 6. Now the 8-cylinder engine is dominant. There were 12- and 16-cylinder engines in 1930 Cadillacs.

Cylinder Arrangements. How the cylinders line up also varies. In the early engines the cylinders were strictly in-line. American

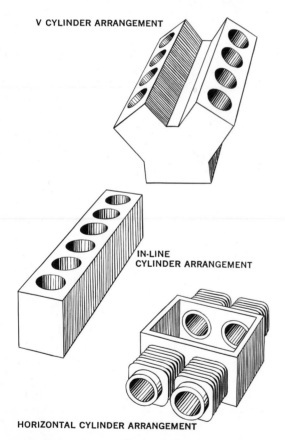

V CYLINDER ARRANGEMENT

IN-LINE CYLINDER ARRANGEMENT

HORIZONTAL CYLINDER ARRANGEMENT

Typical engine configurations. The V and the in-line are familiar. The horizontal, or "pancake" design, is found on Volkswagens and on Corvairs, no longer produced.

cars have appeared as in-line 4s, 6s, 8s, 12s, even slanted 6s. Another type is the V-engine in which the cylinders are arranged in two banks, usually at 90 degrees to each other. These may have any even number of cylinders—V-4, V-6, V-8, or V-12. The main advantage of this design is that the engine is much shorter than an in-line with the same number of cylinders. This allows less flexing of the crankshaft and cylinder block, thus a capability of higher running speeds and higher power output.

The rotary engine has found its greatest application in aircraft. It has appeared on only one car—the 1906 Adams-Farwell. This engine has all the cylinders radiating from a common center, like the spokes of a wheel. All connecting rods are attached to a common crank. The Wankel engine, which first appeared on 1959 NSU (German) cars and is now installed in the Mazda, is also a rotary engine, but not a piston type.

Another engine shape, made famous by Volkswagen, is the so-called "pancake engine." Here the cylinders are horizontally opposed. This pancake engine is very much like a V-engine except that the pancake is flattened. The pistons move horizontally; the crankshaft is in the middle. The Corvair was the last U.S. car with such an engine, but it was not the first. The White Truck Company introduced a pancake 12-cylinder engine for buses and trucks in 1933.

Valve Arrangements. Engineers have a few choices as to where to place the valves. They can be arranged in a number of positions in the cylinder head or in the engine block. According to the designer's reckoning, each configuration is supposed to resemble a capital letter, thus certain arrangements are termed L-head engines, I-head, and F-head.

The L-head has all the valves lined up in a row in the engine block. Each intake and exhaust valve, along with a piston, represents a complete unit. The L is a rugged and dependable design. However, the space requirement for the upward opening of the valve limits size of the combustion chamber. This is a drawback, since engineers are forever dreaming of ways to reduce the size of the chamber in order to further compress the fuel-air mixture for more power.

The I-head is extremely popular today. Here, all the valves are located in the cylinder head; hence its popular name, overhead valve engine, or OHV. Since the valves are "upside-down" as compared with the L-head engine, they move downward to open. In the in-line engine, such as a typical overhead-valve 6 cylinder, the valves are arranged in a single row. In a V-8 the valves can be either in a single row on each bank or in a double row on each bank.

The F-head is no longer very popular. It is a combination of the L-head and I-head, since the intake valves are in the cylinder head and the exhaust valves are in the cylinder block.

Cooling Classification. Another way of characterizing an engine is by the method used for cooling. This is covered in depth in Chapter 5. However, as a reminder, there are two types of cooling systems: air and water. In the air-cooled engine, each cylinder barrel is separately exposed to the outside air, metal fins helping to dispose of engine heat by radiation. The Volkswagen and Corvair are contemporary examples of

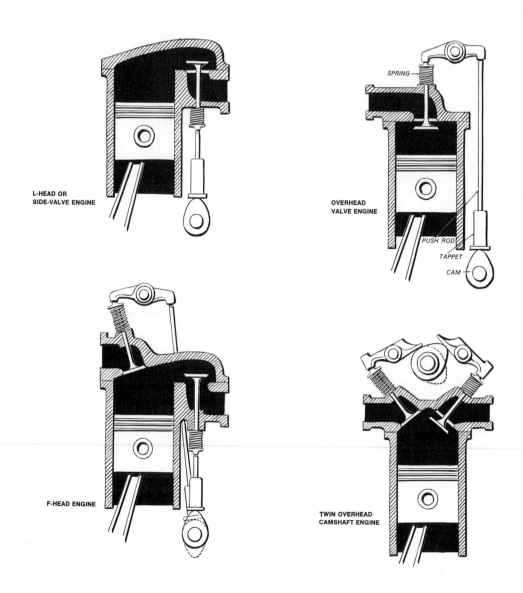

L-HEAD OR
SIDE-VALVE ENGINE

OVERHEAD
VALVE ENGINE

SPRING

PUSH ROD

TAPPET

CAM

F-HEAD ENGINE

TWIN OVERHEAD
CAMSHAFT ENGINE

VALVE ARRANGEMENTS OF OTTO ENGINES

this type of cooling, though a number of models have used it in the past. The other, more popular method of engine cooling uses a medium such as water mixed with antifreeze. The coolant circulates through passageways, picking up heat and disposing it to the outside via the radiator.

Cycle Rating. As described, the Otto cycle consists of four strokes. But this is not the only way for an engine to operate. There is also an engine with a two-stroke cycle. It works by combining the intake with the compression stroke, and the power with the exhaust stroke. Thus a power stroke is furnished with every crankshaft revolution, rather than with every two turns as in the four-stroke. Since the last American car to have the two-stroke engine was the 1906 Oldsmobile, the two-stroke hardly occupies any position of importance. The Saab (Swedish) did have a 3-cylinder, two-stroke engine in the U.S. market until 1970, but because this is a particularly "dirty" engine in terms of air pollution, it will probably drop to obscurity as a source of power for automobiles. However, the two-stroke engine is still quite popular on motorcycles and nonvehicular equipment.

Fuel Usage. The final designation given to engines concerns the type of fuel used. Most cars use gasoline. Some makes, like certain models of Mercedes Benz, use diesel fuel. There are even limited-use vehicles which employ liquified petroleum gas (LPG).

If anyone asks you to describe your particular engine, you might simply say: "It's an 8-cylinder, V-type, overhead-valve, water-cooled, four-stroke cycle, gasoline-burning, internal-combustion engine."

Now that you have a basic understand-

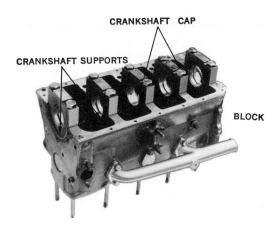

A stripped engine block upside down. Note the five crankshaft supports.

ing of the engine and the various ways it is classified, let us examine the various parts and see how they contribute to the functioning of the whole.

THE ENGINE BLOCK

The engine block is the torso, the foundation for all parts of the engine and for parts serving other systems necessary for engine operation. Its name is apt for it is indeed a large, heavy block of metal. In most cases the block is made of cast iron mixed with nickel or molybdenum for strength. Sometimes the block is made of aluminum.

From the outside, the block appears fairly simple. However, beneath its surface is a sophisticated combination of passageways and openings. The main feature of the block is the cylinders. Surrounding them are the continuous water jackets used to circulate the coolant for carrying off engine heat. Also inside the block are many oil passages for lubricating the crankshaft. The lower section of the block is somewhat flared out to make room for the revolving crankshaft. Part of the casting also contains the supports for holding the crankshaft. This section is the crankcase.

To make an engine block, with its maze of avenues and openings, a casting method is used. First, a sand mold is made. It is formed as a "negative." All areas that must end up as metal are left hollow. All areas that must end up hollow are shaped with a special sand. With the mold formed, molten metal is poured into it.

A variation of this process is to inject the metal into an enclosed mold under pressure. The latter method is favored because there is less chance for air bubbles to be trapped inside the metal after it has cooled.

When the metal turns to a solid, the sand is removed from openings in the block, called *core holes.* The block is washed and the machining process begins. The core holes are plugged and can be seen at the sides of the engine. A number of holes are tapped into the block and many surfaces are machined to accept the attaching parts. Most important is the milling, or planing, of the top of the block. This is the mating surface for the cylinder head.

Of course, the most important holes in the block are the cylinders. These are the homes of the pistons. It is in the cylinder where most of the action of engine operation takes place. The cylinders are given careful treatment during the machining process. The final step is honing them with fine stones to make them perfectly round and straight. A difference of .0005 inch between the diameter at the top and at the bottom of the cylinder is considered a normal tolerance. In addition, the surface of the cylinder must be polished and smooth to reduce friction of the moving piston to a bare minimum. When the cylinder bore is part of the cast, the method of manufacture is called *enbloc.*

There are certain instances when the cylinder is *not* a part of the block casting. This occurs when the engine design calls for a cylinder to be of another material than the engine block. In these cases a special sleeve is used. This is a machined cylinder which is installed in special cutouts in the engine block. These sleeves are replaceable when wear takes its toll. For this reason they are often found in truck engines where the block is made of cast iron while the sleeve is made of steel. Until recently, iron sleeves were required in aluminum blocks. A new process which includes the adding of silicone to the aluminum makes this practice unnecessary. The process gives the light aluminum the hardness necessary for piston operation and avoids adding weight to the engine. The first production car to use this type of engine was the 1970 Chevrolet Vega.

Two types of sleeves are used in engine blocks. One is called a *dry sleeve.* Here the cutout in the block is a solid hole. The sleeve is driven into the hole and completely surrounded and supported by the block over its full length. The other type is the *wet sleeve.* Here the cutout in the block exposes the water passageways. The coolant can then contact the side of the sleeve. In this case the sleeve is contacting the block only at the top and at the bottom. The sleeve metal must be thicker for wet sleeves than for dry sleeves.

There are a number of ways the sleeve is held to its assigned spot in the block. Where a rugged steel or cast-iron sleeve is used in an aluminum block, the sleeve is installed just prior to the pouring of the molten metal. Thus the sleeve is cast in place. Another method is the use of friction to hold the sleeve. That is, the hole in the block is of such a size that driving the sleeve in under pressure is enough to hold it there. Holding power is not always reliable here. A more dependable method is to make the sleeve with a large flange at the top. The sleeve fits easily into the block cavity, but is held in place by the cylinder head clamping down on the flange.

CYLINDER HEAD

Acting as a cover for the cylinders and as a lid for the combustion chambers is the cylinder head. It is usually made of the same material as the block, but not always. Many cars have engines which have cast-iron blocks and aluminum heads. Some engineers are partial to aluminum heads because the metal is a good heat conductor and is less likely to harbor hot spots.

Requirements for a cylinder head include that it be rugged and inflexible. The movements of the pistons, coming up on the compression stroke and going down on the power stroke, imposes a heavy pressure on the cylinder head; thus it is rugged and is held to the block by many large bolts.

Another essential feature of the head is that one of its surfaces must be machined to near-perfect flatness. This surface must match the planed surface of the engine block. When the two are joined, with a gasket in between, the combustion chamber is absolutely sealed—at least at the top. (There will be more on gaskets later in this chapter.)

The cylinder head is almost as complex as the block. It, too, has internal passageways for the flow of coolant. These avenues must match up with those of the block when the head is installed. In the case of the V-8, I-head engine, the head

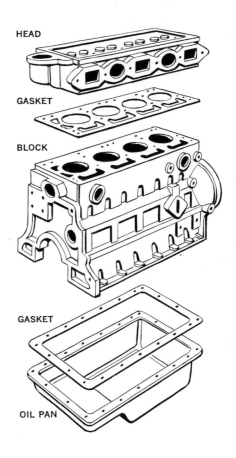

HEAD

GASKET

BLOCK

GASKET

OIL PAN

An engine block and mating parts.

must also contain the supports for the valve-operating mechanism, the valve ports and the valves themselves. The head must also have a machined and threaded hole at each cylinder to accept the spark plugs.

All of these jobs have been imposed on the cylinder head, a large slab of metal which still has as its major responsibility the sealing of the cylinders.

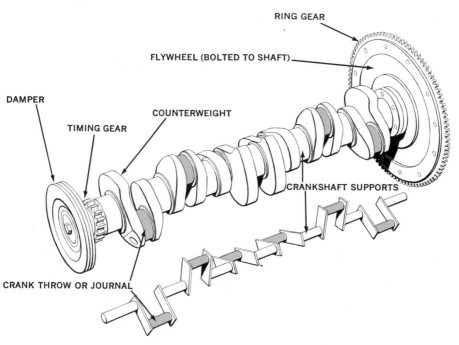

RING GEAR

FLYWHEEL (BOLTED TO SHAFT)

DAMPER

COUNTERWEIGHT

TIMING GEAR

CRANKSHAFT SUPPORTS

CRANK THROW OR JOURNAL

A 6-cylinder crankshaft with flywheel and damper. The shaft rotates on its supports. The crank throws, or journals, rotate in a wider arc. The piston connecting rods are attached to the journals. Thus, owing to the journals, rotary motion of the crankshaft is converted to up-and-down (reciprocating) motion of the rods.

THE OIL PAN

If the cylinder block could be called the house and the cylinder head the roof, then the oil pan could be called the basement.

The oil pan is a large tub made of thin steel which is stamped to conform to the shape of the underside of the engine block. It is often misnamed the crankcase, which is actually the lower part of the block enclosing the crankshaft. To be perfectly accurate, we should call the oil pan the lower crankcase.

The pan is secured to the engine block with small cap screws. The large bulge at the bottom of the pan is called the *sump*. It contains a supply of oil which is used by the oil pump to get lubrication to the vital engine parts. To keep the oil from splashing while the car is in motion the pan has one or more baffles on the inside. Oil is drained from the sump by removing a large threaded plug on the underside of the pan.

The framework is complete. Now it is time to examine the important moving parts which make the engine work.

THE CRANKSHAFT

As mentioned before, the crankshaft is the receiver of power generated by the other parts above it. In return, it supplies a constant turning force to such components as the transmission drive shaft and the rear wheels. Though the pistons and connecting rods go up and down, the motion of the crankshaft connected to them is rotary. This is made possible by the offsets called *crank throws.*

To get a clear idea of the throws, imagine a carpenter's brace and bit. The drill bit and the knob are on a centerline. The handle section must be turned around the centerline for the bit to turn.

The shaft at the centerline is called a support. Where it offsets, it is called a crank throw or a journal. With the exception of V-8 engines, there are as many throws as there are cylinders. In the case of V-8s, there are usually half as many throws, since two connecting rods share the same journal. Thus a shorter crankshaft is necessary. The supports are not confined to the front and rear of the shaft, but in-between as well. Many engines have five support points, others have three.

The shaft is made of a one-piece heat-treated alloy steel which is either cast or forged. It must be very strong to withstand the downward thrusts of the piston, which often reaches a force of 4,000 pounds for each power stroke. Distortion must be minimal.

Despite the terrific pounding, the shaft must be balanced so that it can turn at all speeds without vibration. Balancing is the function of the counterweights, which are part of the casting. Counterweights are so called because they have the job of countering the off-center weight imposed by the crank throws. A close examination of the counterweights of any shaft will reveal some oddly placed blind holes. These are drilled at the factory to achieve a correct balance. Precision is so important in the balancing process that the removal of a

half-ounce of metal from a 40-pound shaft can make the difference between a shaft that will perform properly and one that will vibrate to a breaking point.

Another feature of crankshaft design is that the bearings (to be discussed later in this chapter) receive constant lubrication by way of the oil passageways drilled into the shaft. These are called *oil galleries* and lead from each of the supports to the surrounding throws. Oil is fed to the supports via the oil pump and is routed to the throws via the galleries. Therefore, what appears to be a solid shaft is really a shaft that is rifled with holes for lubrication.

The Flywheel. Energy is supplied by the shaft only during the power stroke. This means that a 6-cylinder engine will deliver six power blows in one full cycle (two crankshaft turns). On an 8-cylinder engine, eight power thrusts are delivered in one cycle. Even if the engine is a 16-cylinder plant, the power delivered to the shaft is still a series of separate and distinctly individual efforts. These pulsations of power could easily cause the crankshaft to "stutter."

To avoid this, the crankshaft is fitted with a flywheel at the rear flange. It is made of thick cast iron and is very heavy. The weight of the flywheel keeps the crankshaft rotating smoothly at a constant speed. Since the flywheel is so heavy, it tends to slow down the shaft just a bit when the power impulse hits. Then, in between the pulses, when the crankshaft has no power delivered to it, the flywheel carries the shaft around. The ultimate effect is that the flywheel aids the shaft to turn at a constant speed. The lag between power pulses is minute and is hardly detected when the engine idles. However, not having a flywheel can have a marked effect on engine performance when the shaft spins at two or three thousand revolutions per minute.

Besides keeping the crankshaft revolutions at an even pace, the flywheel has two other functions. Welded or force-fitted to its outer rim is a ring of teeth. This is called the *ring gear*. This gear is engaged by the starter motor pinion gear when the starter circuit is activated. When the starter pinion turns, it turns the ring gear, causing the flywheel to turn. This of course turns the crankshaft, making the pistons go up and down. The direction of power flow is then reversed when the combustion process begins above the piston.

Another function of the flywheel is to provide a base for the clutch. This is explained in greater detail in Chapter 7.

The front section of the crankshaft contains a gear which helps to synchronize the opening and closing of the valves, by operating the camshaft.

Vibration Damper. The crankshaft also has a device called by such names as a *vibration damper, harmonic balancer,* or *torsional balancer.* Its purpose is to prevent a phenomenon known as torsional vibration, caused by the shaft's turning at high speed.

The vibration damper does what the name says; it dampens or softens the twisting effects. There are a number of designs in use. However, the most popular involves a small, heavy metal disc, a mini-flywheel, which is secured to a somewhat lighter steel flange pressed on the crankshaft. It is important to point out that the heavy disc is not attached to the shaft. Its only link to the steel flange is by rubber plugs with rivets through them.

As the crankshaft (and the steel flange)

twists, it imparts the twisting action to the heavy disc. But since the rubber plugs are interposed, much of the twisting energy is dissipated by the slight twisting of the rubber. Now, when the firing pressure is removed, the shaft cannot snap back. The

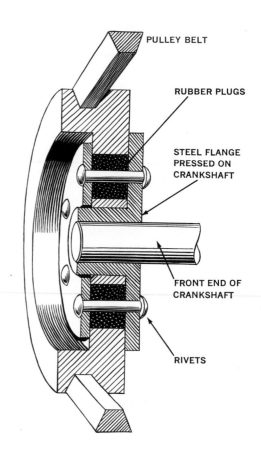

PULLEY BELT

RUBBER PLUGS

STEEL FLANGE PRESSED ON CRANKSHAFT

FRONT END OF CRANKSHAFT

RIVETS

The vibration damper. Located in the front of the crankshaft, this heavy pulley is mounted on rubber plugs which absorb the twisting energy of acceleration and deceleration.

twisted rubber plugs have enough energy stored in them and tend to keep the shaft turning. Thus the twisting action is softened, and the possibility of vibration is thwarted. Understandably, with a short shaft, as found on a V-8, the problem of torsional vibration is less serious than with a longer one. Often a vibration damper isn't even used.

The foremost attachment to the shaft is the pulley which drives a variety of belts. The most common power taps are for driving the alternator, power steering pump, water pump/radiator fan, airconditioning compressor and, in some cases, emission-control air pumps.

The crankshaft, then, performs several important tasks. It reroutes energy from the up-and-down motion of the pistons into a rotary motion. It provides the power for the turning of the rear wheels. It provides the power for driving auxiliary systems. It also responds to energy from the starter motor for getting the engine going. In doing all these jobs the shaft is expected to work smoothly without excessive vibrations. Is it any wonder that the crankshaft is often called the most important part of the engine?

THE PISTON ASSEMBLY

The piston assembly is also a receiver of power, but it is much closer to the source. A sliding plunger within the cylinder, it responds to the explosions of the fuel-air mixture and transfers that energy to the crankshaft. However, the power stroke is not the only instance when the piston is working. It also plays an important role in the entire combustion process, during all the strokes of the cycle.

On the intake stroke, the piston helps

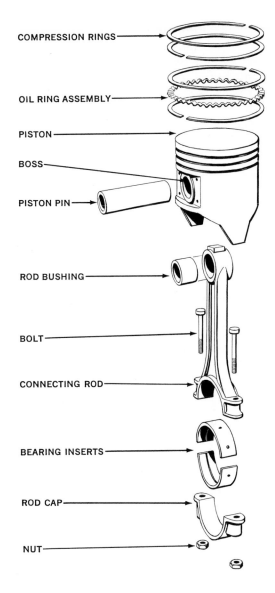

COMPRESSION RINGS

OIL RING ASSEMBLY

PISTON

BOSS

PISTON PIN

ROD BUSHING

BOLT

CONNECTING ROD

BEARING INSERTS

ROD CAP

NUT

A typical engine piston. A heavy pin is fitted through the pin boss and through a connecting rod (not shown).

create a vacuum to draw fuel and air into the cylinder. On the compression stroke, it squeezes the mixture into the small combustion chamber. On the power stroke, the piston is the first moving part which responds to the energy released by the explosion. On the exhaust stroke, the piston actually shoves the spent gases out of the cylinder.

Though the piston is one solid piece of metal, its various areas have specific names. The top of the piston is the *head.* This is the portion which responds to the blasts of the combustion process. About one-third of the way down the sides of the piston are two holes. These accept a steel pin which links the piston to the connecting rod. Between the head and the pin holes are a series of grooves cut into the piston body which hold the piston rings. The lower part of the piston is called the *skirt.*

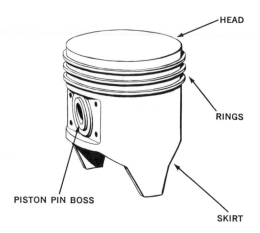

Piston and connecting rod assembly.
The rings fit in slots around the pistons. The lower end of the connecting rod attaches to the crankshaft journal and is held by the rod cap. Bearing inserts fit between the rod and the cap.

In moving up and down inside the cylinder, the piston comes to a complete stop each time it reaches the limit of its travel. To counter inertial forces, the piston is therefore made as light as possible. The ideal metal is aluminum. Cast iron is sometimes used in slow-speed engines, but is considered too heavy for the modern automobile engine. Aluminum machines better and conducts heat more readily. The aluminum is often anodized by electrically oxidizing the metal to give it a hard protective coat of aluminum oxide. Some pistons are also given a thin coat of tin, which is supposed to rub off on the cylinder walls and speed engine break-in.

One of the big problems for engineers is to keep the piston fitting tightly in the cylinder throughout the wide temperature range produced by its movement—550 degrees at the head and 275 degrees at the bottom of the skirt. When the engine is cold, a piston that is too loose will tilt from side to side as it goes up and down. This phenomenon is called "piston slap"— a condition which cannot be tolerated for long without wearing down the piston and the cylinder walls. A close fit when the engine is cold leads to problems when the engine gets hot—specifically, the risk of the piston jamming inside the cylinder due to heat expansion.

A number of solutions have been devised to counter these problems. One is to put a cut or a T-slot in the piston skirt. As the engine heats up, the cut or slot takes up the expansion and over-all piston size is barely affected. Another, and more popular solution, is to grind the piston so it is slightly egg-shaped, rather than fully round. Cam grinding, as this is called, makes the piston somewhat narrower at the non-thrust sides of the piston. The

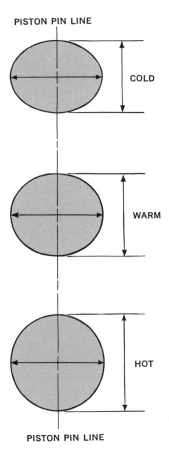

PISTON PIN LINE

COLD

WARM

HOT

PISTON PIN LINE

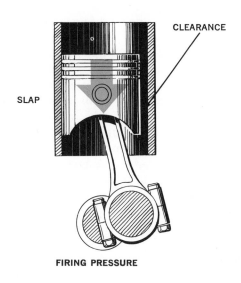

CLEARANCE

SLAP

FIRING PRESSURE

Piston configuration changes with temperature. When the engine is cold, the piston is oval shaped. Gradually, the piston becomes round as it gets hot. The oval shape is exaggerated here for emphasis.

egg-shaped condition prevails only until the engine warms up. Then heat expansion causes the piston to assume a more fully rounded shape.

Another trick employed by engineers to deal with expansion is to make the head of the piston smaller in diameter than the

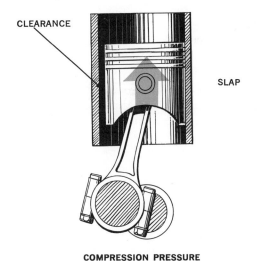

CLEARANCE

SLAP

COMPRESSION PRESSURE

Loose piston fit that causes slapping. Note the clearance between the piston and the cylinder wall, exaggerated for emphasis.

17

skirt. For reasons soon to be explained, the head of the piston cannot be cam-ground, but must be a perfect circle. However, since the head is the hottest part of the piston when the engine is operating, it will expand the most. Therefore, by making the head 30 to 40 thousandths of an inch smaller (.030–.040), expansion is tolerable.

One more modification of piston design is worth mentioning. This is the partial skirt design, produced by cutting away piston material at the non-thrust sides. Advantages include a further lightening of piston weight without sacrificing strength. In addition, it allows the piston to extend deeply into the cylinder without the possibility of striking the crankshaft. The cutaway piston is known as a *slipper.* If it is not cut away at the skirt the piston is called a *full trunk.*

Designers have also given attention to the shape of the piston head. In accordance with the principle that the greater the compression of the air-fuel mixture, the greater will be the explosion, the configuration of the piston head has been modified from the traditional flat top to a dome. An array of irregular shapes is used to assist in swirling the gases to produce more complete combustion. Some piston heads have a notched top to make room for the valves in an I-head engine. A wedge top is also used to achieve higher compression.

Piston Rings. The force with which the explosion drives the piston down depends on how well the cylinder is sealed. Given a great deal of space between the piston and the cylinder wall, most of the energy of the blast will be lost. It would be like trying to fire a rifle bullet from a cannon.

If the area between the piston and the cylinder wall is totally sealed, the full effect of the explosion is then concentrated on the moving piston.

Actually, it is impossible to make a piston that will totally seal the cylinder and yet be free enough to move up and down. You can prove this yourself by examining a simple football pump. The plunger is made of metal, as is the cylinder. If the disc at the end of the plunger was carefully machined to be airtight against the cylinder, it would be almost impossible to work it up and down. Instead, a strip of leather or plastic is used as a seal. Since the softer material is flexible, it can contact the cylinder walls tightly, yet allow free movement of the plunger.

The piston in the internal-combustion engine cannot use leather or plastic because of the tremendous heat generated during engine operation. Instead, rings made of cast iron plated with chromium or molybdenum are fitted to the piston. Each ring is a split circle which is compressed when the piston is installed in the cylinder and expands against the cylinder wall to provide a good seal.

In addition to making the cylinder airtight, the rings have two other functions: (1) they assist in conducting heat from the piston to the cylinder walls, where it can be carried off by the coolant in the water jackets; (2) they control lubrication on the cylinder walls.

Piston rings are classified as either *compression* or *oil-regulating* rings. Some engines are designed so that the piston has two of each type. Other, more modern engines have two compression rings and only one oil-regulating ring. As a rule, all rings are located above the piston pin.

Sometimes one oil ring is located at the very bottom of the piston skirt.

Compression rings are always the first two rings from the top of the piston. The face of the ring, that part which contacts the cylinder wall, has a variety of configurations to create a stress in the ring. The most popular is the simple bevel. On the upstrokes, the ring tilts and can glide over a thin film of oil on the walls. On the

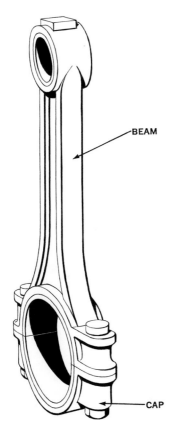

A piston connecting rod. The upper opening accepts the pin to secure it to the piston. The lower opening wraps around the journal of the crankshaft.

downstrokes, the bevel acts as a scraper to accumulate the oil and, more importantly, to help seal the cylinder.

The oil-regulating ring has the job of scraping the excess oil from the cylinder walls. The ring is not a solid band but has a series of slots. The ring groove in the piston is also punctuated with a series of holes. The oil that escapes the scraping action enters the ring slots and ring-groove holes and drips down the inside of the piston skirt into the oil pan.

Wear of the rings and the cylinder is inevitable. In time, compression and exhaust gases will get through from the combustion chamber to the crankcase. This condition is called blow-by. Only a resurfacing of the cylinder walls and replacement of the oil rings can cure this condition.

Connecting Rods. The important link which ties piston movement to crankshaft movement is the connecting rod. It is made of strong alloy steel which is forged to an I-beam shape, then machined. In the top of the rod there is a hole through which the piston pin is inserted to connect the piston and rod. The piston pin, otherwise known as the *wrist pin,* is hollow in order to keep weight to a minimum.

The lower end of the rod is a split circle. When the two parts of the circle are separated, they can be wrapped around one of the crank throws and held together with nuts and bolts. As the crankshaft turns on its supports, the crank throws are actually spinning inside the connecting rods as they make their revolutions.

The final feature of connecting-rod design is the provision made for lubrication at the points of friction. In the beam of the

Pistons, pins, rods, crankshaft and bearings.

THE VALVES

A broad definition of a valve is that it is a device to control the flow of a liquid or a gas. Though automotive engine valves have the same function, their shape is not exactly what you might find at the kitchen sink. Engine valves look like long-stemmed mushrooms. Each valve is a one-piece unit made of special alloy steel to resist heat. The head of the valve is at right angles to the stem, but the face is at a 45-degree angle. Some engineers prefer 30 degrees, but the figure is unimportant.

Camshaft, valves and valve springs.

rod is a hollow passageway. One end is at the bottom of the rod, at the upper half of the big circle; the other is at the hole which accepts the piston pin. With this arrangement, engine oil can travel from the crank journal up the rod and keep the pin well lubricated.

Most of the engine is now put together. The block holds the crankshaft, which is driven by the pistons with the connecting rods serving as the link between the two. It is now necessary to consider the mechanism which sets up the combustion process so that these heavy parts can do their assigned job.

It is the angled face that is vital in allowing the valve to seal properly.

Every cylinder of a 4-stroke engine must have an *intake valve* and an *exhaust valve*, at least one each. Some engines of the past had two each at every cylinder. The intake valve allows the entry of the air-fuel mixture into the cylinder; the exhaust valve allows the spent gases to escape from the cylinder.

Every valve is fitted so that the angled face fits into a similarly angled seat. The seat is a carefully machined rim of an opening in the engine block or cylinder head. The opening is called the *valve port*. The port is a vestibule serving the chambers which feed fuel mixture or carry away exhaust gases. The former is called the *intake manifold;* the latter, the *exhaust manifold.*

Just as no kitchen faucet is doing its job if it drips, no automotive valve is effective if it leaks. Leakage here is not due to a defective washer, either. Due to the large amount of heat in the area of the valves, no outside materials can be used for sealing. The exclusion or the retention of the gases results from metal-to-metal contact. In position, the valve fits in a metal holder called the *valve guide.* When the valve is shut, its face is in firm contact with the valve seat. With an assist from the pressure of the gases in the cylinder and the *valve spring,* the valve face and the valve seat make a firm seal. But a great deal depends on the valve guide. The fitting between the stem and the guide is designed rather closely. Only about two or three thousandths of an inch (.002–.003) is tolerated. If the clearance is excessive, the valve may tip slightly and the valve face will not make positive all-around con-

tact with the seat. The result is leakage and a drop in engine efficiency.

Operation of the Valves. Reviewing quickly the valve operation during the four strokes of the cycle will help in understanding how the valves work. On the intake stroke of the piston, the intake valve opens, allowing mixture to flow from the intake manifold, through the intake port, past the valve seat—into the cylinder. When the piston comes up on the compression stroke, both valves are tightly shut. No leakage is allowed. The piston then descends on the power stroke. Again, both valves are closed; no leakage is allowed, either. Coming up on the exhaust stroke, the exhaust valve opens, permitting spent gases to be pushed from the cylinder, past the exhaust valve seat, through the exhaust port into the exhaust manifold, through the exhaust pipe and into the air.

Now, during each of the strokes of the cycle, the valves seem to know how to act—just when to open and close. How? The valves opened because they were told to do so by a specially programmed engine component—the *camshaft.*

A cam is actually a revolving lever which can do some work each time around. Cam operation is called eccentric motion. An eccentric can be defined as one circle within another not sharing the same center. This is the opposite of concentric—two circles, each sharing a common center.

Find something flat and round, like a saucer. Hold it upright with one hand by clamping it between your thumb and your index finger. Make sure that your fingers are placed exactly in the center of the saucer. When you spin the saucer it will revolve in a perfect circle, like the wheels of a car. The distance from the edge to the center of the dish is the same all around the rim. Now, move your fingers about two inches off the center. Spin the saucer and it will go around in a bumpy manner. The dish will seem to have a low and high point as it passes your palm.

Try to visualize a stick piercing a stack

of saucers. Each saucer will accept the stick in the same spot—an inch from dead center. Now, when the stick is twirled, each of the saucers will be riding up and down. With a few adjustments some dishes could be coming up while others are going down.

A camshaft is like that stick with a series of "bumps" machined around a

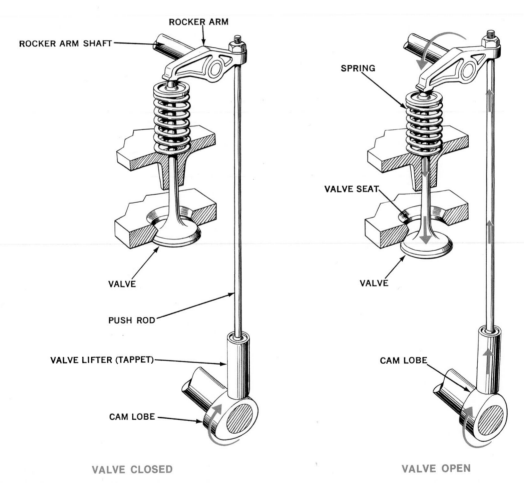

VALVE CLOSED   VALVE OPEN

Overhead valve (OHV) operating mechanism. Only the rocker arms, shaft and valve are visible. Springs are visible when the valve cover is removed. The valve is opened when the cam lobe pushes up on the lifter (right), which raises the push rod, tips the rocker arm, and opens the valve. When the cam lobe turns (left), the valve spring tips the rocker arm and pulls the valve shut.

common axis. Each of the bumps is a cam. The high point of the cam is called the *lobe*. The shaft itself is made of forged steel and the cams are case-hardened. The camshaft also has a special gear for turning the distributor shaft, a gear for turning the oil pump, and a special cam for operating the fuel pump.

A simple camshaft for a one-cylinder engine will have two cams, one for operating the exhaust valve and one for operating the intake valve. The lobes are spaced in such a manner under the valve stems that they can raise the valve (open) at the appropriate moment in the cycle. As the shaft turns, the #1 cam will contact the intake valve and raise it at the start of the intake stroke. By the time the intake stroke is completed, the lobe has passed by the intake-valve stem and the valve is forced shut by the spring. Since no cam is in touch with the valves during the compression and power strokes, both valves remain closed. At the exhaust stroke, the #2 cam contacts the exhaust valve and raises it to open position. Continued turning of the camshaft causes the #2 cam to leave the exhaust valve stem, closing the valve, but the #1 cam is now again opening the intake valve.

It is clear that the operation of the camshaft is directly related to the operation of the piston, more precisely, the crankshaft. Therefore, camshaft and crankshaft turning must be synchronized. In front of each shaft there is a gear. Sometimes the gears are in contact, and sometimes there is a chain which links them. Regardless of how they are joined, the important fact is that the gears are of two different sizes. Since it takes four strokes of the piston to complete the Otto cycle—two up strokes and two down strokes—this means that the crankshaft makes two complete revolu-

tions per cycle. (Each up-and-down movement of the piston is equal to one revolution.)

As for the camshaft, note that during each full cycle the intake valve opened and closed only once, and the exhaust valve opened and closed only once. This means a cam contacts a valve only once during each cycle. Thus the camshaft must revolve only one full revolution during the cycle.

The ratio between the crankshaft and camshaft during one cycle must then be set so that two turns of the crankshaft give one turn of the camshaft—2 to 1. This ratio is fixed by the size of gears, one double the size of the other. Which one should be the larger?

Since the camshaft travels only one full turn for every two turns of the crankshaft, the camshaft gear must be twice the size of the crankshaft gear. Put another way, the gear must be made to go twice as far around in order to be half as fast. Because the gears synchronize the action of the piston movement and the valve opening, these gears are called *timing gears*. The chain that is used to link them is called the *timing chain*.

Lifting the Valves. It is easy to get the impression that the lobe can, in time, inflict much wear on the valve stem. This would be true, if it were not for an important part in the valve mechanism called the *valve lifter*, commonly called a *valve tappet*. This is a special metal cylinder that is closed at both ends and hardened. It serves as a buffer between the cam and the valve stem. It also contains a special bolt within it that is important for providing a correct spacing between itself and the valve stem.

Correct clearance between the tappet

and the valve is important to the proper seating of the valve face, to counter the effects of heat expansion. When the engine is cold, there is about eight or ten thousandths of an inch (.008–.010) clearance between the stem and tappet. When the engine gets hotter, the stem lengthens, narrowing but not closing the gap. If there were no gap provided when the engine is cold, the expanded stem would not permit the valve to seat when the engine is hot — even when the tappet is in contact with the low side of the cam. The space provided is often called *valve lash*.

Described above is a solid-type lifter. In recent years, oil-filled lifters have come into general use. This is a small version of a hydraulic pump. Its essential parts are a body, a spring, a plunger, and a ball-check valve. When the cam lobe is down and the valve is closed, the spring pushes on the plunger, extending it fully to contact the valve stem. Oil under pressure is forced in under the plunger. As the cam comes around, the ball check seals the chamber under the plunger. Full of oil with no place to go, the lifter acts as a solid body. The valve rises. As the lobe passes pressure from the valve, springs push the valve down, the ball check leaves its seat, and some of the oil in the lifter is allowed to bleed off. The important advantage of the lifter is that it always maintains zero lash between the stem and the lifter — and can maintain it through a wide range of temperatures. As the stem expands, less oil is required to fill the chamber. As it cools, a bit more oil is needed.

Valve Arrangements. There are two vastly differently styles for arranging the valves and their mechanisms. The valve-in-block

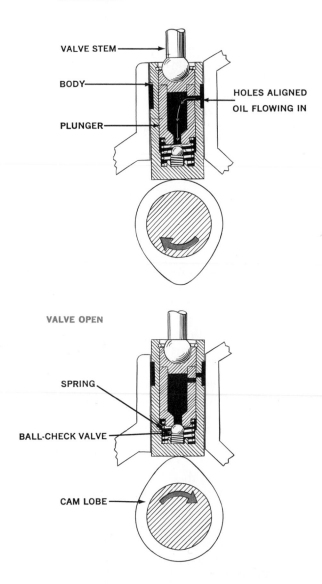

Hydraulic valve lifter in operation. In the top drawing, the cam lobe is down; lifter body is also down. The holes in the body and plunger are aligned. The plunger can fill with oil. When the cam lobe comes up (bottom), the body is pushed upward. The holes are no longer aligned. Thus the plunger is sealed, and the column of trapped oil raises the push rod.

design shows up in the L- and F-type engines. The valve-in-head design is found in I-type engines. In the valve-in-head design, the rocker arm and shaft, the valve and spring, the valve port and seat are all part of the cylinder head. In the valve-in-block design, no part of the valve mechanism is in the head. For illustrations, refer back to page 8.

Getting Rid of Heat. Considerable heat develops during the combustion process. The intake valve runs relatively cool since it passes a mixture of cool vapor and air. The exhaust valve operates under different circumstances and may actually glow red with heat. Average temperatures are about 1,300 degrees.

The main method for getting rid of the heat is to pass it off to the valve guide and the valve seat. Both of these components are close to the engine water jackets. Thus, in addition to the need for adequate sealing, full contact with the valve seat is important to valve cooling.

Timing. One final point about valves. From the preceding descriptions of the action of the valves during the strokes of the Otto cycle, you might be under the impression that the intake valve opens only when the piston starts going down on the intake stroke, and that the exhaust valve opens only when the piston starts to come up on the exhaust stroke. This is not exactly accurate.

When the piston goes down on the intake stroke, the intake valve does open, but it stays open after the piston reaches its bottom dead center (BDC) and starts coming up. After about 45 degrees more of crankshaft rotation, once the piston has started upward, the intake valve will

close. This gives additional time for the cylinder to fill up with a charge of mixture.

Similarly, the exhaust valve starts opening at 45 degrees of crankshaft rotation before the piston reaches BDC of the power stroke. The exhaust valve stays open while the piston comes up and remains open for 5 degrees of crankshaft rotation after the piston comes past the top dead center (TDC) and is already headed downward on the intake stroke. This gives a little extra time for the cylinders to clear out. The juggling of the valves in this manner is called *valve overlapping.*

BEARINGS

Without motion inside the engine there is no motion of the car. All motion has its own demon to contend with—friction. Even a wheel spinning off the ground still has to overcome the friction between the hub and the axle. All friction results in wear. Therefore, friction must be kept to a minimum.

Friction and wear are reduced by *bearings.* A bearing can best be described as an expendable part that is put between two moving parts to cut friction and take the wear.

There are numerous types of bearings used in the engine. They are located where the crankshaft is supported by the cap and block (main bearings). Where the connecting rod contacts the journal (rod bearings). Where the camshaft is supported by the engine block (camshaft bushing). Where the wrist pin contacts the connecting rod (pin bushing). The word "bushing" means a bearing of one-piece construction.

The bearings at the crankshaft supports and all the connecting rods are made up of

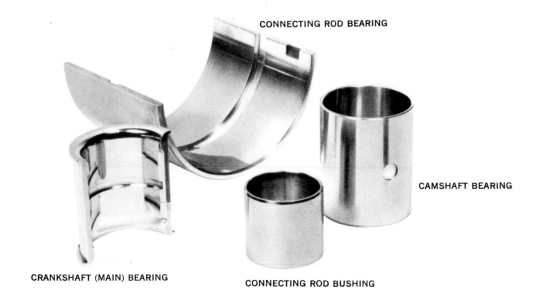

CONNECTING ROD BEARING

CAMSHAFT BEARING

CRANKSHAFT (MAIN) BEARING

CONNECTING ROD BUSHING

Various flat bearings used in the engine.

two pieces. Technically, they are described as two-piece, precision-insert, flat bearings. That is, the bearing is a flat (though curved) piece of metal which is inserted between the cap and the shaft below and between the support and the shaft above. For the connecting rod, the two *shells*, as they are commonly called, are installed between the cap and journal and between the rod and journal. The bearings are fixed. They do not turn. To do so would be to defeat the purpose of the bearing.

The bushing used at the wrist pin looks like a wide wedding band and is driven into the connecting rod hole. It is usually made of bronze. The camshaft bushings look like wide bracelets and are fixed to the large holes cast in the clock for holding the shaft.

The base metal for bearings is steel, but on top of this base are layers of softer metal. Every bearing maker has his own formula for what he thinks is a winning combination. Soft metals employed as layers include copper, lead, tin, mercury, antimony, cadmium, silver. Yet, the bearing must not grow softer as the heat increases.

LUBRICATION

Regardless of the careful machining of engine parts and the quality of the bearings, friction can never be entirely eliminated. The main weapon against friction is lubrication. Specifically, a lubricant such as engine oil or grease is a substance which provides a thin film between two moving parts. Since the film has low friction characteristics, the two moving parts move more easily because they are never in actual contact with each other but are moving on a "slippery" film.

Engine oil is processed from crude oil. Besides providing that film which we call lubrication, oil has other jobs:

Oil is a coolant. Because oil can transfer heat, it is kept in circulation within the engine. The cooling-off spot within the engine is the sump of the oil pan where heat picked up by the oil is passed to the surrounding air.

Oil is a sealer. Because it has body, oil is the final seal between the piston rings and the cylinder wall, also between the valve guides and the stem.

Oil is a cleaner. Regardless of the cleanliness of the air sucked into the combustion chamber, an engine produces "dirt" of its own. Chemical processes create carbon, gums, sludge. A good detergent-type oil can clean these impurities from the moving parts and hold them in suspension until the oil is drained.

Oil Thickness. When oil is processed, it ends up with a certain thickness. The technical term, *viscosity*, denotes a fluid's tendency to resist flow. A heavy oil is more viscous; a light oil is less viscous. The thickness is given a grade number by the Society of Automotive Engineers (SAE). The higher the number, the heavier the oil. Thus SAE #40 is thicker than SAE #10. The purpose of varying the thickness is to counteract the effects of weather in starting the engine. Cold makes the oil thicker; heat makes the oil thinner.

In common use today is a multi-viscosity oil. It meets the requirements for a light oil at low temperature and a heavy oil at high temperature. A can of this type of oil is usually marked "SAE 10W–30."

Bearing Clearance. If oil provides the film between the bearing and the moving part, it is clear that a space must be provided for the film to reside there. This space is called *bearing clearance* and is about $1\frac{1}{2}$ to 2 thousandths of an inch (.0015–.002).

If the oil is to do other jobs besides lubrication it is not enough to dip the parts in oil at the assembly plant and let it go at that. What is required is a complete circulation system. On modern cars a pressure system is popularly used. However, in the past and in limited use today, are a splash system and a combination splash and pressure system.

The splash system depends on the dipping of the connecting rods and journal into a puddle of oil in the sump. On the upswing, the oil is spread over the parts. This system is not very efficient for high-speed engines.

The full pressure system is very complex and involves many parts. It starts at the *oil pickup* which is a tube with a screened opening located in the sump. It is there to suck up oil from the reservoir in the sump. Many pickups are on a hinge so the screen always floats on the oil, thus avoiding the sediment which settles to the bottom of the sump.

The Oil Pump. The next unit in the system is the oil pump. This small unit has the job of sucking up the oil from the sump and delivering it to the various units. Some cars have the gear-type pump which is a simple combination of two small gears.

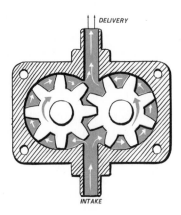
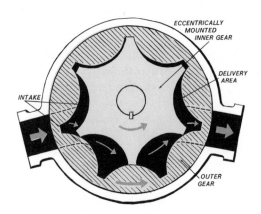

Two types of oil pumps used in automobiles. Left is a gear pump. Right is an eccentric pump. A pump draws oil from a sump (oil pan) and distributes it to the engine's moving parts.

One is driven by the special gear on the camshaft. As the driving gear spins, it scoops the oil and transfers it to its partner, which whips it through the pump outlet. The rotary pump is set up like a cross within a star. The cross is driven by the camshaft gear and "walks" around the inner perimeter of the star. In so doing, it picks up oil from the sump and sends it through the pump outlet.

Before the oil is allowed to the various bearings it must first pass an oil-pressure relief valve. This a traffic cop which makes sure the oil pressure does not build up too much when the engine is at high speed. The "brain" of the valve is a special spring which shuts off oil flow at a predetermined pressure and opens when pressure drops below the limit.

After passing the relief valve, the oil is then admitted to the galleries cast into the block. These lead to the main bearings of the crankshaft, the rod bearings, up the bore in the connecting rod to the wrist pins. In addition, oil is pumped to the valve system. In the overhead valve setup, the oil must go all the way to the top of the engine to keep all the rocker arms well lubricated. The route can be through hollow push rods or through a special oil line which is routed to the top. Not to be overlooked is the oil supplied to the two timing gears at the crank and camshaft and to the camshaft bearings themselves. Pressurized oil is also utilized by the hydraulic valve lifters.

When the fresh oil comes up, it displaces the "old" oil, which drips down back to the sump for cooling. Necessary to complete the system is a method by which the oil can be cleaned of impurities each time around. Enter the *oil filter*. Numerous filtering materials have been used. Among them are cotton waste, special fibers, porous metals and even full rolls of toilet tissue. Most cars have settled on specially treated filter paper. Nevertheless, filtering materials do have a limited life span. In time they fill up with the impurities and have to be replaced.

There are two popular types of oil-filter systems in use today. The *full-flow* system is set up so all the oil coming right from the pump is forced to go through the filter. Then it can go to the bearings and the other parts. The *bypass* filter system is set up so that only a portion of the oil coming from the pump is sent through the filter and then back to the oil sump. The bypass filter is considered the safer of the two. In case of filter clogging, the oil-circulation system remains unaffected. The only thing that happens is that no more oil will be filtered. The full-flow system contains a special bypass valve. In case the filter clogs, the valve opens and permits the oil to circumvent the filter. However, there is also the danger that the bypass valve will clog. In that case, oil starvation will take its toll in burned bearings and other components.

EXHAUST

Whenever the engine operates, vapors are created in the crankcase. These come from the mixture of water moisture and

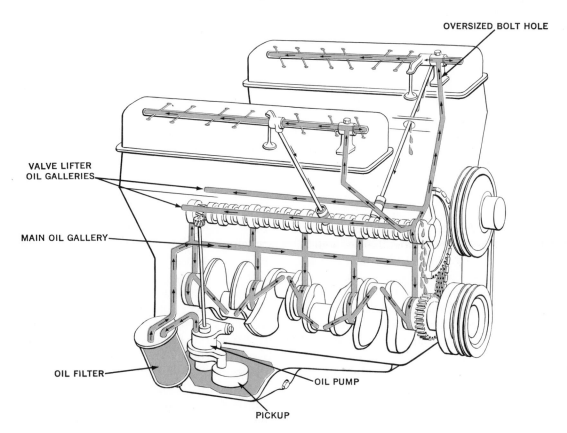

Oil flowing through the engine block. The oil provides lubrication for all engine moving parts. Force for the flow is provided by an oil pump operating from power supplied by the camshaft.

gasoline which manages to slip by the rings. These vapors must have an outlet or an explosion can occur. In the old days, the crankcase was ventilated by air entering the crankcase through the oil-filler pipe, circulating around the crankcase and going out through a tube called a breather pipe. The only problem was that the breather pipe was vented to the outside air. Since we and the engineers have been made more conscious of the quality of the air we breathe, a slight modification was put into mass production in 1959. Here, the outlet for the fumes from the crankcase is rerouted to the carburetor where it is eventually burned in the combustion chamber. Metering the fuel to the carburetor is the *positive crankcase ventilation* valve, know as the PCV valve. It is the function of the valve to dole out the fumes in such a manner that the carburetor does not become choked up with these fumes and cause poor engine performances. (See Chapter 4, "Exhaust System.")

SEALING THE PARTS

It is impossible to machine parts so that they will fit perfectly together as well as seal out or seal in liquids or gases under all conditions. To cope with this problem, various gaskets are used between many mating parts of the engine. A gasket serves to take up the minor imperfections of the two mating parts. Placed between them and crushed, it fills these imperfections and prevents leaks. These gaskets can be made of steel, copper, paper, cork, or asbestos. They are shaped to the configuration of the mating parts and punched with the proper holes to allow bolts to pass through them. Sometimes a special

liquid or paste sealer is used in addition to the gasket, never instead of it.

To seal in water and pressure of the exploding gases, a steel or copper gasket is used between the cylinder head and the block. To seal in oil at the oil pan, a cork or neoprene gasket is used. To seal in exhaust gases between the manifold and the exhaust pipe, an asbestos ring is used. Gaskets are also employed at the intake manifold, under the rocker-arm cover, between the fuel pump and the engine block and in a variety of locations which require sealing.

THE ROTARY ENGINE

As mentioned before, the 4-stroke, internal combustion engine has been around since before the automobile. Nevertheless, it appears that its days are numbered. There are many reasons for this. High on the list are this engine's low efficiency and its attendant pollution. Another cause for its low prospect for the future is the need for engines that use fuels other than gasoline or diesel oil. In addition, a source of increasing concern is the need to conserve our metal resources. As a result research is under way in many quarters towards finding new methods of propulsion.

The first engine other than the piston type to be accepted on a large-scale, commercial basis was the rotary engine. While it still burns gasoline and while it still is considered to be a "dirty" engine, the rotary does represent a departure and for that alone it rates some attention.

A rotary engine is one in which the major component makes a circular motion, giving off its power to a rotating crankshaft. The opposite, of course, is the

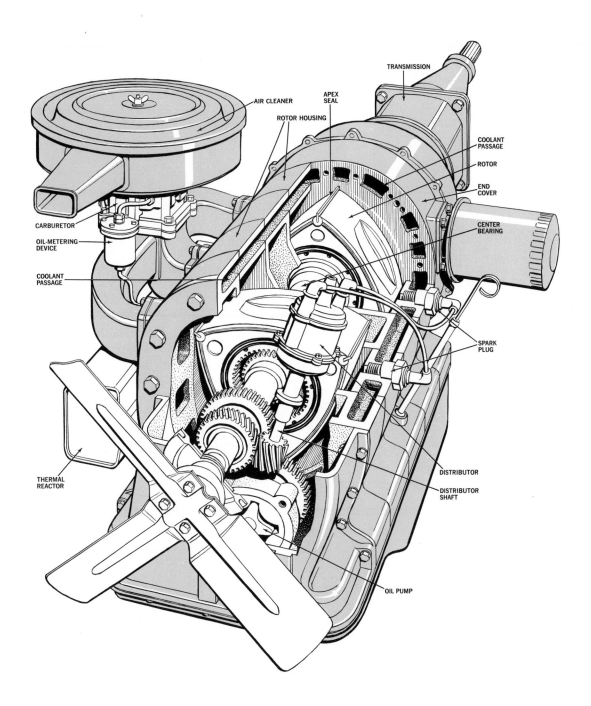

AIR CLEANER

APEX
SEAL

ROTOR HOUSING

TRANSMISSION

COOLANT
PASSAGE

ROTOR

END
COVER

CENTER
BEARING

CARBURETOR

OIL-METERING
DEVICE

COOLANT
PASSAGE

SPARK
PLUG

THERMAL
REACTOR

DISTRIBUTOR

DISTRIBUTOR
SHAFT

OIL PUMP

CUTAWAY OF THE WANKEL WITH ACCOMPANYING PARTS

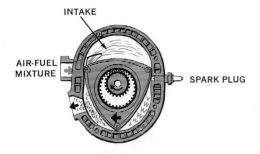

INTAKE

AIR-FUEL MIXTURE

SPARK PLUG

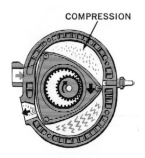

COMPRESSION

POWER

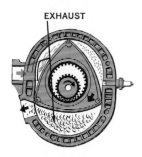

EXHAUST

Four phases of the Wankel cycle.

reciprocating (up and down) motion of the piston which must be "translated" to the rotary motion of the crankshaft.

The inventor of the rotary engine in popular use today is a German engineer, Felix Wankel. Though his development work started in the 1920s, it wasn't until 1957 that the engine was bolted to its first car, the German NSU. The first car to be mass-produced and sold in the U.S. with a rotary engine was the 1969 Mazda.

Few Parts Required. The essential parts of the rotary engine are the special rotor chamber, the triangular rotor, and the gear within the rotor.

The rotor chamber is shaped like a race-track oval, except that it has a slight pinch at the sides. Technically, this geometric figure is called an epitrochoid. The three apexes of the rotor are in constant contact with the chamber wall. Thus in any position, the rotor faces and the chamber form three separate compartments.

It is essential that each compartment be sealed from the other. To accomplish this, each rotor apex is equipped with a special flexible seal which will allow rotation around the irregular surface without leakage. Due to the unusual configuration of the chamber, the size of each compartment will vary as the rotor turns.

Operationally, the rotary engine's four phases accomplish the functions of the four strokes of the Otto cycle. The rotor gear is located in the center of the rotor and is attached to a shaft which acts like the crankshaft in that it transmits rotary power to the transmission. The gear turns three times with each turn of the rotor.

In a comparison between the rotary and piston engines, it is notable that the piston can accomplish only one stroke at a time while the rotary is performing three phases (strokes) at any given moment of operation. While one compartment is sucking in the fuel/air mixture, the next one is compressing its own charge, and the third one is exhausting its spent gases. In order to create enough power to run an automobile, two, three and four such rotary engines are coupled in a line, turning a common shaft.

While the rotary engine is still an internal combustion engine and still uses fossil fuels with poisonous exhausts, it does have some advantages over the piston engine. Its construction is quite simple, with fewer parts used. It has half the weight for a piston engine of similar horsepower. There are no valves or valve mechanisms required. Due to its rotary action, vibration is greatly reduced. And, it can burn a low-octane fuel.

Among its disadvantages, the rotary engine requires a complete tearing down to replace the apex seals, and its fuel economy is not much greater than that of a comparably-powered 6-cylinder engine.

2
ELECTRICAL SYSTEM

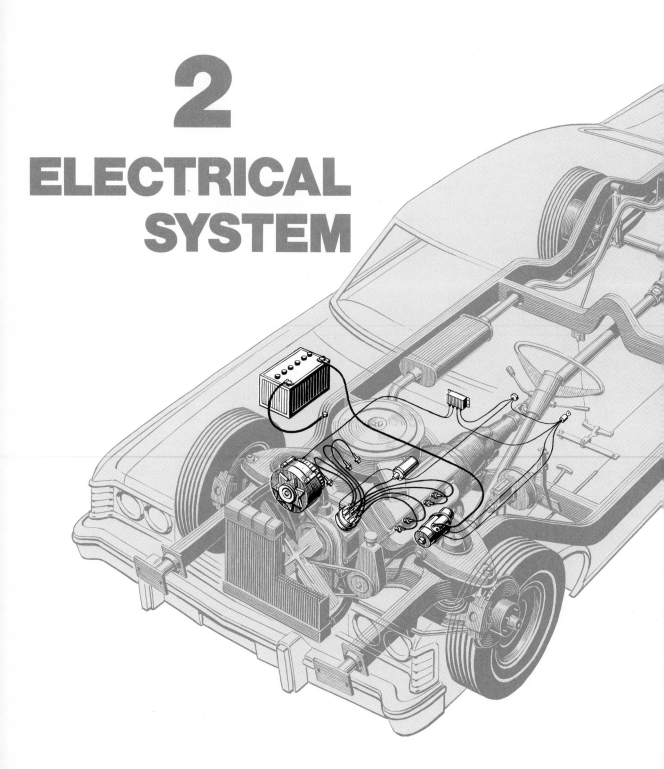

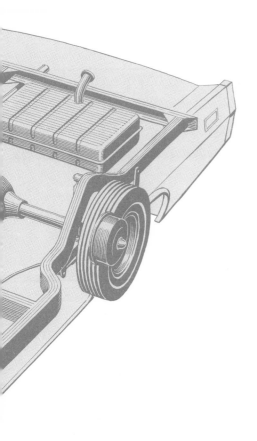

ower to move a car comes from the engine, but power for almost everything else on the vehicle comes from electricity. Not only are all the safety and comfort features electrically powered; electricity is the life-giving pulse that systematically ignites the air/fuel mixture in the combustion chamber.

So widespread is the use of electrical power in the car that, to explain the electrical system, it is necessary to divide it into three subsystems: charging, ignition and starting. Although these depend on the battery as the main source of power, they are independent of each other and can be examined separately. Lighting is discussed in Chapter 6.

THE BATTERY

The source of all electrical energy in the car is the battery. But that is its abbreviated name. The correct name for the heavy black box with thick cables attached to it is *storage battery*. And storing is just

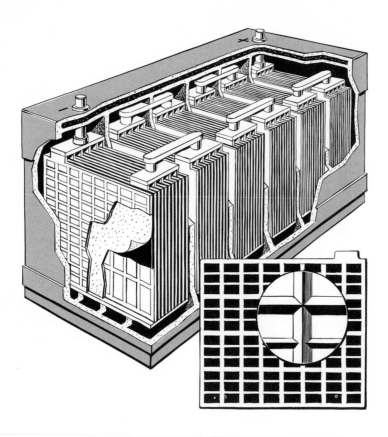

Lead-acid battery (cutaway).
Each section of plates is a cell,
capable of providing two volts.
The inset shows the grid-work
construction of each plate.

what the battery (group) of plates does. Power is stored as chemical energy, then converted and released as electrical energy when called to do so. Energy conversion is common in a car. Heat energy of the exploding gas/air mixture is converted to the mechanical energy of piston movement. Mechanical energy of the turning crankshaft is converted to electrical energy by the spinning alternator. Electrical energy of the starter motor is converted to mechanical energy by the turning of the flywheel.

A battery consists of a number of identical cells. To construct one cell, we start with a *grid* made of lead alloy bars criss-crossed on a frame. Pure lead in powdered form is mixed with a few chemicals to make a paste, which is spread on the grid. Now we have a plate that can do little by itself. To make it work we need more plates. The greater the number of plates, the greater the amount of electrical energy that can be stored in chemical form.

After a number of grids are pasted, they are dried and subjected to an initial electrical treatment called the forming charge. Some plates will be charged positively and turn brown as the material becomes lead peroxide; other plates are charged negatively and turn gray as the material becomes sponge lead. From here on the positive and negative plates are kept separated.

The next step is to assemble all of one type of plate on a single bar; the other type is similarly assembled. Each of these assemblies is now called a *group.* Both are then lined up so the plates interleaf, with insulating material separating each positive and negative plate. Because the insulator separates the two types of plates, it is simply called a *separator.* At one time separators were made of cedar wood; today they are made of rubber or plastic.

With the plates interleafed and the separators in place we now have a new unit called an *element,* more commonly called a *cell.* The total number of plates in a cell is always an odd number since there is always one more negative plate. A cell with thirteen plates will have seven negative plates, six positive plates and twelve separators.

The cell is then installed in a case. If it is for a 6-volt battery, the case will accept three cells; a 12-volt battery will have space for six cells. Each cell will produce about 2.2 volts when fully charged. This is true of small batteries used in motor scooters or of large ones used in submarines. With the cells installed in the case, all the bars holding the positive plates are linked to a thick post. The same is done to the negative plates. Then a cover is fitted to the case and the edges are sealed. The cover has openings for adding water to the cells and the venting of gases when the battery is in use.

Now we have a number of elements within a common case. But we do not yet have a storage battery. An activator must be added.

The Activator. The solid materials within the battery are inert. To make them active a fluid called *electrolyte* must be added. This is a mix of water and sulphuric acid. The concentration of this mixture is critical. A new, fully charged battery contains one part acid to 2¾ parts water. As the battery is discharged the water content

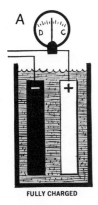
FULLY CHARGED

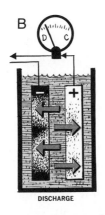
DISCHARGE

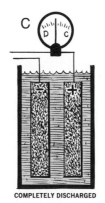
COMPLETELY DISCHARGED

CHARGE

Chemical action in the charge/discharge cycle. In *A*, the negative plate has sponge lead; positive plate has lead peroxide. Electrolyte has a high acid content. In *B* and *C*, sulphate leaves the electrolyte and combines with lead of both plates. Oxygen from the positive plate helps form water. In *D* the process reverses. Oxygen combines with lead to form lead peroxide; sulphate leaves the plates to form sulphuric acid.

increases; as the battery is charged the acid content increases. That is the wonderful feature of the storage battery—the chemical process is reversible. That is, when the available amount of electricity is fully drawn from the battery, electricity from another source can be "pumped" in from a generator and stored in chemical form. However, there are limitations. Each time the battery cycles, some of the lead material drops to the bottom of the case, lowering battery capacity a little. Eventually enough material is lost to prevent the battery from holding a charge.

Chemically, the discharge and charging formula works like this: As the cells discharge, the electrolyte (H_2SO_4) breaks up into hydrogen (H) and sulphur dioxide (SO_4). The hydrogen unites with the oxygen (O_2) found at the positive plates and produces water (H_2O). This dilutes the concentration of electrolyte. The sulphur dioxide combines with the lead of both plates forming lead sulphate ($PbSO_4$). In charging, the lead sulphate on the positive and negative plates converts to lead peroxide (PbO_2) and sponge lead (Pb). Electrolyte strength increases as the sulphur dioxide from the plates combines with the hydrogen from the water to form sulphuric acid.

Specific Gravity. Notice that the acid concentration varies with the state of battery charge. When the battery is fully charged, acid concentration is at its peak; in a fully discharged state the electrolyte is watered down. Therefore, by checking the concentration of the electrolyte, the state of charge of a battery can be determined.

Concentration is determined with a test for *specific gravity*. This is a term used to describe how much heavier a certain

amount of solution is when compared to a similar amount of water. Because 1 cubic centimeter of water weighs 1 gram, water is arbitrarily designated as one (1). If, let's say, 5 ounces of a certain liquid weighs twice as much as 5 ounces of water, then the liquid is said to have a specific gravity of 2.000. If it weighs 1½ times the water then the specific gravity is 1.5.

When sulphuric acid and water are mixed for a new battery, the liquid has a specific gravity of 1.300. When the cell is completely discharged, the reading will be 1.100. Remember, pure water is 1.000. Therefore, a check of the specific gravity will give readings anywhere from 1.300 to 1.100 and the state of charge can be determined. Specific gravity is determined very simply with an instrument called a *hydrometer*.

The accompanying table shows some typical readings taken on a hydrometer and what they say about the battery's state of charge.

Specific Gravity	State of Charge
1.275 to 1.300	100%
1.225 to 1.250	75%
1.200 to 1.220	50%
1.165 to 1.190	25%
1.140 to 1.160	Barely operative
1.100 to 1.135	Discharged

Battery Ratings. We now have a battery with cells producing a little more than 2 volts each. We do not know how much current the battery will produce. Nor do we know how much reserve the battery has. These are important questions to consider when you have to buy a new battery.

There are a number of factors which will decide how much power a battery can put out. These include the number of plates per cell, the size of the plates and their thickness. A battery with thirteen plates per cell, each plate about 5×8 inches and $\frac{1}{4}$-inch thick has more storage capacity than a battery with twenty-three plates half as large and $\frac{1}{8}$-inch thick. The buyer can determine the capacity of the battery without measuring any plates. All that has to be done is to refer to the Ampere-Hour (AH) number stamped on the case.

AH is a standardized test used by all battery makers to indicate the capacity of the battery. The basis of the rating is to determine the battery's ability to deliver continuous power over a twenty-hour period. To arrive at the ampere-hour rate a fully charged battery is slowly discharged at a low and steady current. When the drain causes the voltage to drop to 1.75 per cell (from 2.2 volts at the start) the test stops. By multiplying the amperes used by the number of hours the test ran before the drop to 1.75 volts, the ampere-hour rate is established. If a battery put out 5 amperes for 20 hours, the AH is 100. A battery with more working material will have a higher AH.

About amperage: While a battery may have voltage limits (6 or 12) there are no limits on amperage. It holds this power as your bank holds money. Amperage is drawn to the extent it is needed. A starter motor may need as much as 300 amperes while a dashboard bulb will "pull" as little as two amperes. Naturally, the higher the amperage draw, the faster it will take to discharge the battery. The starter will drain a battery in about thirty seconds of continuous operation while a small bulb may take twenty-four hours to do the same.

Principles of Operation. The battery is built and ready to work. It has two posts protruding from its case. These are labeled positive and negative. In operation, the battery plays a tennis match with electrons. During the discharge process, electrons flow from where they are most abundant to where they are lacking. This electron flow is electricity. After a while a balance is achieved. The positive plates make up their deficit of electrons; the negative plates have unloaded their surplus. This balance sounds good, but the result is a discharged battery.

When the battery is recharged, electricity is used to dislodge the electrons from the positive plates and chase them back to the negative plates. When a sufficient imbalance exists between the positive and negative plates, the battery is charged. Or, it can be said that the battery now has the potential for producing electricity due to its imbalanced distribution of electrons.

THE SINGLE-WIRE SYSTEM

Electricity cannot flow unless it is in a complete circuit. The electrons will not start their journey, so to speak, unless they are assured they can finish the trip. This means that a wire will go from the positive post of the battery to a bulb or heater fan. Then the circuit will continue through the appliance and another wire will run back to the negative post of the battery. This is true in theory; in fact wiring on the car is much simpler. To light a bulb, a wire runs from the positive post to the bulb, but there is no return wire to the negative post. Then how is the circuit completed? *By way of the metal frame of the car.*

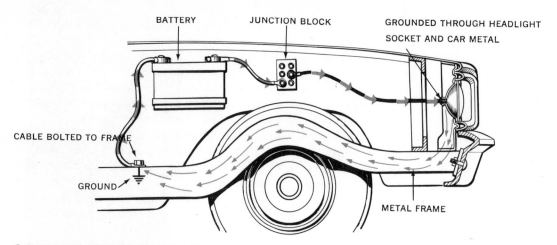

BATTERY   JUNCTION BLOCK   GROUNDED THROUGH HEADLIGHT
SOCKET AND CAR METAL

CABLE BOLTED TO FRAME

GROUND

METAL FRAME

Common-ground electrical system. The car frame is used to complete any electrical circuit on the negative side. Hence only one wire is necessary for any electrical appliance.

At the battery there are two heavy cables. One from the positive goes off to serve all the car's appliances. That is the "hot" line. The other cable is bolted to the engine. In turn, the engine is bolted to the car frame. Now, if we attach a special lamp to the rear fender of the car, only one wire, a "hot" one, will be attached to the socket. The return circuit is handled from the bulb to the lamp housing, to the fender, to the car body, to the frame, to the engine, to the negative post of the battery.

This single-wire system is used to supply electricity to all the car's electrical units. It does not negate the principle that electricity must travel in a complete circuit. The name of the return leg of the circuit is called the *ground*. It gets its name from the time when the ground was used as a common means of return for telegraph circuits. Thus only one wire was stretched from one station to the next while each of the stations had a wire buried deeply in the ground. (British auto manuals still refer to the grounded side of the car circuits as "earth.")

With the basics of the battery understood we can now venture to the subsystem which replenishes it—the charging subsystem.

THE CHARGING SUBSYSTEM

By now a few facts should be clear. 1) All power for the car's entire electrical system is supplied by the battery. 2) The battery does not make electricity; it merely stores it. 3) The electrical energy in the battery is finite and must be replaced as it is spent. 4) This replacement process is called recharging.

The charging unit used on cars is either a generator or an alternator. It does the job by converting the mechanical energy of motion into electrical energy. The early cars had no need of a generating unit. Lights burned either oil or acetylene gas; the horn was sounded by squeezing a rubber bulb; starting was accomplished by turning a crank. There were no air conditioners, heaters, cigar lighters, or power windows. The only need for electricity was for engine ignition, which was supplied by a dry-cell battery or magneto.

Although industrial generators were used since the early nineteenth century, the automotive generator was first seen on the 1906 Buick, which offered it, a regulator and a storage battery as standard equipment. Together these are parts of a team, still used, called the *charging subsystem.*

The Generator. In order to produce electricity there has to be motion. It was Michael Faraday who found that current can be created (induced) when a conductor is passed through the invisible lines in a magnetic field. The field is the name given to that limited area around a magnet which influences iron objects. How effectively a generator produces electricity depends on three factors: (1) the number of conductors cutting through the field, (2) the speed at which they cut through the field, (3) the strength of the field itself.

A simple generator could be made by placing two bar magnets at the edge of two tables so that the north pole of one magnet faces the south pole of the other. Keep them just far enough apart so that they do not draw to each other and touch. Around this immediate area and between the tips of the magnets there is a strong magnetic field. Now, take a wire and move it back and forth between the tips. The wire will feel as if it were cutting through

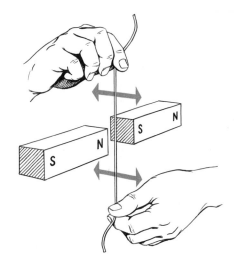

Generator principle. By passing a wire through a magnetic field, it is possible to generate electricity in that wire.

strands of rubber bands stretched across the space. If a meter were connected to the wire it would show that an electrical current was created, or induced, in the wire when it passed through the magnet.

Take this demonstration one step further. Since more current can be induced by cutting through a stronger magnetic field, we can build up the field. Instead of a permanent magnet, an electromagnet is used. This is an iron core with many turns of wire wrapped around it. When a small current is put through this wire, the core becomes a strong magnet. The more turns of wire used, the stronger the magnet. The core will remain a magnet as long as current is sent through the wire; stop the current and the magnet "turns off."

With a strong magnetic field, the induced current made by passing a wire conductor through it is greater than before. But, we can make the induced current yet stronger. Instead of a single wire cutting across the magnetic field, we can use a loop of wire in the simple shape of a bottle. The loop can turn within the area between the two magnets.

Now, if one loop of wire is better than a single strand, then many loops are still better. As this combination of loops turns within the space between the two magnets, lines of force are being constantly cut, inducing a continuous flow of electricity. The problem now is to collect this accumulation of induced current. Since the wire loops are in motion, it is difficult to make any electrical attachments at these loops. The answer is to allow the loop ends, the neck of the bottle, to brush up against a stationary object which will

conduct the built-up electrical charge. For our lab generator, a metal strip will do if it has positive contact with the wire loops all the time. Now if a wire is run from the brushing conductor to a light bulb, and another wire from the bulb to one of the electromagnets, the bulb will glow when the wire loops are turned.

Thus we have the basic generator. It consists of a series of wire loops that turn in a magnetic field. Each time one of the magnetic lines is cut, electricity is induced. This current is then tapped off by a conductor brushing up against the wire loop ends. The faster the wire loops spin, the greater the induced current.

The automotive generator is quite similar to the one just described. The heart of the unit is the part that holds the wire loops. This is called the *armature*. The

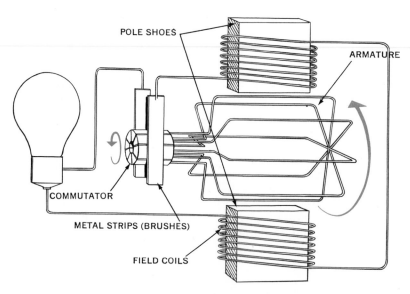

A simple generator. A magnetic field is created at the pole shoes. Wires from the armature cut through the magnetic lines, creating a current which is picked up by the brushes at the commutator.

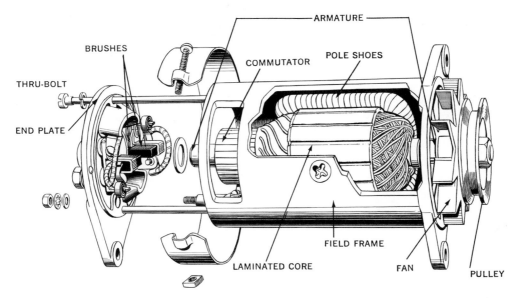

Automotive generator (cutaway). Compare the description of parts relationships in the text with parts identified in this illustration.

A typical generator.

thin, soft-iron discs in its middle section are notched to create furrows. This section is called the *laminated core.* Each of the wire loops starts at the "neck" end of the armature shaft, runs up one furrow to the end of the laminations, across to another furrow on the opposite side, and back to the neck. Of course, many loops are used, all wound in a similar manner.

Each wire end is soldered to a flat copper segment attached to the shaft, but insulated from it and from its neighboring segments. The insulation material is usually mica. The rounded section containing the copper segments is called the *commutator.*

The armature fits into a heavy metal cylinder called the *field frame.* That's the part which is visible to you under the hood. Screwed to the inside of the cylinder are two soft-iron pieces called *pole shoes.* Around each shoe are several loops of very heavy wire called *field coils.* As demonstrated earlier, wire wrapped around a soft-iron core is the basis of an electromagnet.

The cylinder is closed at both ends by covers called *end plates.* On one end a fan and pulley is attached to the armature shaft, permitting the armature to be turned by a belt also attached to a pulley on the crankshaft. The fan blows away heat created by generator operation.

The opposite end frame holds the carbon *brushes,* which ride against the copper segments of the commutator, when the mechanism is assembled, to pick up the induced current. But they also have another job. As you may recall, in the simple generator it was possible to induce a stronger magnetic field by switching from permanent magnets to electromagnets. Also, remember that the field frame is fitted with pole shoes with heavy

wire wrapped around them. Those electromagnets now need some current to make them work. The job falls to the brushes.

One of the brushes rides on the commutator and is wired to the housing. This is called the grounded brush. The other brush, which also rides on the commutator, has two wires. One of them goes to the thick, threaded post, labeled "A" on the outside of the field frame; the other is connected to the heavy wires running around the field shoes, making them electromagnets. The field shoes are wired to the thin, threaded post, labeled "F." Because some of the output of the generator is shifted, or shunted away to the fields, this type of charger is called a "shunt type" generator.

When the engine is cranked for starting, the armature spins slowly. Some, but very little, current is induced. After the engine fires, the armature spins much faster and generator output is increased. Some of this output is tapped off to feed the field coils, thus creating a stronger magnetic field. Then the generator is functioning fully. A strong magnetic field produces a greater output; this makes a still stronger magnetic field, which raises output. But unless some controls are used, the generator can burn itself out.

Regulating Output. The generator pours out electricity as long as its armature turns. The faster the armature turns, the higher the production of electricity. To prevent damage from overproduction, a regulating device is required that will route electricity to the battery when needed and guide it away when the battery is satisfied.

Until the 1940s generator output was regulated by a third carbon brush at the commutator. This brush was adjustable and placed between the "A" and "F" brushes. Generator output was determined by where the third brush was positioned in relation to the two standard brushes. This was a crude way of regulating the generator. While the charger was limited from putting out beyond a certain fixed voltage, the speed at which the battery was recharged depended, to a great extent, on how fast the engine was running.

The system that succeeded the third brush is still in use today on cars with generators. This system employs a three-unit regulator consisting of a cutout relay, a voltage regulator relay and a current regulator relay.

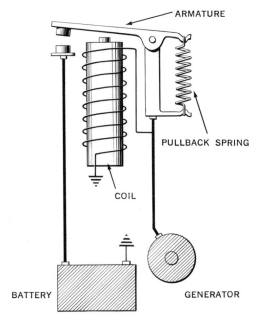

Simple cutout relay of voltage regulator. With the engine off, the spring pulls the contacts apart. Battery cannot discharge. When engine is running, the generator current makes an electromagnet of the coil, pulling the contacts together. Current can now flow from the generator to the battery.

An electrical relay transfers current and voltage from the generator to the battery. And, in the case of the cutout relay, it *prevents* transfer of voltage from the battery to the generator. The relay is actually a switch that operates magnetically. One electrical circuit controls the magnet; another circuit is cut in and out by the action of the magnet.

Cutout Relay. Its function is to connect or disconnect the generator-to-battery circuit. This is a perfect example of an automatic switch that operates by electromagnetism. Its core has two windings, one of heavy wire and one of fine wire. Both are wrapped in the same direction. When the engine is off, spring tension holds the contact points apart. When the engine operates and the generator begins to produce electricity, some electricity is carried in the fine winding, turning the core into a magnet. This pulls the metal strip downward and causes the two contact points to meet. Now the circuit is complete so that the generator current can flow to the battery via the heavy winding.

When the generator stops charging, voltage in the fine winding drops, weakening the electromagnet. Current from the battery is now greater than the current coming from the generator; thus it flows from the battery to the generator via the heavy winding. In doing so, it completely wipes out the magnetism in the core. With no magnetism to hold the metal strip, the contact points separate and the circuit between the battery and the generator is broken. The cutout relay is found on all vehicles using a generator system.

Voltage Regulator. To better understand the role played by the voltage regulator, picture the battery and the generator

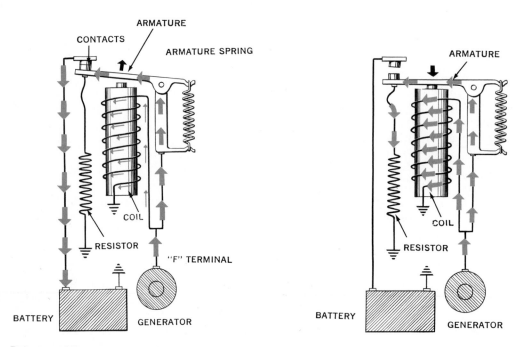

Relay used for current or voltage regulation. When the contacts touch, in the left-hand illustration, the generator charges the battery. When the contacts separate, in the right-hand illustration, the generator output goes through the resistor.

on a see-saw. When the battery is discharged, it is down and the generator is up. There is considerable *difference* between the voltage available at the battery and the voltage available at the generator. As the generator charges the battery, the voltage difference between the two units decreases. When the battery is fully charged, both sides are almost equal—no significant *difference* in voltages. With a satisfied battery, both voltages oppose each other so generator output is cut down to almost zero.

The function of the voltage regulator is to limit the maximum voltage the generator is capable of producing. Though the voltage regulator is also an electromagnetic switch, it is designed somewhat

differently from the cutout. The retracting spring is set so the contact points are held together when the generator is not operating. Also, an electrical resistor is connected as an alternate path from the generator to ground.

When the battery voltage is low, the contacts touch and there is a clear line from the generator to the battery. Answering the call for a supply of voltage, generator output begins to climb. When the charging voltage reaches a safe predetermined value, the little magnetic core of the relay attracts the metal strip downward, breaking the flow to the battery as the contact points separate. Instantly, the generator output is forced to flow through the resistor, where it is dissipated as heat. Output is then made difficult for the generator. Thus it starts cutting back. As the generated voltage drops, the relay core starts losing some of its magnetic powers and releases the metal strip which is pulled upward by the retracting spring. Thus the contacts are joined and generator output to the battery is resumed. Again the buildup occurs, and the core pulls the contacts apart. Flow is again detoured through the resistor and reduces generator output. These cycles of opening and closing contact points are repeated many times a second, holding voltage fairly constant. Because the contact points operate so rapidly, this type of electromagnet is called a vibrating relay.

Current Regulator. The purpose of this unit is to prevent the generator output from exceeding a safe maximum. It operates very much like the vibrating relay of the voltage regulator. Wiring for this unit comes from the generator fields. When the contacts separate, routing the current through a resistor, the generator field strength weakens. This causes a drop in generator voltage. Consequently, current is reduced.

A typical voltage regulator.

When the engine is running, the voltage and current regulator never operate at the same time. When the battery is low and many accessories are turned on, increasing requirements, the current regulator operates to assure battery recharge and to prevent the generator from exceeding its specified maximum. The voltage regulator does not operate at this time because generator voltage never reaches a high enough level to require regulation. When the battery comes up to charge and the accessories are turned off, voltage output climbs and reaches a value at which regulation is required. Consequently, generator output tapers off so that it falls below the value at which the current regulator would operate.

The generator system is vanishing in cars. It is being replaced by an improved type of charger—the alternator. For the same reason the three-brush replaced the dry-cell batteries, and the two-brush generator with regulator replaced the three-brush unit, the alternator replaced the generator—that is, to keep up with the increased electrical demands built into modern car design.

The Alternator. The alternator not only produces more electricity, but keeps charging the battery at the lowest of engine speeds —in fact, even at idle speeds. Though it first appeared in mass production on the 1959 Valiant, the alternator was used many years before on police cars and refrigerator trucks. Its widespread use today in passenger cars was encouraged by developments in the field of solid-state electronics.

Before examining this efficient charging device, let's look at the nature of the electricity in the car's charging system. The generator provides DC (Direct Current) power. This means that power flows in only one direction—from the generator to the battery, from the battery to the electrical appliance, to ground. The counterpart of DC is AC (Alternating Current), in which the generated electricity rapidly shifts forward and back (oscillates) many times per second. Each oscillation is called a cycle, and current is rated in the number of cycles it makes a second. Household electricity is usually AC and has a rating of 60 cycles.

AC for home and industrial use is practical. The generator at the power company creates the flow and sends it directly to homes and shops where it is consumed. But in a car there is a battery that stores power and doles it out as needed. The function of the generator is to replenish the battery rather than produce electricity for immediate use. Alternating current is useless when a battery is present. The only way to charge a battery is with Direct Current.

The most significant difference between the generator and the alternator is that the former operates on the principle of wire coils (the armature) cutting magnetic lines created by stationary field coils. The alternator operates on the principle of a revolving field having its lines cut by stationary wire coils. The second major difference is that the generator has a field that is fed internally by current shunted from one of the brushes. The alternator has a field that is fed directly by the battery.

In a typical alternator the part that turns like the generator armature is a tightly wound coil of wire with an iron shaft at its center. Surrounding the core are two pieces of soft iron resembling six-point tulips. The pieces are positioned so the "petals" of the tulip interlace. The coil, shaft and the pole pieces are called the rotor assembly.

What we actually have is a circular magnet. Current flows from the battery to one of the brushes, then, via the slip rings, to the coil of wire on the shaft. After

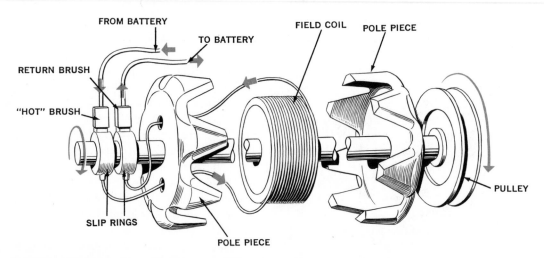

Exploded view of an alternator rotor assembly. A magnetic field is created at the field coil. The coil is energized by the battery through brushes on the slip rings.

coursing through the windings, current returns to the battery via the other slip ring and the brush. This flow is called the field current. As current flows through the coil, a strong magnetic field is created and the 12 "petals" of the pole pieces adopt an alternating polarity. Thus we have a series of fingers polarized north, south, north, south, etc. The entire rotor assembly is designed to fit within a housing. A pulley pressed to one end of the shaft makes it possible for the shaft to be turned by a belt attached to the engine.

Inside the housing the rotor assembly is placed within a ring of stationary wire loops called the *stator*. The most basic stator can be a single loop of wire positioned close to the rotor. As the magnetic field of the spinning rotor is cut by the single wire, voltage is induced in the

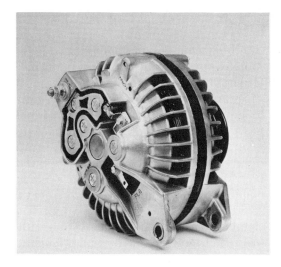

An alternator.

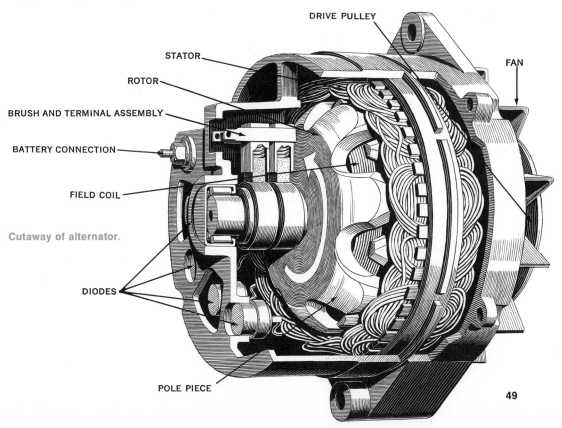

Cutaway of alternator.

DRIVE PULLEY

FAN

STATOR

ROTOR

BRUSH AND TERMINAL ASSEMBLY

BATTERY CONNECTION

FIELD COIL

DIODES

POLE PIECE

loop. In order to increase the voltage the rotor can be spun faster, field strength can be raised, or the number of stator loops can be increased. The modern alternator uses all three methods.

Naturally, the alternator is not going to get by with a single loop of wire. It has three separate long windings of wire wrapped around an iron ring to form a tight circle. The ends of each wire winding are joined together forming a Y connection; the other ends lead away from the stator. (We'll pick them up later.) The stator assembly is positioned around the inside perimeter of the alternator housing. When the rotor with its magnetic field turns, the stator provides many loops of wire to cut those lines of force.

We now have all the essential ingredients for the making of electricity. But since the stator loops will be cutting through magnetic lines emanating from a series of north and south poles, the direction of the current will keep shifting — first in one direction then in the other. Alas, we are back to AC and the only way to charge a battery is with DC. Some changes now must be made if the battery is to get any help at all.

If this were an old-time AC generator and a conversion to DC had to be made, it would require a large and bulky converter — a *rectifier*. Today, a better answer lies in solid-state electronics.

To change the nature of alternator output a device called a *diode* is used. A diode is to electricity what a check valve is to plumbing — it permits flow in one direction and not in another. Inside a typical alternator there are six diodes. Three are attached directly to the housing and are thus negative, or grounded, diodes. The other three are positive, or un-grounded, and placed in an insulated ceramic called a *heat sink*, also located in the housing end frame.

The term heat sink is frequently found in electronic literature and is often misunderstood. It serves the same function for heat as the kitchen sink does for water flowing from the tap. In some cases the tap will discharge more water than the drainpipe can handle. The sink serves to hold the water until the water can drain off. In electronic equipment there are times when more heat is produced than can readily be dissipated. The heat sink serves as a reservoir to hold the excess heat while it is being drained off.

The positive diode allows an electrical flow in only one direction, *to* the positive battery post. A negative diode allows an electrical flow in only one direction, *from* the battery negative post. Soon we will illustrate how a combination of six diodes in the alternator is used to get a continuous flow of DC power.

As mentioned previously, the stator has three separate coil windings, and one end of each winding is joined together to form a Y connection. Each of the remaining ends is connected to a positive diode. In turn, each positive diode has a wire running to a companion negative diode. All of the plus diodes are insulated from each other but lead to a post called the *alternator output terminal*. Since the negative diodes are pressed into the metal end frame of the alternator, they are, in effect, connected to the negative battery terminal via the common ground system. The wiring to the diodes is called the rectification circuit, since it will rectify AC current to DC.

Meanwhile the field rotor assembly spins independently, getting its power directly from the battery, at a very low current, via the brushes and the slip rings.

Rectification goes through six stages in a typical alternator; two stages equal one phase. Each stage forms a complete circuit to the battery—that is, current just induced will flow to the battery via the positive diode and some will drift back to the stator windings through the negative diodes, forming a complete DC circuit. Each of the six stages occurs for only a very brief instant and overlaps with the next as the rotor twirls inside the stator ring. The six stages repeat themselves several times during one single revolution.

The six stages can be charted and plotted. It is the position of the rotor with its north-south tulip tips that determines which stage the alternator is in at any given moment. Stage 1 is arbitrarily chosen here, but stages 2 through 6 are the logical follow-ups. Since it takes only two wires to form a complete circuit, one stator winding is always neutral while the other two serve as the "going" and "coming" channels. In all six stages, current entering the positive diode from its "going" winding has but one way out—through the alternator output terminal. Current cannot bridge the connecting wire to the negative diodes because the diodes are a one-way valve. It cannot return through the positive diodes in the heat sink because they are insulated from each other. Flow to the battery is always in one direction.

Alternator Regulator. Alternator output, like generator output, requires some regulation. However, the job of keeping the alternator in tune with battery needs is far less complex than for its older brother.

While the generator requires a cutout, a voltage regulator and a current regulator, the alternator requires only two controls—a field relay and a voltage regulator. Even the former has been eliminated on cars with ammeters rather than charging lights.

The cutout is unnecessary because the diodes do the job of preventing battery discharge through the alternator when the engine is off. Current attempting to flow back from the battery is stopped by the diode.

Current regulation is unnecessary because the very design of the alternator makes it self-limiting. This self-limiting phenomenon is called *inductive reactance*. The faster the rotor spins, the more AC is produced. But this increase builds up a counter-reaction which opposes current flow. Therefore, at top speed, current is balanced by the opposing voltages and the alternator is safe from damage.

The Field Relay. Though the diodes prevent battery feedback, drainage could occur at the carbon brushes. They are in constant contact with the grounded rings and the battery and represent a complete circuit. The field relay is a simple magnetic switch that permits or prohibits battery current to flow to the field coil. When the ignition key is off, the field relay opens and current to the rotorcoil is aborted. When the key is turned to "On" the contacts of the relay close and the circuit is complete. As mentioned, the field relay is found only on cars with a charge indicator lamp.

Voltage Regulator, Again. The voltage regulator controls current flowing to the revolving field core in the center of the alternator. In turn, the amount of current flowing to the field coil decides the number of lines of force cut with each field revolution. When the field coil turns faster and wants to pass more lines of force through the stator coils, the voltage regulator reduces the field current; thus the amount of cut lines is held down and alternator voltage is limited.

The voltage regulator has a three-part job, which it can only do one at a time. It controls alternator output by (1) sending full line voltage to the field rotor, (2) introducing a resistance to reduce the voltage sent to the field, (3) cutting off voltage going to the field entirely. The basic circuit consists of a wire coming from the ignition switch, through the regulator, then through one slip ring, through the rotor coil and back to ground via the other slip ring. The actual regulator is a typical magnetic relay. Positioned over the wire core is a moveable metal strip (the armature) with contact points on top and bottom surfaces. The armature is sandwiched between upper and lower stationary contact points. Resistors are used to limit the voltage. The electromagnet core of the unit senses electrical needs and acts to attract the armature above it. Offsetting

the magnetic pull is a spring which tends to pull the armature away from the coil.

THE IGNITION SUBSYSTEM

Engine operation is actually a continuing process of explosions in each cylinder. Lighting the fires at the correct moment, with the correct intensity, over and over again is the job assigned to a series of electrical and mechanical components called the ignition subsystem.

Its focal point is that very small combustion chamber that remains under the cylinder head when the piston is in its fully extended position. The spark that explodes the air/fuel mixture is the end of the line for a series of events that occur at extreme speed, fast enough to enable a car going 60 miles per hour to use 200 sparks per second. But rapidity is not the only concern of the ignition system. There is also the problem of creating enough voltage to produce a spark in the highly pressurized combustion chamber. In addition, the ignition system has to parcel out the voltage impulses to each of the

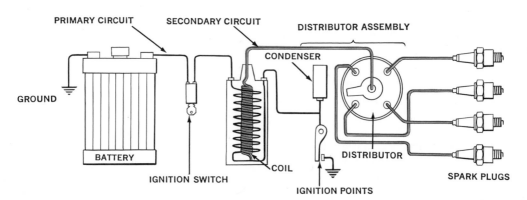

Drawing of ignition system. All parts involving thinner wires are in the low-voltage primary circuit. Heavy wires are in the high-voltage secondary circuit.

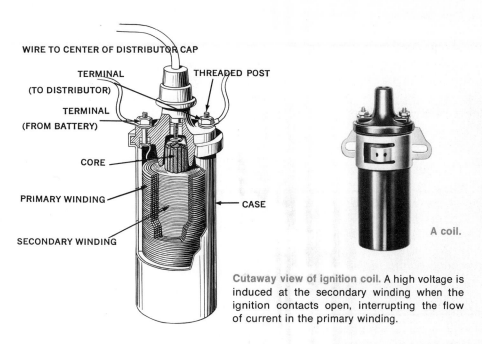

WIRE TO CENTER OF DISTRIBUTOR CAP

TERMINAL
(TO DISTRIBUTOR)

THREADED POST

TERMINAL
(FROM BATTERY)

CORE

PRIMARY WINDING

SECONDARY WINDING

CASE

A coil.

Cutaway view of ignition coil. A high voltage is induced at the secondary winding when the ignition contacts open, interrupting the flow of current in the primary winding.

cylinders at the correct stroke in the cycle and to modify the exact moment the spark will occur based on various operating conditions.

Therefore, the three main functions of the ignition system are:

1) To convert low battery voltage to high voltage.

2) To distribute and deliver electrical impulses to each cylinder.

3) To time the impulse for producing combustion at the moment it will do the most work.

Converting the Voltage. The ignition system is divided into two departments, or circuits. In electrical language these circuits are called the primary (low voltage) circuit and secondary (high voltage) circuit. The terms here mean "first" and "second" rather than implying that one circuit is more important than the other. First, a look at the primary circuit and its components:

The Battery. All electrical power begins at the battery. From here the ignition system gets the starting voltage it must eventually boost. Battery power is indiscriminate. It will flow through any conductor attached to it in a circuit. Since almost all ignition-system components are conductors, a way must be provided to control battery flow to the system.

Ignition Switch. The classical way to control the flow of electricity is with a switch. In the car it is called the ignition switch and it is equipped with a variety of electrical terminals. The most important one is the post that accepts the feed wire, the wire coming from the battery. Next to it are the terminals that control all the electrical accessories and the terminal for the starter motor. Turning the key bridges the battery and the starter motor terminals. Immediately next to the starter motor terminals are two ignition terminals. Both have wires leading to the ignition coil. One has a fixed electrical resistance in its path, the purpose of which will be made clear shortly. For now, assume there is one wire. The moment the starter motor is activated, the circuit to the ignition coil is completed.

The Coil. Outwardly, the coil looks like a baby bottle. It is made of bakelite or metal. Under its skin are several hundred turns of copper wire, called the primary winding, which is the low-voltage circuit. Each end of the wire is attached to a small threaded connector on the outside of the unit. The wire from the ignition terminal of the switch runs to one of the threaded posts on the coil. So far we do not have a complete circuit because nothing is grounded. Voltage can go only from the battery to the ignition switch, to the coil post, through the wire winding, and stop at the other post.

Though nothing is happening now, a potentially useful situation has developed. The ignition coil is actually a transformer, creating high voltage from lower values. When electricity is fed into the wire winding, a magnetic field is created. When the current is abruptly shut off, the field will collapse and induce a high voltage. Once more, we need a switch that will suddenly abort the current flow to the wire windings.

The Distributor. The central mechanism of the entire ignition system is the distributor. Actually, the name is not entirely accurate. For although it does have the function of distributing the high voltage to the spark plugs, as we shall soon see, the distributor also operates the contact breakers and regulates the timing of each spark occurrence at the cylinders.

The contact breakers, popularly called ignition points, are located in the top section of the distributor. They serve as a switch to open and close the ignition primary circuit.

When the points are touching, the current can resume its flow from the coil, through the points to ground—a complete circuit from the battery, through the ignition switch, through the coil, ignition points and ground. With the current flowing through the windings, a strong magnetic field is created in the coil at a low voltage. To collapse this field and create a high induced voltage, the points will have to open, breaking the circuit. The job of separating the points is accomplished mechanically, the rubbing block and distributor shaft playing the leading roles.

The lower end of the distributor shaft is fitted with a gear that meshes with a gear cut into the camshaft. Gear ratio is 1:1. The upper part of the distributor shaft is machined with as many lobes as there are cylinders in the engine. This is the distributor cam. One of the points is fitted with a fiber rubbing block that presses against the cam. When the block is between lobes, the points are closed. As the shaft turns, the lobe pushes the rubbing block and opens the points, then rides past and permits them to close again—an on-off sequence.

When the points are open, there must be a specified distance between them. Most systems require .015 to .018 inch. The precise size of the gap is important because it dictates the length of time the points are allowed to stay together. This time is called the *contact dwell.* If the dwell is too long or too short it will affect the strength of the magnetic field in the coil, the strength of the high voltage de-

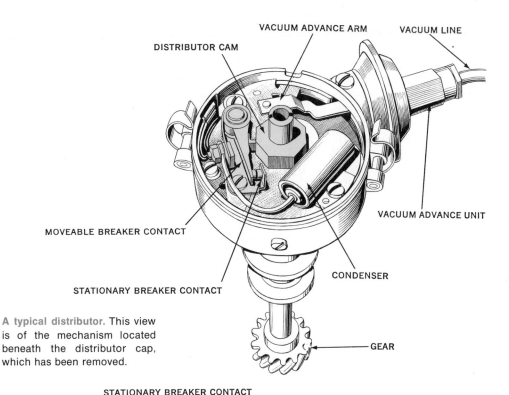

VACUUM ADVANCE ARM

VACUUM LINE

DISTRIBUTOR CAM

VACUUM ADVANCE UNIT

MOVEABLE BREAKER CONTACT

CONDENSER

STATIONARY BREAKER CONTACT

GEAR

A typical distributor. This view is of the mechanism located beneath the distributor cap, which has been removed.

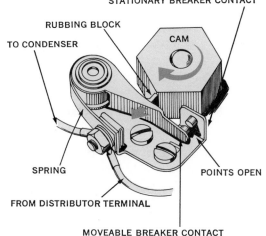

STATIONARY BREAKER CONTACT

RUBBING BLOCK

CAM

TO CONDENSER

SPRING

POINTS OPEN

FROM DISTRIBUTOR TERMINAL

MOVEABLE BREAKER CONTACT

Close-up view of distributor's ignition contacts. As the edge of the cam touches the rubbing block, it opens the contacts. When the rubbing block rides the flat sides of the cam, the contacts close.

livered to the spark plugs and, ultimately, the engine's performance. Electrically, the primary circuit is complete when the points are together and the magnetic field is created in the wire winding. When the points are separated, the field collapses. The primary circuit ends at the base of the stationary breaker contact. From there, the secondary circuit in the ignition coil takes over. However, there is one small problem which must be resolved before we leave the primary circuit.

The Condenser. At the moment the points of any electrical switch begin to separate, current flowing through them tends to keep going and jump across the tiny air gap that is created as they separate.

The result is a small, seemingly harmless spark called an arc. Sometimes you can see this arc when you flip a wall switch. This arc can burn or pockmark ignition points and shorten their life. In addition, arcing drains some energy from the primary coil magnetic field, weakening ignition performance. The problem is solved by the condenser, whose job it is to draw off the current from the points just as they are about to open and send it back to the coil.

The outside of the condenser looks like a lipstick tube with a small wire protruding from one end. Inside the tube is a tight roll of alternate layers of aluminum foil and insulating paper. Every odd layer of foil is connected to the wire lead; even layers are connected to the tube.

The wire lead is connected to the distributor post while the tube is connected to the distributor body. Just as the points are about to crack open, the condenser starts to "load up," drawing off the current at the moveable point that wants to jump across to the stationary point. By the time the condenser is fully loaded, the points are too far apart to arc. This produces a clean break of the ignition points and an abrupt collapse of the magnetic field at the primary winding. While the points are open, the loaded condenser will discharge back to the coil via the lead wire at the distributor post. By the time the points close, the condenser is "empty," ready for the next time the points open.

Secondary Circuit. The secondary circuit begins at the inside of the coil. Under the heavy primary winding is another wire winding. This one consists of several thousand turns of very fine wire insulated with a special shellac. This is called the *secondary winding*. The thin wire is

A distributor.

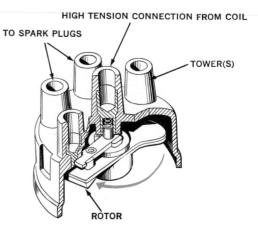

HIGH TENSION CONNECTION FROM COIL

TO SPARK PLUGS

TOWER(S)

ROTOR

Cutaway of distributor cap showing the rotor. Heavy wires run from each side tower to the spark plugs. The center tower holds the wire coming from the coil.

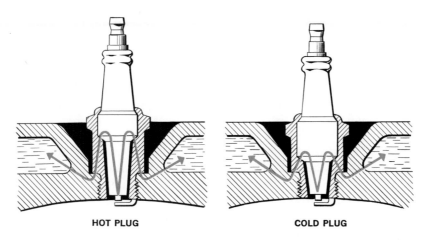

HOT PLUG   **COLD PLUG**

Hot and cold spark plugs. Arrows show the path that the heat follows. The hot plug, used in cars operated mainly on open highways, has a longer heat path. The cold plug, which has a shorter heat path, is used in cars driven in heavy traffic.

wrapped around a core of soft iron strips. One end of the fine winding is connected to the same threaded terminal as the wire running from the ignition switch. The other end is connected to a piece of metal inside the tapered nose of the ignition coil, the high-voltage terminal.

The field that is created by the flow of current through the primary winding completely surrounds the secondary winding. As the current is interrupted by the opening of the ignition points, the magnetic field collapses inward, toward the soft-iron core. As it does so a tiny current is induced in each turn of wire. All the tiny currents add up to a big blast of voltage. Now the job is to get this bundle of energy delivered to the spark plugs.

Distribution. An important part used to get the high voltage directed toward the engine cylinders is the *distributor cap.* Made of plastic, it sits atop the distributor and has a number of towers arranged

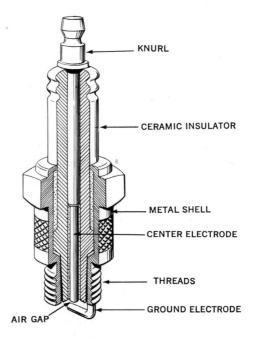

KNURL

CERAMIC INSULATOR

METAL SHELL

CENTER ELECTRODE

THREADS

GROUND ELECTRODE

AIR GAP

Cutaway view of spark plug. The spark occurs at the air gap, the space between the center and ground electrodes.

around its top rim. There are as many towers as there are cylinders—plus one more located in the center of the cap. The center tower is used to hold a thick wire that comes from the coil's secondary terminal. As the high voltage is created, it flows through this wire to the distributor cap. To help distribute the pulse a *rotor* is used. This piece fits directly on top of the distributor shaft under the cap. Though it is a fraction of an inch from the distributor cam, it has nothing to do with the primary circuit.

One end of the rotor's brass strip is directly beneath the center tower of the distributor cap and the other end is below any one of the other towers that ring the cap. In operation, the high voltage blast comes from the wire, through the center tower to the rotor's tip. From there it is conducted to the other tip. It then jumps upward to metal contacts under the other towers. From there, the pulse is conducted to the cylinders by the heavy wire fitted to each of the towers and each of the spark plugs. By the time the rotating distributor shaft moves the rotor tip to the next tower, the points have closed, the primary winding has built a magnetic field, the points have opened and another high-voltage discharge is on its way to the rotor.

In essence, the rotor and the cap are the real distributors of the electrical pulses. What now remains is to get the high voltage into the cylinders. This is the job of the spark plugs.

Delivering the spark. The spark plugs are screwed into the cylinder head, one for each cylinder, and extend into the combustion chambers. Each plug consists of two heavy wires called electrodes. The center electrode runs from one tip of the plug to the other. The other, the ground electrode, is welded to the lower threaded section. A ceramic jacket insulates the electrodes, which develop high heat when electrical surges are sent through them.

Spark plugs are given "hot" and "cold" designations. The hot plug retains its heat longer, owing to a longer ceramic tip, and is used on cars traveling mainly on open roads. A cold plug dissipates heat quickly, owing to its short ceramic tip, and is used on cars traveling mainly in heavy traffic. There are "in-between" heat ranges as a compromise for cars used in both kinds of driving.

The function of the spark plug is *not* to create a spark. It is to provide a gap between two electrical conductors in the combustion chamber. The high voltage carried from one of the towers through one of the heavy wires travels down through the center of the spark plug to its lower end. The pulse leaps across to the ground electrode and creates a spark, igniting the air/fuel mixture in the chamber.

If the gap between the electrodes is too small, the spark will be too small to burn the fuel charge. If the gap is too wide, the high-voltage pulse cannot jump across to get to the grounded electrode. Thus there is no spark. Specifications for the spark plug gap are approximately .028 to .035 inch.

Timing the spark. For the engine to produce peak power, the spark must occur at the correct moment. This is when a chamber is charged with fuel and the piston is ready to go down on the power stroke. In each engine, the cylinders fire in a specific order, determined by the balanced shape of the crankshaft.

A 4-cylinder engine is a good illustra-

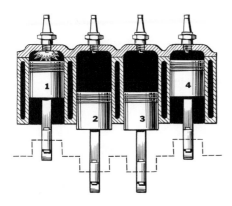

Firing order of 4-cylinder engine. Though the cylinders are numbered 1-2-3-4, the spark plugs fire in 1-3-4-2 order.

tion. Note that the cranks are 180 degrees apart. Pistons 1 and 4 are up, 2 and 3 are down. Each set is said to be *companion pistons.* If 1 is firing its plug, 4 cannot fire, but goes down with it on the intake stroke as 2 and 3 come up. Then piston 3 fires, going down with piston 2. Pistons 1 and 4 come up and 4 fires; 2 and 3 come up and 2 fires. Thus the firing order is 1-3-4-2. On a 6-cylinder engine the firing order is 1–5–3–6–2–4. On V-8s there is no typical firing order, but it is not consecutive.

Because the rotor must deliver the electrical pulses in the designed order as it spins under the cap, the wires to the spark plugs from the cap towers must be installed in the proper sequence.

The next problem is to get the spark to occur in each cylinder at the exact moment calculated to produce the most power. In the explanation of the Otto Cycle in Chapter 1, it was assumed that the spark occurs when the piston is at top dead center of its travel (TDC) and ready to go down on the power stroke. This is only approximately correct. If the spark occurs at TDC the piston might be halfway down by the time the explosion is

over. In this case the available time that power is applied to the piston is reduced.

Full power is achieved when the spark and the explosion start and finish before, during and slightly after the piston is at TDC. This is only possible if the time-consuming spark and explosion occur well before the piston reaches the top. How much before depends on the engine horsepower, type of gasoline used and the general power requirements of the driver.

The timing of the spark relative to piston position is adjustable. This setting is measured in degrees of crankshaft revolution. As an example, let's take a typical specification — 10 degrees before top dead center (10 deg. BTDC). To help determine where the piston, or crank throw, is in relation to TDC, the engine's crankshaft vibration damper has some lines

Timing marks on the vibration damper.

scribed into it. As the damper turns, the lines pass a fixed pointer secured to the timing case cover. These marks say what is happening to cylinder 1, and thus provide a reflection of what is happening to the other pistons. When the zero mark is lined up with the pointer piston 1 is at TDC. If the crankshaft is slowly turned backwards to the 10 mark, the piston is adjusted to 10 degrees before TDC.

According to the specifications, at this point the ignition contacts should just open and the rotor should be under the tower containing the #1 spark plug wire. What if this is not the case and the rubbing block is between the lobes with the points closed? Then the distributor shaft must be turned so that the points are about to open. To get the distributor shaft to turn, the camshaft must be turned. To get the camshaft to turn, the crankshaft must be turned. But, if the crankshaft is turned the piston will move and will no longer be at 10 deg. BTDC. This may appear to be a dilemma, but there is a way.

If the distributor shaft cannot be turned to get the lobe to the rubbing block, then the rubbing block and the entire contact set is brought to the lobe. The distributor body itself is designed for a limited amount of turning. Thus the rubbing block is brought to the edge of the cam so the contact set will just open when the crankshaft is turned.

Ignition timing is set at idle speed with the use of instruments. This is the basic starting point. However, as the engine operates, timing requirements change with engine speed. Our demonstration engine requires a 10-degree advanced spark setting for the explosion to be completely finished by 5 degrees after TDC at the very latest. When the engine is operated at faster speeds, the spark has

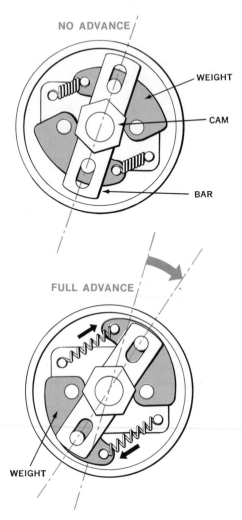

Distributor's centrifugal advance mechanism. At low speed (top), the weights are close to the shaft. At higher speeds centrifugal force pushes weights outward (bottom).

to take place still sooner to be completed in the allotted time. It is impossible for the driver to advance the spark every time the car is accelerated. What is required is a fully automatic system for advancing the spark in accordance with engine speed. Since the distributor shaft is an accurate reflector of engine speed,

VACUUM ADVANCE UNIT MOVES BREAKER PLATE

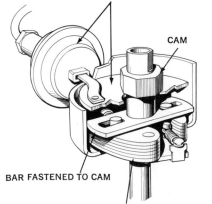

CAM

BAR FASTENED TO CAM

CENTRIFUGAL ADVANCE UNIT MOVES CAM

Vacuum advance at the distributor. Vacuum from the engine will turn the plate, advancing the spark when the engine is at part throttle.

it is used to provide the automatic spark advance. Immediately below the contact breaker plate are two elongated weights. As distributor-shaft speed increases, centrifugal force throws the weights outward causing the bar to rotate. Since the bar is firmly attached to the distributor shaft, it is forced to rotate slightly, advancing the spark. When the engine slows down, the weights retract and the bar unwinds, putting the timing back to its initial idle setting. This advance mechanism comes into full use at high engine speeds. To provide an automatic temporary spark advance at moderate speeds a vacuum *device* is employed.

Vacuum advance mechanism. The vacuum device is a special metal chamber, usually screwed to the side of the distributor body. At idle speeds there is no vacuum in the small tube; spark advance is provided by the initial spark adjustment. At the opposite extreme, when the throttle is wide open, spark advance is handled by

the weights. But, at part-throttle, vacuum conditions in the intake manifold are such that the pistons get less than their full measure of air/fuel mix and the burning process is slowed down considerably. To compensate for the increased time it takes to burn a charge, the spark must be advanced if the driver is to get any fuel economy.

At part-throttle the high vacuum in the manifold is brought to the vacuum diaphragm by the small tube. As the diaphragm is pulled back, it pulls the link attached to the breaker plate. Thus the breaker plate turns, advancing the spark. If the throttle is opened further, vacuum falls off and the centrifugal weights take over. The spring inside the diaphragm chamber pulls all the parts back to their relaxed state.

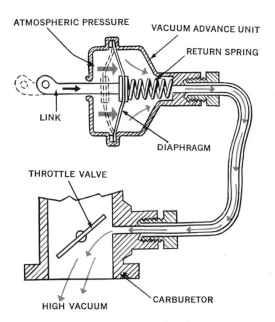

ATMOSPHERIC PRESSURE

VACUUM ADVANCE UNIT

RETURN SPRING

LINK

DIAPHRAGM

THROTTLE VALVE

HIGH VACUUM

CARBURETOR

Vacuum advance mechanism in operation. High vacuum pulls the diaphragm and link attached to distributor plate, creating an advance. At low vacuum, the spring pulls the link back.

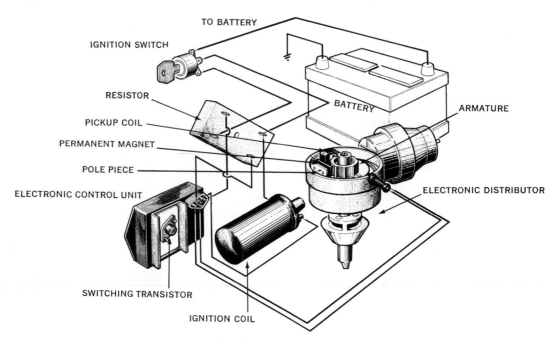

TO BATTERY

IGNITION SWITCH

RESISTOR

PICKUP COIL

PERMANENT MAGNET

POLE PIECE

ELECTRONIC CONTROL UNIT

BATTERY

ARMATURE

ELECTRONIC DISTRIBUTOR

SWITCHING TRANSISTOR

IGNITION COIL

Diagram of electronic ignition. The system uses no wearing parts. Instead of contact points a fixed permanent-magnet pickup assembly is used. The spinning armature sends a signal to the electronic control unit, inducing the ignition coil to produce high voltage for use at the spark plugs via a regular distributor cap.

Thus the ignition system has taken battery voltage, boosted it and delivered it to the cylinders at the right time.

ELECTRONIC IGNITION

Today no technology is exempt from improvement and change. The conventional ignition system with its contact points is no exception.

New in this area is electronic ignition. Though it appeared briefly on some Chevrolet Corvette and Pontiac Grand Prix cars in the 1960s, electronic ignition was first presented as standard equipment on a full line of cars by the Chrysler Corporation in 1974.

In electronic ignition the following parts are eliminated: breaker points; breaker mounting plate; rubbing block; condenser; cam lobes on the distributor shaft. However, the following parts are retained: distributor base; distributor cap; rotor; vacuum and centrifugal spark advance.

The heart of the system is a low-voltage generator built into the top of the distributor. Fitted to the top of the distributor shaft is a round device resembling a gear. It has as many "teeth" as the engine has cylinders. This is called the armature. To the side of the armature is a pole piece with a permanent magnet. Both are at a fixed, preset distance from each other.

Also inside the distributor is a small pick-up coil, very much like one of the recording heads on a tape recorder. Mounted to the firewall in the engine compartment is the electronic control unit. It is essentially a circuit board that connects various transistors, resistors, diodes and capacitors.

As the armature turns, a low voltage is generated at the magnet, which is picked up by the coil and sent as a signal to the electronic control unit. Here the signal is fed as a pulse to the ignition coil, which operates in a conventional manner by transforming low-voltage input to high-voltage output. The electronic control unit also regulates the dwell angle. This would be the number of degrees of rotation the conventional breaker points are closed. But, in electronic ignition, dwell angle regulates coil build-up and discharge.

There are quite a number of advantages to electronic ignition. It maintains a higher voltage throughout all the speed ranges. The higher voltages allow the ignition system to "forgive" worn or fouled spark plugs. Electronic ignition is also very reliable at high speeds when the more conventional system is likely to experience ignition contact bounce or inadequate build-up times in the coil. The new system also allows an 18,000-mile spark plug life. Because of its advantages, experts presume that electronic ignition will soon become standard equipment on all cars.

THE STARTER SUBSYSTEM

Though the operation of the engine is self-perpetuating, there is the problem of putting the entire combustion process into motion. This is strictly a mechanical problem—that is, the pistons of the engine must be moved physically up and down to cause the first combustion blast, leading to an operating engine. Turning the crankshaft, that moves the pistons, is the job of the starter motor.

Back in the "good old days" initial movement of the pistons was accomplished by muscle power. The driver would turn on the ignition switch, shift the gears to neutral position, insert a crank in the front of the engine and give it some hefty turns by hand. The crank was connected directly to the engine crankshaft. Once the engine was started, the crank handle was supposed to be nudged, disengaging itself from the crankshaft. Often it did not uncouple and the handle would kick back, causing physical injury.

Starter Motor. Though many better methods for starting were developed over the

A starter motor.

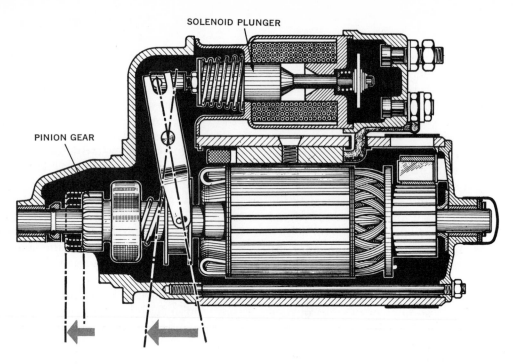

SOLENOID PLUNGER

PINION GEAR

Cutaway view of starter motor. When the key is turned, the solenoid plunger is pulled forward, forcing the starter gear rearward into the ring gear on the flywheel.

years, the ultimate solution was introduced on the 1912 Cadillac. This was the electric starter motor developed by Charles F. Kettering.

Basically, the electric starter is a special type of motor which converts electricity to mechanical energy. But, provisions are made to use the turning force of the motor to turn the crankshaft.

In a typical setup, the flywheel, which is bolted to the crankshaft, is fitted with a large ring containing many teeth. This is called the *ring gear*. The starter motor has a specially designed tailpiece that includes a small gear on its armature shaft. This gear is called the *pinion gear*. The idea is to engage the pinion gear with the ring gear. The rotating pinion turns the ring gear and disengages when the engine is running under its own power.

In most cars today the starter switch is contained inside the ignition key lock. In earlier times it was located on the floor. The driver stepped on a button that activated a rod extended through the engine firewall. The opposite end of the rod came to rest at the top of a lever at the rear of the starter motor. As the rod was pushed forward, the top of the lever pushed a button switch connecting the starter motor to the battery; the lower half of the lever pushed the pinion gear backward into the ring gear. With both conditions operating, the engine was "turned over." This system was called the *positive shift starter*.

In time, starting was made easier by the use of a pushbutton on the instrument panel and a magnetic switch under the hood. When the driver turned the key to "On," not only was the ignition circuit

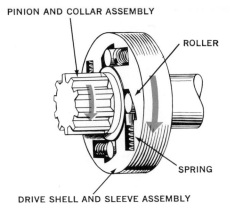

PINION AND COLLAR ASSEMBLY

ROLLER

SPRING

DRIVE SHELL AND SLEEVE ASSEMBLY

Overrunning clutch drive. This device locks to the starter motor armature shaft when the engine is cranking and disengages when the engine is running.

engaged, but an additional circuit as well —this one from the battery to an electromagnetic switch. Attached to the switch were cables from the battery and to the starter motor and a thin wire leading to a button on the dashboard. When the driver pushed the button, the wire coil inside the switch became a magnet. Inside the coil was a heavy metal plunger that was pulled upward by the magnetic force. The plunger bridged the contacts connected to the heavy cables. Thus the current could flow to the starter motor. Releasing the button, destroyed the magnet in the switch and the plunger receded, breaking the circuit from the battery to the motor.

The most important development in starter motor circuits was the introduction

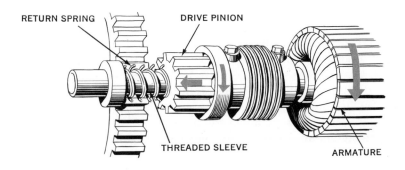

RETURN SPRING

DRIVE PINION

THREADED SLEEVE

ARMATURE

The Bendix drive.

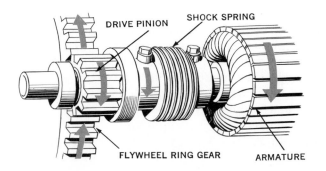

DRIVE PINION

SHOCK SPRING

FLYWHEEL RING GEAR

ARMATURE

of the *starter solenoid*. This does the same job as the magnetic switch, with the additional feature of actually moving the pinion gear into the ring gear. In other words, the solenoid accomplishes what the positive shift device did, but it works electrically rather than mechanically.

When the key is turned, the coil in the solenoid is energized and the plunger completes the heavy-duty starter circuit and pushes the pinion gear into mesh. With the ignition circuit activated, the turning crankshaft will soon be spinning under its own power. Now there is a problem of getting the starter gear out of there before the starter motor is destroyed by the excessive speed developed by the crankshaft. The flywheel gear has about 15 times more teeth than the starter gear. Even at a moderate speed of, say, 1,000 rpm, the starter gear will be forced to rotate at 15,000 rpm. Speeds like this are not healthy for the starter motor.

The part of the starter motor that saves the starter gear and the motor armature is called the *starter drive*. There are two distinct designs for the drive. These are called the *overrunning clutch* drive and the *Bendix* drive. For both, engagement and disengagement works on the inertia principle.

The overrunning clutch. This is a device that locks to the starter motor armature shaft when the engine is cranking and disengages from the shaft after the engine is running. The main parts of this clutch can be divided into two groups, the driving members and the driven members. When the ignition key is turned and the solenoid gets the message, its plunger is pulled in, sending the pinion back toward the flywheel.

As the pinion moves rearward, it is not yet spinning. In a nonrotating state the small springs inside the hub push the rollers to the narrow end of the tapered oval slots. This has the effect of wedging the outer hub and pinion against the inner hub making them, in effect, as one with the pinion gear.

The solenoid plunger is set up so the pinion starts spinning a split second before it is about to engage the ring gear. When the gears do contact, the entire starter drive is spinning as if it were a solid unit. As soon as the engine is running, flywheel speed is imposed on the pinion gear. Thus the driven members go faster, or overrun, the driving members. Centrifugal force then moves the rollers out of their jammed position to the wide part of the taper. Now the pinion and the hub are independent of the motor armature. The effects of the high-speed flywheel operation cannot be transmitted to the starter. By this time the driver realizes that the engine is running and releases the key. The solenoid de-energizes, releasing the plunger and the pinion gear withdraws to rest position.

The Bendix drive. This drive works on the spinning nut principle. The drive unit consists of a sleeve which fits over the armature shaft. On the outside, the sleeve has a coarse spiral thread. Consider this as the bolt. The pinion gear has a similar thread cut to its inside rim. This gear is screwed onto the sleeve. Consider this as the nut. The spiral is such that it allows the pinion gear to travel about 1½ inches in about a quarter of a turn. The pinion gear is heavily weighted on one side.

When the driver turns the key, the starter motor armature starts spinning. In so doing, the threaded sleeve revolves with it. Remember, this is the bolt. Because the gear (nut) is unbalanced, it does not revolve with the sleeve; it "walks" its way backward on the threaded sleeve. The heavy spring at the end absorbs the shock as the gear reaches the ring gear. Now the armature shaft and the Bendix drive become one unit, cranking the flywheel.

When the flywheel starts to turn the pinion gear at operating speed, which is much higher than armature shaft speed, the pinion will then "walk" down the sleeve, out of mesh with the flywheel gear. Thus the gear is sent back to home position.

Over the years there have been slight modifications in the starter drives. However, the basic design has been the same, using the motion of the flywheel to get the starter drive to its original position.

3
FUEL SYSTEM

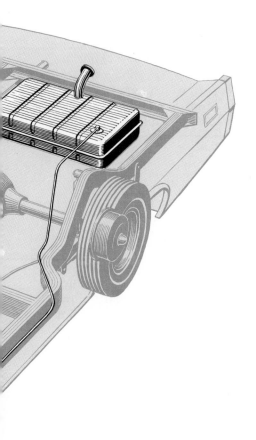

Motion is energy unleashed. Fuel is energy packaged. The function of any engine is to release the energy within fuel and convert it into motion. The car engine does this too. However, in order for the crankshaft to turn and produce the motion to propel the car, three conditions must prevail:

1) The engine must have compression. This is provided by the piston rings and gaskets.

2) The engine must have ignition. This is provided by the battery, coil, ignition points and spark plugs—the ignition system.

3) The engine must have fuel. This is provided by the fuel tank, fuel lines, fuel gauge, fuel pump and carburetor—the fuel system.

THE FUEL

Gasoline is a substance composed mainly of hydrogen and carbon atoms, called hydrocarbons. It will burn and liberate heat energy when it is mixed with oxygen. Gasoline is derived from crude oil through an extensive process of distillation. Before it goes to market it is purified, blended with additives and mixed with a variety of other gasolines.

The essential quality of gasoline is its ability to change from a liquid to a vapor so that it can mix with air to make a combustible mixture. This quality is called *volatility*. How volatile a gas is as it enters the throat of the carburetor is the result of all the mixing and blending prescribed by the refinery chemists. Gasoline for sale in Tampa, Florida, may be less volatile than the same brand of gas sold in Boise, Idaho, since warmer climates aid combustion and colder climates impede the process.

The chemists are forever doing a balancing act in designing the volatility of the fuel. A gasoline which is too volatile will vaporize readily and produce vapor lock. A gas which is not volatile enough will cause hard starting and poor engine performance.

Gas Ratings. The measure by which a gasoline can burn properly without knocking is called the *octane number*. The rating is obtained from the blending of high- and low-quality fuels to match various engine sizes. A high-compression engine will require a high-octane gasoline blend. The reverse is true of a low-compression engine.

In addition to the blending of various fuels, there are anti-knock additives used by the refinery. They include tetra-ethyl lead (TEL) and tetra-methyl lead (TML). The lead in these additives acts as a heat sink. That is, the lead absorbs the high heat created in front of the flame wall in the cylinder and prevents the mixture from igniting itself. In recent years, there has been a tendency to design engines to operate at lower compressions, making the use of lead unnecessary. Lead deteriorates catalytic converters, which remove poisonous emissions from the engine exhaust, and it is a dangerous pollutant.

THE BURNING PROCESS

The actual combustion of an air-fuel charge in the combustion chamber is not a single explosive act, but a chain of events which lasts for a fraction of a second. Keep in mind that an explosion is defined as very rapid combustion. After the air-fuel mixture is compressed and the spark jumps the gap at the spark plug, combustion occurs in three stages.

The first stage is called the *nucleus of flame*. As soon as the pulse jumps across the spark electrodes, a small ball of blue flame develops in the spark plug gap. The ball slowly enlarges, but there is no measurable pressure or heat created.

The second stage is called *hatching out*. Now the original ball of flame breaks up and spreads to the fuel-air mixture in that corner of the combustion chamber close to the spark plug. There is now a slight rise of temperature and of pressure in the combustion chamber.

The last stage is *propagation*. Now all the portions of the flame in the corner of the combustion chamber unite to form a solid wave of fire sweeping across the entire chamber. The flame is swift and builds up an intense heat and pressure, which bears upon the piston and sends it down with a powerful force.

The transition from one phase to the other must be swift but smooth if the piston is to get the full benefit of the energy created by the process. However, if a grade of gasoline is used that is not suited for a particular engine, an intense counter-reaction occurs. This is called *detonation,* and it can rob much energy and also ruin the engine.

Commonly called engine knock or ping, detonation produces a sound that is much like steel marbles rolling around in an empty can. It occurs only in the last stage, propagation. As the flame front moves across the combustion chamber, the un-burned fuel-air mix ahead of it is heated and compressed. A proper grade of gas can withstand this pressure. An improper grade of gasoline will cause the mixture on the far end of the chamber to ignite spontaneously and set up its own flame wave — headed at the original flame wave. The result is a collision, an uncontrolled rapid burning and a misdirection of energy. As a consequence there is a power loss and a buildup of extra heat. Occasional detonation is tolerable. However, if the engine is permitted to knock for a steady period it can cause damage, especially to the piston head.

At the opposite end of the problem scale is a phenomenon called *pre-ignition.* This is the ignition of the fuel-air mix before the precise moment it should start burning. The major cause of pre-ignition is an ignition timing that is too far advanced. But there are other reasons for its occurrence. They include the accumulation of deposits in and around the combustion chamber which get so hot that they glow and set off the gas charge before the spark plug can do it.

The two terms, detonation and pre-igni-

tion, should not be confused. Pre-ignition takes place *before* the spark plug fires; detonation takes place *after* the plug fires.

FUEL STORAGE

The fuel system starts at the tank. In most of today's cars the tank is located in the rear of the vehicle. However, throughout the years it has been found in the front, under the seats, or behind a fender. With the developments in new plastics it will soon be possible for the car makers to shape the tanks in almost any form and place them almost anywhere in the car.

The major considerations in positioning the fuel tank are (1) protection in the event of a collision, (2) protection against bottoming on the road as the car bounces, (3) protection against flying stones and pebbles picked up by the tires of other vehicles.

The tank is a box made of sheet steel. Inside are a number of short walls, or baffles, which slow down the sloshing of the gas as the car stops and goes. Attached to one of the sides of the tank is a filler neck which leads to the outside of the car. Some provisions are made to vent the tank to atmospheric pressure. This is important for both filling the tank and for the slow draining of gas when the car is in use. The idea is to help the air from the atmosphere replace the gas leaving the tank.

Let's start with an empty tank. The attendant inserts the gas-pump nozzle into the filler neck and gas starts pouring into the tank. In so doing, it begins to displace the air which had occupied the area. The air has no other outlet but the filler neck. Since that route is partially clogged by a filler nozzle, the vent pipe, fitted to the side of the filler neck, eases the situation.

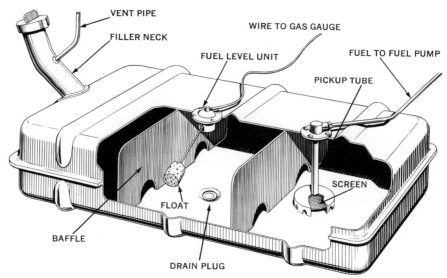

VENT PIPE

FILLER NECK

WIRE TO GAS GAUGE

FUEL LEVEL UNIT

FUEL TO FUEL PUMP

PICKUP TUBE

SCREEN

FLOAT

BAFFLE

DRAIN PLUG

Cutaway of a fuel tank. On all cars from 1972 on, the vent pipe is fed into a canister of charcoal. In turn, a tube leads from the canister to the carburetor. Thus the gas fumes cannot go into the atmosphere, and the tank is vented.

Air can now exit through the vent pipe and gas can enter rapidly.

When the engine is running, the gas that is drained from the tank must be replaced with air. If not, a vacuum will form in the tank and atmospheric air pressure will collapse it. On some cars, the same tube that vents the air also draws it in. Other cars have a vented gas cap—that is, a cap that allows air to be drawn into the tank through a special opening, though the cap is firmly secured to the neck.

We know from research into the sources of air pollution that gasoline fumes are responsible for large quantities of raw hydrocarbons in the air. Therefore, a completely enclosed system has been developed for venting the tank on late-model cars. Fumes which are forced from the tank must go through a charcoal filter linked to the carburetor. In this manner the fumes are burned off rather than set free in the air.

The tank has three attachments. The first is a drain plug at the very bottom. This is used for emptying the tank prior to its removal from the car or for draining a contaminated gas supply. The second attachment is a tube which is the beginning of the fuel line to the engine. The tube opening is situated about a half inch above the tank floor. This location reduces the chances of drawing water and sediment into the fuel system, for these impurities usually sink to the bottom. The third attachment to the tank is the float unit which indicates fuel level. It is usually inserted into the tank from the top. This unit is explained in Chapter 14, "Instruments and Accessories."

FUEL PUMP

From the gas tank the gasoline is carried to the engine via the *fuel line,* made of

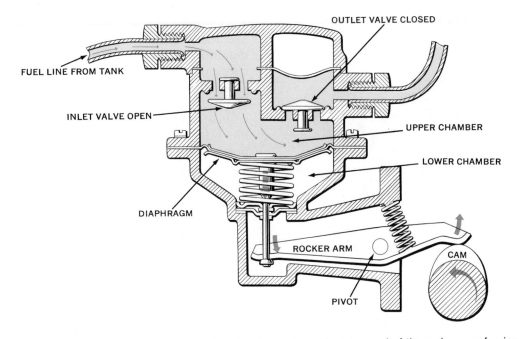

OUTLET VALVE CLOSED

FUEL LINE FROM TANK

INLET VALVE OPEN

UPPER CHAMBER

LOWER CHAMBER

DIAPHRAGM

ROCKER ARM

CAM

PIVOT

A typical fuel pump in operation. In the top drawing, a cam raises one end of the rocker arm, forcing down the other end, pulling down the diaphragm. Suction pulls the inlet check-valve open and draws gas from the fuel line coming from the tank.

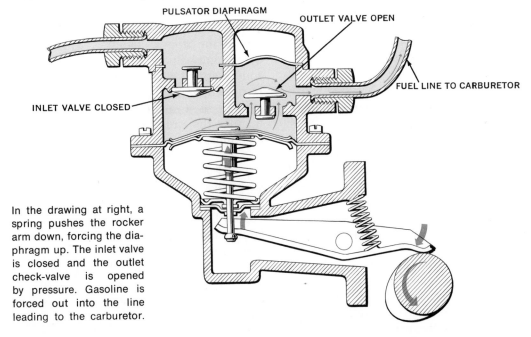

PULSATOR DIAPHRAGM

OUTLET VALVE OPEN

INLET VALVE CLOSED

FUEL LINE TO CARBURETOR

In the drawing at right, a spring pushes the rocker arm down, forcing the diaphragm up. The inlet valve is closed and the outlet check-valve is opened by pressure. Gasoline is forced out into the line leading to the carburetor.

A fuel pump. The housing is of aluminum. Note the thick flange to the left of the rocker arm. Here is where the pump is bolted to the engine.

copper or steel, which runs underneath the car. Care is taken to protect the line from damage either from flying stones or from rubbing against any of the under-car components.

The line terminates at the *fuel pump*. A pump is necessary because the gas in the tank is at a lower level than it is at the engine. There was a time when the tank was perched well above the engine and the fuel was fed by gravity. Since the position of the tank on today's cars makes gravity feeding impossible, a pump is essential.

The conventional pump is mechanically operated, very much like the old-fashioned pump used to raise well water. The "handle" of the pump, called the rocker arm, reaches into the engine to contact a special cam on the engine camshaft. As the shaft turns it moves the rocker arm up and down, activating the diaphragm. The diaphragm is composed of several layers of fabric impregnated with compounds which make it resistant to wear and deterioration. It is stretched across the center of the pump housing, dividing the pump into an upper and lower chamber. The main job of the diaphragm is to activate the important check valves in the upper chamber.

As the diaphragm is pulled downward by one motion of the rocker arm, a suction is created in the upper chamber, moving the inlet check valve from its seat and pressing the outlet valve against its seat. Gas is pulled in from the tank line while the line to the carburetor is sealed. When the rocker arm "pumps" the other way, the valves reverse their modes. The inlet valve is sealed while the outlet valve leaves its seat and gas is pumped to the carburetor under pressure. By that time the cam lobe has come around to produce another movement of the arm, another downward pull of the diaphragm, and another intake of gasoline.

The fuel pump delivers gasoline in spurts or pulsations that could be harmful to some delicate parts in the carburetor. To reduce these pulsations, many pumps have an additional diaphragm across the top of the upper chamber. This second diaphragm separates the gasoline from some trapped air above valves. As the gas is pulled in and forced out, the trapped air acts as a cushion or damper. In this manner the pulsations are leveled off to an almost constant flow.

Double Pump. A variation of the mechanical pump described above was in use on many cars from the late 1930s until the late 1950s. This one was the combination fuel and vacuum pump. It was designed to overcome the main disadvantage of the vacuum-operated windshield wipers.

In those days the power for the wipers came from engine vacuum. A small tube was connected from the engine's intake manifold to a vacuum motor under the dashboard. The wipers would operate only when the engine was running. This system had its drawbacks. When the engine labored up a hill, or when the gas pedal was suddenly depressed, engine vacuum dropped and the wipers stopped working.

To solve this problem and have the wipers operate at a more uniform rate, the combination fuel pump provides a steady vacuum supply to operate the wipers. Now that all cars are required to have two-speed electric wipers, the combination pump has almost disappeared.

Electric Fuel Pump. The ultimate in fuel delivery is the electric fuel pump, found on many foreign and race cars. It has certain advantages. It can be located almost anywhere on the car. (Some cars even have the pump submerged in the gas tank.) In addition, the pump will start working as soon as the ignition is on, rather than waiting for the engine to be cranked or running.

Inside the electric fuel pump, the check valve setup is similar to that in the mechanical pump. The pumping action varies, however. Some models use a diaphragm; others use a bellows which provides the vacuum and pressure necessary to move the gasoline.

Vapor Lock. As a rule, fuel pumps are trouble-free, but sometimes they succumb to a problem known as vapor lock. This is the malady which attacks on steaming hot days, usually in traffic jams. When the under-hood temperatures get very high, some of the fuel in the pump and in the fuel line to the carburetor will vaporize. When the rocker arm goes up and down, all that results is a compression of the vapor bubbles. Hence, the pump cannot move any liquid fuel. Naturally, the car will then stall due to fuel starvation. Since the pump cannot purge the vapor bubbles, all the driver can do is wait for the pump to cool off, allowing the vapor to return to a liquid state. Or he can pour cold water

Four-barrel carburetor.

on the pump to speed the process. A more permanent solution is to see that the fuel pump is insulated from heat.

The fuel line going to the carburetor is the last piece in the fuel-delivery system. The next stop is the unit which deals with converting fuel to power—the carburetor.

THE CARBURETOR

The carburetor's main function is to measure and mix the best combination of gasoline and air to satisfy all engine speeds and loads. This may not appear to be a tall order. But the carburetor must perform instantly and automatically, and these requirements have resulted in making the carburetor a complex device.

Little can be learned by taking a carburetor apart. Most of it is a casting with a variety of hidden passageways. Essential to unlocking the secret of the carburetor is knowing some of the basic physical principles governing its operation.

- Air has weight.
- Air pressure at sea level is 14.7 pounds per square inch (atmospheric pressure).
- Air pressure below normal atmospheric pressure is called vacuum (suction).
- Liquids and gases are classified as fluids.
- Fluids take the shape of the containers that hold them.
- Fluids are moved by application of pressure (pushing) or by vacuum (pulling).

Keeping these principles in mind, let's examine a simple carburetor. To be pre-

cise, the three basic tasks of the carburetor are (1) to atomize, or break up, the fuel, thereby increasing its ability to burn, (2) to mix the fuel with air, (3) to measure, or meter, the fuel and air in correct proportions for all operating conditions—all instantly and automatically.

The first requirement for a carburetor is a reservoir for the fuel—a bowl. Except for the fuel line coming from the fuel pump, a vent hole and a discharge tube, the bowl is fully enclosed. Gasoline sent by the fuel pump will be stored in the bowl and used as engine conditions demand.

To get the fuel out of the bowl, a discharge tube is inserted into the side of the bowl at an angle, much like a drinking straw in a glass of soda. The level of the gas in the tube will always be the same as the level in the bowl.

Now we need some method of drawing the gasoline up the tube—a source of vacuum. The best vacuum generator in the

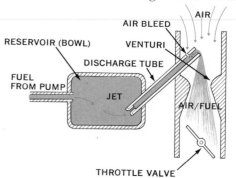

A simplified version of a carburetor. The basic elements are the air horn (right), fuel reservoir and discharge tube. Downward movement of the engine pistons sucks air into the horn, pulling gasoline from the tube. The throttle valve regulates the flow of the mixture to the pistons.

car is the engine itself. Every time a piston goes down, it creates suction. The combined suction of all the pistons is brought to a focal point at the intake manifold. The carburetor is bolted to the intake manifold. Thus it can take advantage of the concentrated vacuum in this area.

When the pistons start working, the air each of them draws in comes through the top of the carburetor, down its length. Thus there is a constant stream of air sucking through. Appropriately, this section of the carburetor is called an *air horn*.

The Venturi. Though the vacuum in the air horn is strong, it is not sufficient to assure a steady pull of gasoline up the discharge tube. The vacuum could be strengthened by making the pistons larger or by making the air horn smaller. But that means re-engineering the whole engine. A simpler solution is to pinch the air horn somewhere along its length and cause a partial restriction. Because the flowing air will then "bunch" up above the restriction, it will push hard to get through it. The faster the air moves past this restrictive point, the more reduced is the atmospheric pressure, and the stronger is the vacuum. The restriction is called the *venturi tube* (after the Italian physicist G. B. Venturi, 1746–1822).

Now, if we drill a small hole on the side of the air horn, just at the venturi, we can insert the discharge tube through it and bolt the fuel bowl to the horn. Conditions are now ripe for getting a steady flow of gas out of the bowl. Air is sucked into the air horn by the pistons. As it passes the venturi the vacuum is increased. Thus a very high vacuum (low air pressure) is present at the tip end of the discharge tube. Gasoline is then drawn up the tube and flows into the air horn, where it is swept along to the manifold. Atmospheric pressure in the fuel bowl is greater than the pressure at the discharge tube. Thus it can bear down on the surface of the fuel in the bowl and force some of it up the tube. Many carburetors have a double or triple venturi, one inside the other, for greater vacuum at the discharge point. With a few more modifications we will have completed a very primitive carburetor.

The air-bleed. Since gasoline has to be mixed with air to form an explosive mixture, it is an advantage to have the mixing take place early in the game. The gasoline in the bowl is a liquid. As it comes out of the discharge tube, it is a spray. On its way down the horn becomes a mist. In the intake manifold it turns to a vapor. To boost the process along air bubbles are mixed with the gas before it comes out of the tube. This is done simply by drilling a hole in the tube near the tip. Then as the gas is pulled up the tube, some air is sucked into the new hole which leads to the gas being discharged. The name of this new opening is called an *air bleed*. You can get an idea of how the air bleed affects the process by puncturing a drinking straw close to the top. The resulting soda that is drawn out will contain a great number of air bubbles.

The Jet. A carburetor jet is merely a brass plug with a hole drilled in its center. The jet hole is a precise size and helps control the flow of fluids. Jets are either screwed or pressed into the openings in the carburetor casting. The main discharge jet is located at the bottom of the discharge tube, and it places a limit on the amount of fuel which can be drawn from the bowl.

Throttle Valve. This is the most important part of the carburetor, for it controls the speed of the car. The valve is actually a flat disc attached to a shaft. It has the vital job of controlling the amount of air and gas flow entering the manifold. Thus it is placed in the air horn at the carburetor base. Attached to the shaft is sophisticated linkage which ends up at the driver's gas pedal. When the pedal is left alone, the disc lies flat and blocks the air horn. As the gas pedal is depressed, the plate assumes a stand-up position. At half-throttle position, the plate is roughly at a 45-degree angle. At full-throttle position (the pedal to the floor), the plate is in full stand-up position, and there is no blockage of air/fuel flow.

Thus we've built the basic carburetor, but it is still useless for normal car operation. As yet, the engine will stall if the throttle plate is fully closed. When the throttle is jerked open quickly, there will be a slight lag until enough gas is drawn from the tube. When the throttle plate is held fully open for a while, not enough gas can come from the tube to sustain the engine at full-speed operation. If the engine is cold it will be difficult to start with this carburetor. Apparently then, further additions are needed to make the carburetor work at all times and under all conditions.

Since the carburetor operates under varied conditions, such as low speed, high speed, cold starting, etc., the basic carburetor must be modified to deal with each condition. The changes exist as seven independent systems within the carbu-

retor. Sometimes they are called circuits. Though each of these circuits has its own job, each shares a common goal with the others: to provide the engine with the proper air-fuel ratio under all operating conditions.

Float Circuit. The float circuit, or system, has the job of maintaining a correct level of fuel in the carburetor fuel bowl. Unless a correct level is maintained, the fuel ratios will be affected. If too much fuel is permitted into the bowl, the level of gas in the discharge tube will be too high, fuel will flow too easily, and the mixture to the cylinders will be too rich. Too low a level will produce a lean mixture because not enough fuel will come out of the tube at any given time.

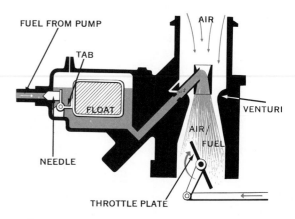

Float circuit. A brass float controls the small valve for admitting a pre-selected amount of gas in the bowl.

The mechanism for controlling the fuel level is a scaled down version of the mechanism in a typical toilet tank. The controlling piece there is the hollow float which is connected to a water valve. As the water level rises in the tank, the float rises until the float arm turns off the water valve. In the carburetor, the float has a tab instead of an arm. This tab rests against a small tapered bit of metal called a *needle*. The needle fits within a special fitting called a *seat*. Both are located at the bowl end of the metal line which comes from the fuel pump.

When the fuel level is low, the float drops, relaxing the float arm's contact with the needle. Fuel can now be pumped into the carburetor bowl. When the fuel reaches a predetermined level, a tab presses the needle into the seat. Pressure against the needle is maintained by the high position of the float. When the fuel level lowers, the float will drop and relax its contact with the needle. With the needle off the seat, fuel will enter under pressure. Then the cycle starts all over again.

Idle Circuit. The function of the idle circuit is to provide an air-fuel mixture to the cylinders when the throttle is closed. Described in detail earlier in this chapter,

the throttle plate controls the amount of air/fuel mix drawn in by the suction of the pistons. Thus, if the plate is closed, blocking the air horn, no mixture will be drawn in; there will be no low-pressure area at the venturi and discharge tube; no gas will be pulled in from the fuel bowl. And the engine won't operate.

But the carburetor is built with a bypass avenue called the *idle circuit*, which sneaks fuel and air to the cylinders *under* the closed throttle plate and permits the engine to operate at slow speed.

Low-speed Circuit. The low-speed circuit provides enough mixture for an engine

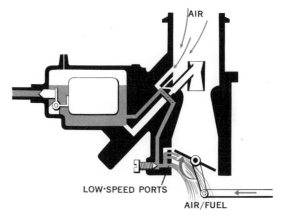

Low-speed circuit. The air/fuel mixture passes through ports exposed by a partially-opened throttle plate.

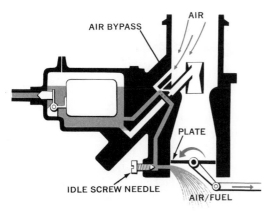

Idle circuit. The air/fuel mixture gets into the cylinders after entering the manifold below the closed throttle plate.

operating slightly faster than idle speed but too slow to pull gas from the discharge tube. This is accomplished by a vertical row of holes (ports) in the air horn just above the throttle plate.

When the throttle plate is closed, the fuel-air mix comes out only at the idle screw port under the throttle. When the plate is cracked open just a bit, mixture emits from the idle screw port *and* the lowest hole in the row. As the throttle plate tilts a little more, another hole is exposed; finally, the third hole is exposed, and the mix pours from all four openings.

In all positions of the throttle plate for low-speed operation, the mix comes from the same routes which supply the idle circuit. These ports provide additional outlets for the mix.

High-speed Circuit. When the throttle plate is tilted beyond the three holes, the air flow down the horn is sufficient to pull gas through the main discharge tube, as is the case with the basic carburetor previously described. With the throttle in this position, vacuum drops at the air bleed, and fuel will no longer flow through the idle or low-speed circuit.

The fuel flow from the discharge tube is sufficient to allow the car engine to operate at a fairly high speed, but at a cruising mode. This means a fairly steady throttle with no real power demands by the driver. When there is need for more power, another circuit takes over.

High-speed, Full-power Circuit. To understand the full-power circuit it is necessary to return to the carburetor fuel bowl. If you recall, a main discharge jet was mentioned. The jet has a fixed opening for allowing a metered flow from the bowl. The size of this opening allows maximum flow of fuel when the driver wants full power. Unless the hole is made smaller, the fuel permitted through the jet during

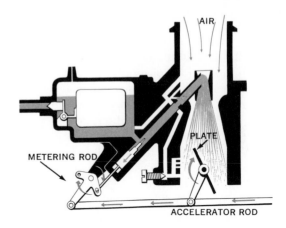

High-speed, full-power circuit. When the throttle plate is fully opened, full suction brings the gas from the bowl into the throat through the main discharge tube. Additional gas is supplied through the metering rod opening.

idle or low speeds will produce a very rich mixture.

To shut down some of the fuel flow during lower engine speeds and allow the maximum during sustained higher speeds, a special "plug" is used. This is called a *metering rod*. Usually made of brass, this rod looks like a long darning needle with several steps cut into it. The bottom of the rod is the thinnest part, graduating upward in thickness. The top of the rod is connected to the carburetor linkage.

When the throttle plate is set for idle or low-speed operation, the rod is deep within the main discharge jet. That is, a small amount of fuel can pass through the jet. As the throttle plate is opened, the rod is raised so that a slightly thinner section blocks the jet and more fuel can pass. At full throttle, the thinnest part of the rod is in the jet opening and allows maximum fuel to pass.

Some metering rods are mechanically operated. They are attached to the linkage in such a manner that the rod will raise and lower in accord with throttle position. When the gas pedal is pressed down to a certain point, the metering rod is raised to a certain step. On other carburetors, the rod is connected to a vacuum diaphragm or a vacuum piston. At the bottom range of high-speed operation, engine vacuum will hold the metering rod in place for minimum fuel flow. When the driver wants to go faster and pushes the accelerator, the engine vacuum will, for a brief moment, drop. The diaphragm or piston will relax its hold on the rod and a spring will push it for maximum fuel flow.

Some carburetors use both mechanical and vacuum control for the rod. Either a drop in vacuum or a certain throttle position will activate the rod. Yet another variation for metering the fuel without the use of a rod, utilizes an opening called the *power jet*. This orifice is found in the fuel bowl and remains covered until the additional fuel is required. Then, either mechanically or by vacuum, the orifice is uncovered and more fuel can enter the air horn.

Acceleration Circuit. The function of the acceleration circuit is to quickly supply a measured amount of fuel necessary for sudden bursts of speed.

When the car cruises at high speed and the gas pedal is depressed suddenly, an extra supply of air rushes through the air horn to the intake manifold. Since air is lighter than fuel, it will reach the manifold before the fuel, which is normally supplied by the high-speed system. This results in a momentary lean mixture. To prevent the

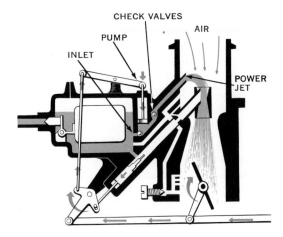

Acceleration circuit. When the accelerator is depressed rapidly, a small pump supplies a momentary injection of gas.

engine from faltering, additional fuel must be force-fed until the high-speed circuit can catch up with the increased volume of air.

The acceleration circuit can be compared to a hypodermic injection. Inside the recesses of the fuel bowl is a special cylinder which has a connection to the main fuel supply of the bowl. This is the inlet. It also has a passageway to the air horn. This is the outlet. Both the inlet and the outlet have check valves, usually steel balls with seats. The cylinder is always kept full of gasoline. Poised on top of this tube is a plunger and a rod. In some cases the plunger is made of metal; in others it is a leather piston. The rod is connected either to the carburetor linkage or to a vacuum diaphragm.

When the driver suddenly depresses the gas pedal, the plunger is forced down in the cylinder. The gas supply cannot go back to the bowl reservoir since this motion forces the ball at the inlet to lock against its seat. The only direction for the pressurized fuel is through the outlet passageway, into the air horn where it comes out as a fine spray through an *accelerator jet*. This spray can be readily seen while looking down a carburetor throat and pumping the accelerator linkage. This is also the spray that "floods" the carburetor when the motorist steps on the gas pedal a number of times while attempting to start the car.

Choke Circuit. The function of the choke circuit is to provide a temporarily rich mixture for starting a cold engine. The emphasis is on the word "starting." Bear in mind that the other circuits discussed so far dealt with an engine that was already operating.

When the engine is cold, there are two ways to get a desirably rich mixture for starting. You can raise the fuel supply or

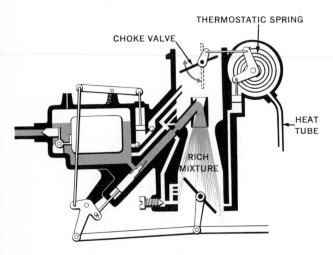

THERMOSTATIC SPRING

CHOKE VALVE

HEAT TUBE

RICH MIXTURE

Choke circuit. When the engine is cold, a thermostatic spring closes the choke plate, cutting off some air to create a rich mixture for starting the engine. As the engine warms up, the choke plate opens.

reduce the air intake. Since an engine turning at cranking speeds does not develop enough of a vacuum to pull a great deal of gasoline from the discharge tube, the easier solution is to cut down on the incoming air. The device which reduces air intake is appropriately called a choke.

The choke is merely a flat, rounded plate, very much like the throttle plate, but with certain refinements, which will be discussed shortly. It is located at the top of the air horn and is controlled either automatically or manually, depending on the design of the system. Most of the world's cars now have an automatic device, though many drivers still prefer the manual type.

In both manual and automatic chokes, the choke plate is attached to a shaft which enters from outside the air horn. The plate is screwed to the shaft. As the latter is twisted, the plate can either close the air horn or remain vertical and have no effect on the air intake.

It is important to realize that the choke does not entirely seal the air horn when it is in closed position. If this were true, then the engine would never start at full choke. There are a number of small aids which prevent a full seal when the choke plate lies flat in the horn. First, the choke shaft does not run through the dead center of the plate. It is located a little to the side of center in such a way that the velocity of air being drawn into the horn will push on the bigger section of the plate and partially open it. Second, automatic chokes have a small vacuum piston which counters the force trying to close the choke as the engine is cranked. Third, a small inlet port is sometimes placed on the underside of the choke plate which can be pulled open by manifold vacuum to admit some air and prevent flooding.

The manual choke is quite simple. A cable runs between the choke shaft and the instrument panel. On starting the car, the driver can pump the gas pedal once or twice to squirt some gasoline to the manifold from the accelerator pump. Then the knob attached to the choke cable is pulled to cut off some of the air supply and start the engine. Once the engine is started, the driver places the choke in a halfway position (about 45-degree tilt) and drives the car. After full warm-up, the choke must be set upright to avoid an over-rich mixture.

The automatic choke is more complex. A typical design will have a plastic housing attached to the choke shaft on the side of the air horn. The housing holds a *thermostatic spring* which is a bimetal coil designed to expand or contract according to temperature changes. One end of the coil spring is attached to the choke shaft and the other is attached to the plastic housing. When the engine is cold, the spring forces the choke plate to close; as engine temperature rises, the spring relaxes and the choke opens.

The problem now is to get temperature information to the spring. A typical solution is to attach a small tube from the plastic housing to the exhaust manifold — the manifold is a good indicator of engine temperature. The place where the tube is secured is called the *choke stove.* However, with the tube installed in the choke stove and the spring housing, heat doesn't travel up to the spring immediately. The solution is to use the reliable force of engine vacuum. The small piston that was mentioned earlier has a direct connection

to the manifold vacuum. Therefore, cut into the small cylinder where the piston operates are a number of grooves or slots. When the small piston is pulled down by vacuum, some of this suction escapes into the spring chamber and starts pulling air from the choke stove up the heating pipe.

One more provision must be made for proper choking. When the carburetor runs with the choke engaged, while the engine is warming up, the engine must operate faster to prevent stalling. On the manual choke, a link is installed between the choke shaft and the throttle linkage. When the choke knob is pulled, the throttle is pulled back at the same time. The linkage is so positioned that a full choke produces a very fast idle.

The automatic choke also has a link from the choke shaft, but the link does not go directly to the throttle linkage. The link from the choke ends at a triangular piece of metal with notches cut in one of its sides. This piece is called the *fast idle cam.* To understand how the cam works, we have to take a brief look at the outside of the carburetor, at the throttle linkage. Like the choke, the throttle plate has a shaft which protrudes to the outside of the carburetor. The shaft is linked to the accelerator pedal to give the driver foot control over the position of the throttle plate — and the speed of the car. Where the throttle shaft meets the linkage is a simple screw, the *idle speed screw,* which regulates the exact position of the throttle plate when there is no pressure on the pedal. The mechanic turns this screw in to get a faster idle or turns it out to get a slower idle.

Now, let's return to the choke fast idle

cam. When the engine is hot and the choke is not engaged at all, the tip end of the idle speed screw is against the lowest step in the cam. However, when the engine is cold and the choke is activated by the driver tapping the gas pedal, the fast idle linkage is pulled up by the closing choke. In turn, the fast idle cam is forced down so the top step contacts the idle speed screw. With the gas pedal fully released, the engine will operate at a fast idle. As the choke plate straightens out by receiving the warm-up signals, the linkage drops a little and the idle speed screw contacts a lower step for a slightly slower idle. At full warm-up the screw is on the last step and the engine is idling (hopefully) at the speed recommended by the car maker.

This is the typical automatic choke. There are many variations found on modern automobiles. On some cars, for instance, the thermostatic, bimetal spring is located in a special well in the exhaust manifold, and it activates the choke plate through a long rod. Nevertheless, a complete automatic choke must have a sensory apparatus which can respond to temperature signals. Plus the choke should have a means for causing a fast idle while the choke is operating.

Other Carburetor Features.   Carburetors have a number of other devices which are aimed at providing good engine performance. Though these devices are important, they are innovations. Hence, not all carburetors have them. Here are some of them:

Anti-icing design. When the outside air is damp and the temperature is about 45 degrees, ice sometimes forms at the throttle valves. This is the result of the cooling effect produced by the sprayed gasoline acting on moisture-laden parts. To avoid icing, some carburetors have a small channel running from the exhaust manifold to the area around the idle port. The small amount of heat which reaches the vulnerable areas is enough to prevent icing.

Anti-percolator. Under extreme conditions such as hot weather during prolonged engine operation, the area under the hood gets hot enough for the gas in the fuel bowl to boil. When the engine is running, the actual boiling is put off by the flow of "cooler" gas from the fuel pump. But, when the engine is turned off, bubbles of boiling gas work their way up the discharge tube, much like what happens inside a percolator coffee pot. If allowed to percolate, raw gas drips into the manifold, causing hard starting later. The solution is an anti-percolator valve which is merely a vertical vent running from the discharge tube and leading to the outside. As the bubbles arise, they diffuse into the vent and prevent gas spillage from the tip of the discharge tube.

Throttle return dashpot. The best analogy for this device is a door check which is used to prevent slamming. Many engines with automatic transmissions have this device. It is attached to the throttle linkage. It consists of a small housing with an air vent, a diaphragm, and a small rod attached to it. When the driver suddenly releases the gas pedal, a lever on the linkage hits against the rod. The shock is absorbed by the air behind the diaphragm. Then the air slowly bleeds from the housing, causing the lever to move slowly to its resting point at which the engine will idle. If the engine did not have a dashpot, a swift closing of the throttle will cause stalling.

Airconditioning idle speedup. When the clutch of the airconditioning compressor is engaged and the engine idles, a very heavy load is placed on the engine, often causing it to stall. A simple solution is to permanently raise the idle speed by turning the idle speed screw. However, this will cause unnecessary racing of the engine when the airconditioning compressor is off. The answer is an automatic device consisting of a small rod and a coil of wire — a solenoid. When the airconditioning clutch is engaged, current flows to the small coil installed within the carburetor body. The coil becomes an electromagnet and it pulls the rod. This action opens an additional channel for increased air flow below the throttle plate and a faster idle.

Vacuum outlets. The carburetor also provides a source of vacuum for control of the spark advance at the distributor.

In addition to these devices, the carburetor has a number of items which reduce exhaust emissions. These are described in Chapter 4, "Exhaust System."

VARIATIONS OF CARBURETOR DESIGN

As mentioned earlier, there are thousands of carburetor designs. Every fuel engineer feels he has the answers for providing the ultimate in fuel mixing and delivery. This same fuel engineer also has the responsibility for making new carburetor designs and variations to fit such developments as automatic transmissions, high-horsepower engines, fuel economy engines, and pollution controls. But every automotive carburetor must provide the right amounts of fuel and air for the various modes the driver demands; every carburetor must have seven systems.

In the foregoing description of the carburetor, the positon of the barrel was assumed to be upright. This is the case for most carburetors but not for all. When the barrel is upright it is called a downdraft carburetor. Some units have it facing to the side or with the opening facing the ground. These are called sidedraft and updraft carburetors, respectively.

Another variation is the multi-barrel carburetor. Our previous discussion examined only the single-barrel unit. Yet a vast number of carburetors have two and four barrels. The two-barrel carburetor is like two single-barrel units mounted side by side. Each barrel has its own throttle valve, discharge nozzle at the venturi, accelerator discharge port and idle port. The parts shared by both sides are the fuel bowl, air horn choke and throttle shaft. The design of the manifold is such that each of the two barrels feeds half of the engine cylinders.

Though the four-barrel carburetor is essentially a bunching of four single-barrel units, the four-barrel feeds the cylinders in a slightly different way. Two of the barrels are called the primary side and function at low and medium speeds. The other two are called the secondary side and function at higher speeds. The linkage is so arranged that the throttle valves of the secondary side remain shut until the gas pedal is depressed a specific distance. Past that point, air is admitted to all four barrels. These carburetors have two fuel bowls with floats, one idle circuit, one choke plate, two throttle valves, a double high-speed and accelerator circuit,

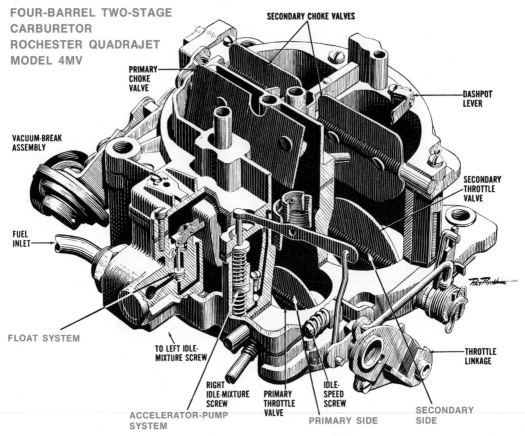

FOUR-BARREL TWO-STAGE
CARBURETOR
ROCHESTER QUADRAJET
MODEL 4MV

SECONDARY CHOKE VALVES

PRIMARY
CHOKE
VALVE

DASHPOT
LEVER

VACUUM-BREAK
ASSEMBLY

SECONDARY
THROTTLE
VALVE

FUEL
INLET

FLOAT SYSTEM

TO LEFT IDLE-
MIXTURE SCREW

THROTTLE
LINKAGE

RIGHT
IDLE-MIXTURE
SCREW

PRIMARY
THROTTLE
VALVE

IDLE-
SPEED
SCREW

ACCELERATOR-PUMP
SYSTEM

PRIMARY SIDE

SECONDARY
SIDE

A four-barrel carburetor. It provides the right air/fuel mixture at all engine speeds. Four barrels permit low-speed operation using only two smaller barrels—while having the throat capacity in larger secondary barrels so that high-rev, large-displacement V-8's get the mix needed for wide-open power.

a single idle and low-speed circuit.

The purpose of the multi-barrel carburetor is to satisfy the "inhalation" requirements of the engine. To illustrate, exaggeration is necessary. Let's say an engine has 12 cylinders, each 4 inches in diameter. This engine will have a voracious appetite for fuel and air. A mere single-barrel carburetor would starve the engine and undermine performance. The single-barrel simply isn't big enough to fill all the cylinders on their every intake stroke.

To get enough of the fuel-air into an engine this size, there must be more than one mouth. Very large engines might require three four-barrel carburetors.

AIR CLEANER

One of the problems with supplying the air necessary for the mixture is keeping airborne dirt out of the engine. This is the job of the carburetor air cleaner. The actual cleaner is a filter which is situated so the

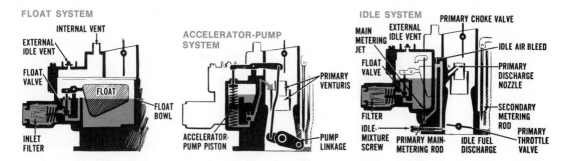

INTERNAL VENT

EXTERNAL
IDLE VENT

FLOAT
VALVE

FLOAT

FLOAT
BOWL

INLET
FILTER

ACCELERATOR-PUMP
SYSTEM

PRIMARY
VENTURIS

ACCELERATOR-
PUMP PISTON

PUMP
LINKAGE

IDLE SYSTEM

PRIMARY CHOKE VALVE

MAIN
METERING
JET

EXTERNAL
IDLE VENT

FLOAT
VALVE

FILTER

IDLE-
MIXTURE
SCREW

PRIMARY MAIN-
METERING ROD

IDLE FUEL
DISCHARGE

IDLE AIR BLEED

PRIMARY
DISCHARGE
NOZZLE

SECONDARY
METERING
ROD

PRIMARY
THROTTLE
VALVE

Three essential functions. The float system, left, maintains the proper level of fuel in the bowl. Center, when the driver depresses the gas pedal, linkage to the carburetor moves the accelerator-pump piston downward, forcing a spurt of fuel to the cylinders. The idle system allows fuel to mix with air and bypass the closed throttle valve.

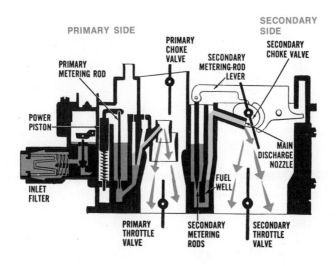

PRIMARY SIDE

SECONDARY
SIDE

PRIMARY
METERING ROD

PRIMARY
CHOKE
VALVE

SECONDARY
METERING-ROD
LEVER

SECONDARY
CHOKE VALVE

POWER
PISTON

MAIN
DISCHARGE
NOZZLE

INLET
FILTER

FUEL
WELL

PRIMARY
THROTTLE
VALVE

SECONDARY
METERING
RODS

SECONDARY
THROTTLE
VALVE

Schematic of four-barrel. Note the similarities to the simple carburetor described earlier. The two barrels on the primary side of the four-barrel carburetor function at low and medium speeds. The two on the secondary side function at higher speeds. The linkage is so arranged that the throttle valves of the secondary side remain shut until the gas pedal is depressed a specific distance.

air drawn into the carburetor throat must pass through it.

The typical filter housing looks something like a skillet with a cover on it. What would be the handle is an air tube. What would be the skillet basin contains a filter.

In the old days, the filter was a screen filled with coarse steel wool. Occasionally oil was applied to the screen to attract dust and foreign matter. The next design used a shallow pool of oil which cleaned the air passing over it. From this evolved the use of an oil-soaked polyethylene sponge.

Today, almost all cars use a dry filter made of special paper, accordion-folded in a holder. This replaceable filter element fits into the basin and cleans the air rushing to the carburetor.

INTAKE MANIFOLD

The intake manifold can be considered the end of the line for the carburetion process or the beginning of the line for the engine combustion process. It is far less complicated than the carburetor, surely less dramatic. But its design is absolutely critical in determining efficient engine operation.

The word "manifold" means many. It is an apt term for a set of tubes which carry the air-fuel mixture from the carburetor to each of the intake valve ports. On V-8 engines it is located in the crotch between the two banks of cylinders. On the 6-cylinder engine it is bolted on one side of the engine block.

Because each cylinder must get the same share of the mix, the engine designer must see to it that all the tubes are about the same length. In addition, there must be no restrictions or sharp corners which would slow up the flow of the mix to the

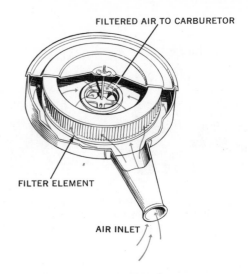

FILTERED AIR TO CARBURETOR

FILTER ELEMENT

AIR INLET

A carburetor air cleaner. The air sucked into the carburetor is forced through a filter element. This prevents foreign particles from entering the engine. Air cleaners on late-model cars have additional tubing for the reburning of exhaust gases as a means of controlling the emissions.

intakes. Even the inside walls of the tubes must be free of roughness. On some rodding and race cars the inside bores of the manifold are actually polished.

A variation of the conventional manifold is a design that provides *ram induction*. The aim of such a design is to have the mixture forced into the combustion chamber under pressure. This is accomplished by mounting a carburetor to each of the two engine sides, making the right side unit feed the left bank and the left side unit feed the right bank. In this manner the tubes running to the cylinders are made extra long. The charge within them has a chance to build up speed on the way to the cylinder. When the intake valve opens, the charge is then rammed into the

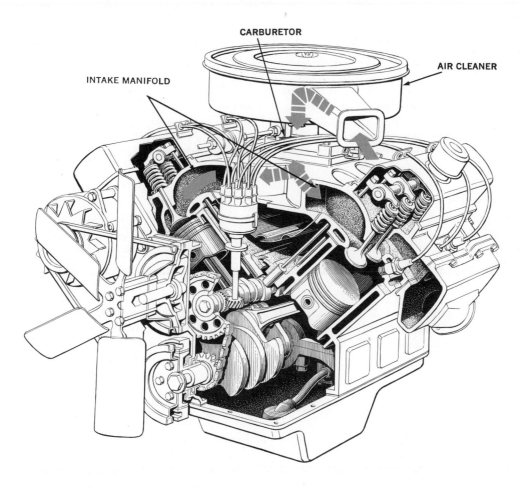

CARBURETOR

INTAKE MANIFOLD

AIR CLEANER

Engine's air-intake system. Air is drawn in through the air cleaner and the carburetor, then through both sides of the intake manifold to each cylinder.

cylinder under considerable force. The result is a more potent power stroke.

MANIFOLD HEAT-CONTROL VALVE

Heat-produced bubbles of gasoline vapor are undesirable at the fuel pump or in the carburetor fuel bowl. However, some heat is desirable to aid in the vaporization of the gasoline. Earlier in this chapter, we traced the progress of a single drop of liquid gasoline from the carburetor bowl; the gasoline goes through various changes of state until it gets to the combustion chamber—from a liquid to a spray, to a mist, to a vapor. It is the conversion at the final stage that is most vital. Liquid gasoline in a combustion chamber spells fouled plugs and poor engine operation.

One of the factors which assures vaporization in the intake manifold is heat. A plentiful supply of heat is no problem since much of the wasted energy produced by the internal-combustion engine is heat. What is of concern is the proper vaporization, which must take place when the engine is just started and is quite cold.

As mentioned in the section on the automatic choke, the exhaust manifold gets hot before any other outside part of the engine. Here is an instant source of heat which is used to raise temperatures inside the intake manifold. The heat is directed by the use of a *manifold heat-control valve.* This is simply a metal plate within the exhaust manifold which is con-

trolled by a thermostatic spring. The gate either allows or blocks warm air from entering a passageway which leads to a chamber containing a small section of the intake manifold.

When the engine is cold, the spring causes the gate to swing so the hot exhaust gases must go into the chamber to warm the intake-manifold section and then flow out the exhaust pipe. As the engine gets hotter, the spring unwinds and the gate gradually swings the other way, channeling some of the heat to the intake and some to the exhaust pipe. When the engine is fully warmed, all of the gases are sent to the exhaust pipe; none go to the intake manifold.

Six- or 8-cylinder engines vary in how they redirect the heat, but the action of the gate and spring is similar. A variation of this method for temperature regulation at the intake manifold is the use of cooling-system water that flows through special jackets around the manifold.

FROM PUMP

FUEL INJECTION NOZZLE

INTAKE VALVE

Typical fuel-injection setup. Rather than having the air/fuel mixture come from a carburetor, each cylinder is equipped with an injector which sprays in fuel at the proper moment.

FUEL INJECTION

In the attempt to get more efficiency from the internal-combustion engine, it is not surprising that the conventional carburetor has some competition. The *fuel injection* method is a viable alternative.

Fuel injection is self-descriptive. Each cylinder is equipped with a special injector aimed at the combustion chamber or at an area just above the intake valve. In addition, a manifold provides a tube running to each of the engine cylinders. When the engine operates, the only fluid carried by the manifold is air. At the cylinders the injectors provide a fine spray of fuel.

There are three basic systems used on fuel-injection engines. In the first, the nozzles send a continuous spray as long as the throttle is open—regardless of the position of the intake valve. Keep in mind that in this system the throttle controls only a flow of air, rather than a fuel-air mix. In the second system, fuel is injected near the intake valves in short bursts timed to coincide with the opening of the valves. The third type of system is similar to the second except that fuel is injected directly into the combustion chamber.

Presently, the only production cars using fuel injection are some models of Mercedes-Benz, Volkswagen, and Saab.

Fuel injection is expensive and not in wide use. However, it is recognized for its efficiency in controlling fuel flow and fuel ratios. Hence, it is regarded as one possible way of reducing harmful exhaust emissions produced by regular carburetion.

4

EXHAUST SYSTEM

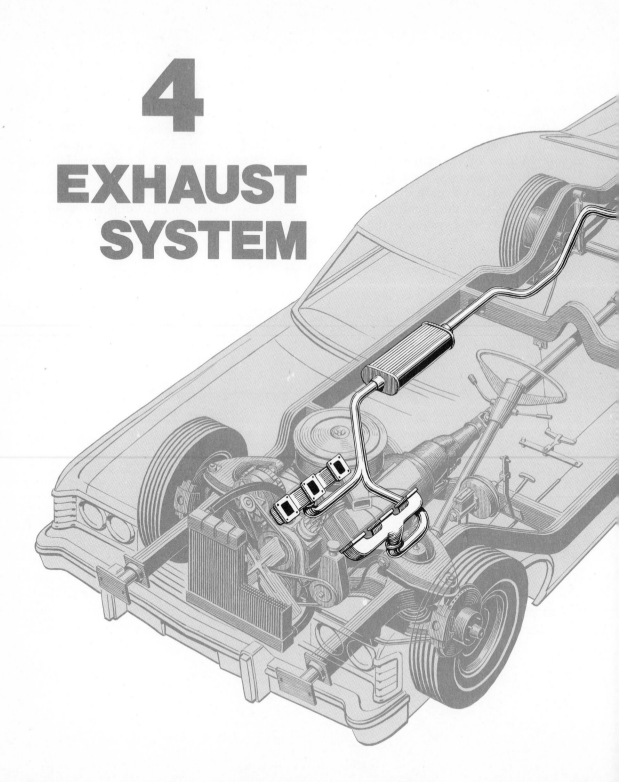

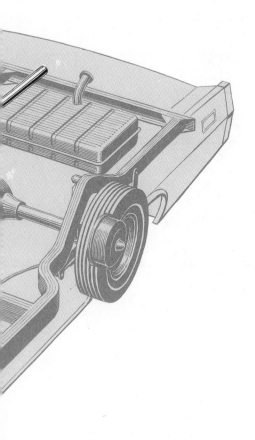

Combustion is a rather messy process. Two products are derived from it— one that we want and one that we don't. The usable product of combustion is heat. And, unless you are dealing with some super atomic furnace, the unusable product is waste resulting from incomplete burning.

If a solid such as coal, wood or paper is burned, you end up with a solid called ashes. When a liquid or a gas is burned, the residue is a vapor. In the previous chapter we explained how liquid gasoline is vaporized and mixed with air to make a combustible mixture. In the section on the ignition system, in Chapter 2, we described how this mixture is set afire in the combustion chamber. In Chapter 1, we explained how the force of the explosion drives the pistons and the crankshaft for the mechanical energy required to turn the rear wheels. Now we take up the problem of what to do with the waste products of the gas-air explosions.

Since these wastes are mostly poisonous, waste disposal is not only a problem

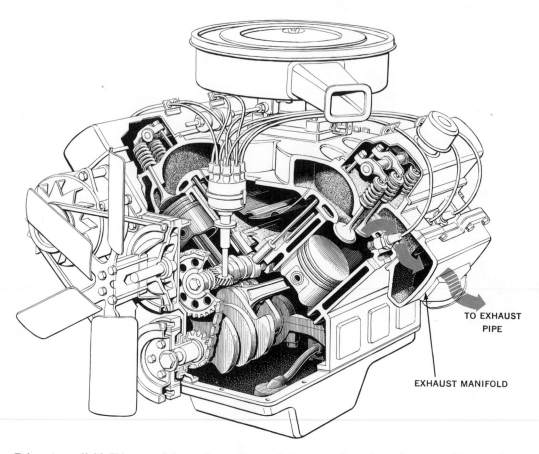

TO EXHAUST PIPE

EXHAUST MANIFOLD

Exhaust manifold. This part of the engine collects exhaust gases from the cylinders and funnels them through the exhaust pipe. It can be easily distinguished from intake manifold because the exhaust manifold's high temperatures during operation result in rust formation on its surface.

for the individual car owner. Keeping air clean enough to breathe has become a broad social problem. All of this comes under the heading of smog control, or, as the engineers call it, "emission control."

The word "smog" was coined to describe a foggy atmosphere created by smoke. In time, this term was enlarged to mean invisible pollutants such as carbon monoxide, sulphur dioxide and hydrocarbons. To this day, debate still rages as to how much the automobile contributes to the contamination of the air above our major cities. Yet, the debate is only over percentages, for there is almost universal agreement that the internal-combustion engine is a major air polluter in most urban areas.

A study in New York City, in 1968, revealed some startling facts. Motorists there consumed about *one billion* gallons of gasoline a year. Based on the quality of the air sampled at various stations around town, it was calculated that about seventy-million gallons of this total was dicharged into the atmosphere as unburned and partially burned wastes.

SOURCES OF AUTOMOTIVE WASTE

There are three different sources of automotive waste.

First, there are burned and semiburned gases in the combustion chamber which manage to squeeze by the piston rings and land in the crankcase. Until 1959 the engine had a pipe called the oil breather, a tube that led from the crankcase to the outside. Air would enter the crankcase at the oil filler cap, circulate through the case and exit through the breather, carrying these blow-by gases with it.

These fumes are almost entirely made up of hydrocarbons. As such, they are not very healthy for lung and throat tissue. Some measure of control is achieved with a Positive Crankcase Ventilation system, (PCV). Instead of allowing the fumes to vent to the outside, this system forces filtered air from the carburetor air cleaner down the crankcase. In turn, the forced draft pushes the blow-by gases up a tube to the area under the valve cover. There another tube, which has a one-way trap

called the PCV valve, picks up the fumes and directs them toward the intake manifold where they are mixed with the fresh air-fuel mixture for another go at burning.

The second source of automotive waste is the fumes from the evaporation of gasoline in the tank, fuel lines and carburetor. This may sound trivial, but when you add the fumes of your car to that evaporated from millions of vehicles, it does diminish the fresh-air supply. Indeed, the problem became so serious in California that legislation was passed requiring evaporation control devices on all cars sold in that state starting with the 1970 models.

One such control system is found in the 1970 Ford Maverick, which was the first mass-produced vehicle so equipped for sale in California. This system has the fancy name of Fuel Evaporative Emission Control (FEEC) and consists of three main subsystems for collection, separation and storage of fuel vapors.

To collect the vapors, the filler cap vent on the gas tank is sealed to the atmosphere. The rising vapors collect in a special plastic chamber located above the tank. This separator is equipped with a valve to make sure that any splashing liquid fuel is re-

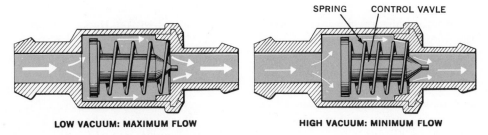

LOW VACUUM: MAXIMUM FLOW   HIGH VACUUM: MINIMUM FLOW

Positive crankcase ventilation (PCV) valve. This device allows fumes in the engine crankcase to vent through carburetor. At high engine speed, engine vacuum is low. The spring forces the valve off the seat (left). Maximum fumes enter the carburetor. At low engine speed, the vacuum is increased. The valve pulls closer to the seat. And fume flow is restricted.

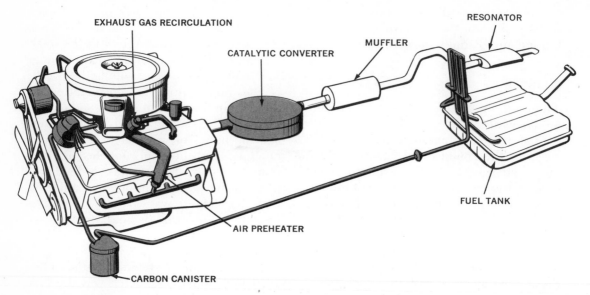

EXHAUST GAS RECIRCULATION

CATALYTIC CONVERTER

MUFFLER

RESONATOR

AIR PREHEATER

CARBON CANISTER

FUEL TANK

Fuel evaporative emission control system. Fumes rising from gasoline in the tank are trapped in a canister of carbon granules. Fumes are sucked into the carburetor and burned when engine is started.

turned to the tank while the vapors are trapped in the collector. The valve also has the job of venting the tank—that is, permitting the air to enter as fuel is consumed.

Running from the tank to the engine compartment is a special tube called the fuel vapor line. The purpose of the line is to direct the stored vapors into a canister containing activated charcoal. These carbon granules absorb the fuel vapors until the engine is operated. Then fuel fumes are sucked into the carburetor air cleaner and mixed with the regular fuel supply for burning. The canister can hold 50 grams of vapor, equal to about three ounces of liquid gasoline. This system is now required on all new cars.

The third and biggest source of wastes produced by the running automobile also comes from fuel combustion, but these

are vented through the exhaust system and are called exhaust gases. When gasoline burns in an engine, it creates a whole roster of waste products. Most of us are familiar with carbon monoxide (CO), the gas that spells doom to those who warm up their car in a closed garage. There are other chemicals spewed out, including nitrogen oxides, hydrocarbons and lead oxides from the antiknock additives in the gasoline. Most of these chemicals are "locked" into the chemical structure of gasoline and are liberated by the incomplete combustion process. If there was a way to make the burning process more thorough, many of the pollutants would break down into more basic and less harmful substances. But this is not possible with existing technology. Some scientists claim that the present internal-combustion engine, powered by gasoline or diesel fuel, can never free itself from these by-products. Others, namely the auto makers and the oil companies, feel that the combustion process can be made more efficient to create less pollution.

Since we have become aware of the emission problem, many methods have been conceived on minimizing the emission of these pollutants into our atmosphere; many more are yet to follow. At the moment, technology has produced two important systems for reducing pollutants. One controls the combustion process; the other uses air injection. The former works on the principle that if the air entering the carburetor is pre-heated it will produce more efficient combustion. To accomplish this, a heat exchanger is placed at the exhaust manifold. Flowing through the exchanger is the underhood air that is destined for the carburetor. As air passes through, it picks up heat radiated by the manifold and proceeds to the carburetor for mixing and burning. Some modifications are necessary for the engine to do its job under these conditions. These include a carburetor which operates on very lean mixtures, increased engine idle speed, and a high-temperature thermostat that allows the engine to operate hotter.

The air-injection system has an engine-driven air pump which picks up filtered air from the carburetor air cleaner and distributes it to a network of tubes leading to the exhaust ports of each cylinder. The theory is that the air will combine with the very hot exhaust gases and help complete the combustion process.

In development are a number of other ideas for reducing exhaust emissions. One of them has the title of Tangential Thermal Reactor—tangential because the exhaust gases are caused to swirl due to the introduction of thermal (hot) fresh air into the exhaust ports.

CATALYTIC CONVERTER

The reason the internal combustion engine produces an exhaust which is harmful is that the burning process does not fully consume its fuel. This incomplete combustion is the object of all the emission control devices required on cars since 1969. However, the EC devices have a major drawback which might be described as a "see-saw problem." If the EC system is designed to reduce hydrocarbons (HC), then the oxides of nitrogen (NOx) emissions go up. If nitrogen emissions are suppressed, the hydrocarbons go up. Somewhere between is a narrow compromise area where both these deadly emissions are reduced.

One way to achieve this compromise is to funnel all the exhaust gases through a chemical substance called a catalyst. A catalyst is a substance that initiates a

Oxidizing catalytic converter. This device mounts under the front passenger seat. As exhaust gases from the manifold flow through, the device chemically converts hydrocarbons and carbon monoxide to harmless water vapor and carbon dioxide.

chemical change without being changed itself in the process. Therefore, if the exhaust gases are forced through a muffler having a catalytic substance, the gases can change chemically before entering the atmosphere. In the past, most catalytic converters could handle only one of the exhaust gases; therefore a multiple system was necessary.

Today, many chemical companies and auto manufacturers say that with a single catalytic system it is possible to reduce hydrocarbons and oxides of nitrogen. Costs for the catalytic mufflers are now projected to be much lower than for the early units —about $60 each with a life span of 50,000 miles. In the near future, we will see the universal use of catalysts on all cars.

EXHAUST PIPE

The job of collecting the exhaust gases and funneling them to the outside falls to the exhaust pipe. The majority of cars have one exhaust pipe, though a typical V-8 engine has two exhaust manifolds. In this case, a crossover pipe shunts the gases to the side bearing the exhaust pipe. In some instances, V-8 engines are equipped with a double exhaust system all the way back to the tailpipe. Here no crossover is required.

In the days before emission controls, cars were equipped with a heat-control valve that was sandwiched between the exhaust manifold and pipe. This valve was equipped with a thermostatic spring. When the engine was cold and just started, the valve would be in a shut position. Then the exhaust gases, which got hot immediately, were redirected through a passageway in the intake manifold to help vaporize the incoming air-fuel mixture. As the engine warmed up, the valve gradually opened to allow the exhaust to take the direct route out, since pre-warming of the fuel and air was no longer necessary.

MUFFLER

After the gases are collected in the exhaust pipe, they are directed below the car through the muffler. The name is quite accurate, for it has the main role of quieting the sounds made by the explosions of the operating engine. The British have a more vivid name for the unit. They call it a "silencer."

The muffler keeps the noise level low by retarding the velocity of the exhaust gases. This is done by forcing the gases through a maze of chambers and tubes. As they enter the front section of the muffler, the gases travel toward the rear of the car. Suddenly, they reach a dead end and are forced to make a U-turn toward the front of the car. This process continues until most of the punch is taken out of the gas flow.

There are some performance-minded people who believe that the muffler robs the engine of power by setting up a back-pressure against the pressure of the exhaust gases trying to escape. Some even have a bypass system which allows the exhaust flow to be switched from the muffler to a straight pipe. The result is a roaring engine. However, it is doubtful that enough power is gained in this manner to really make a difference in a race.

TAILPIPE

When the gases emerge from the rear of the muffler they head rearward, presumably quiet as a kitten's purr. The next job is to get the exhaust gases away from the car so that they can dissipate into the atmosphere. That is the main function of the tailpipe. The odd twists and turns of the tailpipe enable it to conform to the understructure of the car. In traveling from the muffler outlet, which is about the center of the vehicle, the tailpipe has to go over the axle, around the shock absorber and alongside the fuel tank. Engineers in charge of designing the exhaust system are usually consulted after the plan is set for other components under the car.

The length of the tailpipe has a great deal of bearing on driver and passenger health and safety. Have you noticed that the tailpipe protrudes slightly from the rearmost margin of the car? There is good reason for this. You may not realize it, but as the car rolls down the highway it pushes a wall of air in front of it. As a consequence, there is a partial vacuum in the immediate area behind the car. Since physical science says that a vacuum must be filled, air swirling alongside the car and rushing toward the rear is sucked around the rear edge of the car and then toward the *front* of the vehicle. Though most of this air bounces off the rear deck of the car and heads rearward again, some of the air ducks under the rear bumper and manages to blow forward. Because of this phenomenon, if a vehicle had a shortened tailpipe, the exhaust gases would be swirled under the car and up through small holes in the floor pan into the passenger compartment. If the tailpipe protrudes a short distance from the rear bumper, the ejected gases are shot back far enough to get caught into tailstream and clear of the car.

Until recently, owners of station wagons were bothered by exhaust fumes entering the car through the open tailgate window. The problem was solved by relocating the tailpipe opening at the side of the vehicle, directly behind the rear tire. The exhaust was then carried back by the rushing air. In addition, baffles and shields were designed around the window opening to ward off the fumes.

The exhaust pipe, muffler, and tailpipe are made of a light-gauge steel. Because of the high temperatures of the exhaust gases flowing through them, they are subject to rapid oxidation (rust). One of the great enemies of the muffler is the water vapor in the exhaust. When the engine is shut off, this vapor condenses to a liquid and starts rusting from the inside. Some mufflers are made with a drain hole to allow the water to drip out. But these clog easily and are of no value. Because of this problem, the life span of a muffler or tailpipe is short. Exhaust pipes last longer, due mainly to the fact that gases are so hot entering the pipe that water vapor doesn't have a chance to accumulate and condense after the engine is off.

Holding the components of the exhaust system together are a series of clamps and hangers. The former are single and double rings made of steel. These are slipped over the joints, where the various components fit into each other, and are tightened with bolts and nuts. The hangers are also rings, but they have a rubber-fabric strip attached to them. The strip is attached to the floor pan or the chassis of the car while the ring is affixed to the exhaust component. In this manner the entire exhaust system can "give" with the movement of the engine and the vehicle. Thus there is little danger of pipes snapping.

5
COOLING
SYSTEM

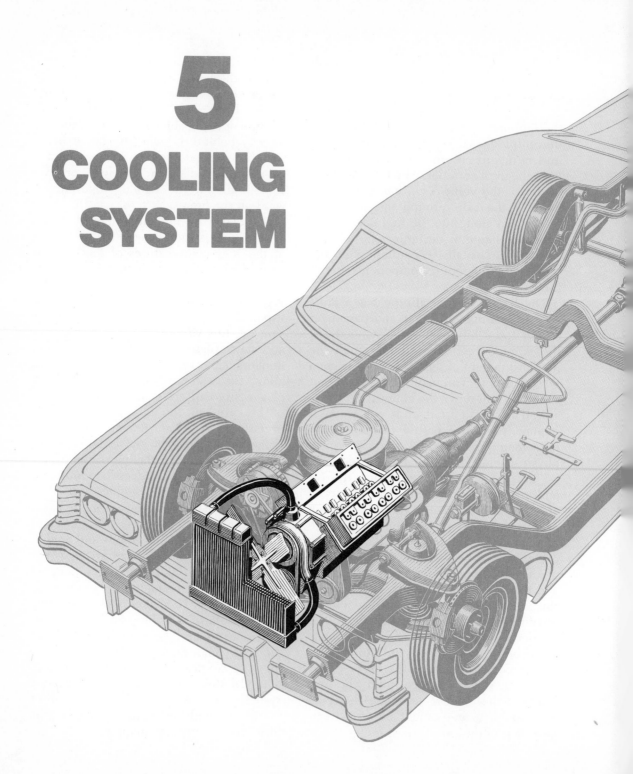

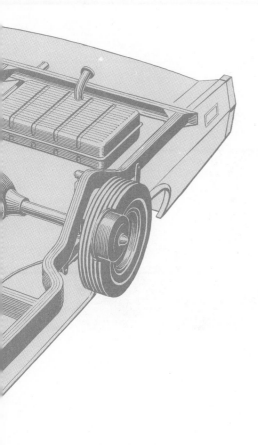

Stated bluntly, the function of the cooling system is to keep the engine from melting. This is no exaggeration. Every time a spark explodes the fuel-air mixture in the combustion chamber, 4500 degrees of heat energy is produced. If it were possible to package all the heat created in twenty minutes of engine operation and direct it back at the power plant, heat accumulations would be great enough to reduce the engine's iron, steel, and aluminum to a molten puddle.

Fortunately for the auto engineers the cooling system doesn't have to handle all the heat created by combustion. Using those 4500-degree blasts as a base unit, let's see where the heat goes. Only 1500 degrees of heat energy is converted to actual power; 1500 degrees goes "up the flue," out the exhaust pipes. Of the remaining 1500 degrees, 500 is allowd to remain with the engine for what the tech men call "thermal efficiency." This is the heat which helps expand the exploding gases which drive the pistons.

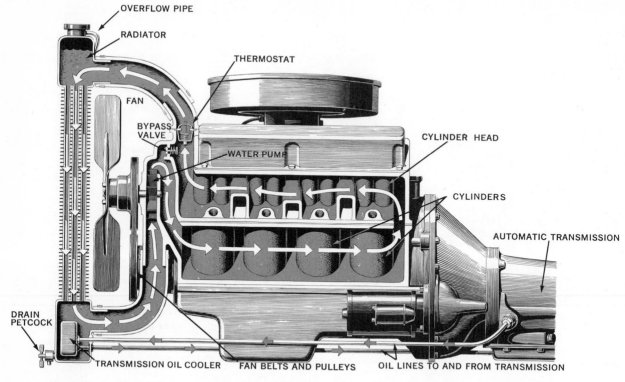

X-ray view of cooling system. Coolant at the radiator bottom is pulled into the engine by a water pump. Coolant circulates inside the engine block and head, absorbing heat. Then it is forced to the top of the radiator and falls through thin tubes. Pulled in by the fan, outside air absorbs coolant heat.

Engineers are constantly striving for greater thermal efficiency. However, the amount of heat allowed to remain in the engine is limited to the temperature at which a film of lubricating oil will stick to the moving parts. Today's technology limits temperatures to about 500 degrees. This leaves about 1000 degrees of heat to be carried away by the cooling system with every blast in the combustion chambers. To be very technical about it, the cooling system is really a temperature regulating system, since it carries away some heat and leaves some for efficient engine operation. But before we see how the cooling system works, it's important to define some terms.

There is no such thing as "cool" or "cold." There is only heat (and the absence of heat). A freezer does not freeze; it withdraws heat. A car's cooling system does not cool; it transfers heat away from the source in the three ways heat can be transferred: by *conduction, convection* and *radiation.*

Think of a soggy day in August. You're sitting in a room in a limp state with a fan blowing the surface heat from your body. It's not too bad now, but the relief is limited. Only that portion of your body directly in the airflow is much affected by this crude mechanical contrivance. You are cooling off by regions. What you need is an all-around, overall, gutsy wrenching of heat from your whole body.

You flip a switch to the airconditioner. Now something else is happening. No longer is a thin stream of air blowing heat from a concentrated area. Now the whole room begins to cool—that is, heat is leaving the room. As your environment loses heat your body begins to cool. Or rather, your whole body gives up heat to a less hot atmosphere.

Why? According to the laws which govern the conduct of heat flow, the direction will always be from the hotter object to the less hot (cooler) object. How fast this rate of flow takes place depends on the difference in the temperatures of the two objects. The greater the differential, the faster the heat flow. In a strange way this is why ice cubes form faster in your freezer when the tray is first filled with hot rather than cold water. Because the heat differential between the hot water and the freezer is quite wide, heat will flow from the water at an accelerated rate; the temperature of the water will fall quite rapidly and the water will change from a liquid to a solid sooner than when cold water is used.

This hot-to-cold process is what the car's cooling system is all about. Engine heat is soaked up by a cooler medium and carried away, much the same way as body heat is soaked up by the cooler air from the conditioner. The two basic processes which cool the engine are called: *heat transference* and *heat dissipation*. Taking the heat from one place and shifting it to another is heat transference. Getting rid of the heat is a simple way of describing heat dissipation. The medium used in the car is water, which from now on we will call *coolant*. It is the task of the coolant to transfer and dissipate engine heat.

All this is done by simple circulation within a complex of components using many of the principles of elementary physics. Though the system is capable of circulating as much as 7,500 gallons an hour, let us follow a single drop in a typical 18-quart system tracing the perpetual journey around the cooling circuit. We'll be stopping at all the components for an explanation of *how* and *why* each is used to keep the engine cool. So, don your scuba suit, and let's take a plunge down the radiator filler hole. Down, down until we are deep inside the engine block.

It is quiet. The engine is still. The chamber we are in is part of a system of passageways called the *water jacket*. This labyrinth surrounds each cylinder and continues through the engine block into the cylinder head. Ordinarily, we think of wearing a jacket to keep warm, to keep body heat in. The engine's jackets are designed for drawing the heat out (conduction) by having the coolant circulate within it. The jacket system is very much like a series of jars containing lit candles sitting in a trough of water. The liquid is free to swirl around and under the jars, influencing the air temperature within them, but not affecting the burning of the candles.

Here in the jacket we can observe our typical drop of coolant. With the engine off there is not much for him to do but sit. But as soon as the ignition key commands the starter motor to whirl the crankshaft, the *water pump* starts circulation in the cooling system.

The water pump is the heart of the cooling system. Without a constant flow of coolant which constantly conducts, transfers and dissipates heat, the whole system goes up in a cloud of steam. Unlike the common backyard pump which has a handle worked up and down for operation, the car's water pump works by spinning around. Hence the name, "centrifugal-type" pump.

Bolted to the engine, just behind the radiator and fan, the pump consists of a cast iron housing with hoses attached to various openings. Inside the pump is a round, flat plate with a series of flat legs, or vanes, around one side of its circumference. This is the all-important impeller. Running from the center of the impeller and through the housing is the impeller shaft, which terminates at a pulley on the outside of the pump.

By attaching a *fan belt* around the pulley and around the crankshaft, the pump impeller turns whenever the crankshaft turns. As the impeller spins, coolant is scooped by the vanes and thrown outward by centrifugal action through the pump outlet into the water jacket. Meanwhile the coolant is drawn from the bottom of the radiator by the pump to replace the coolant forced through the outlet. Thus there is a constant movement of coolant throughout the system whenever the engine is running.

Now, let's keep a sharp eye on the little drop of coolant we isolated earlier. As it is set into action by the pump responding to engine operation, it picks up a little heat from the area close to the cylinder and flows upward into the engine head. (While the droplet is pushed along by pump pressure it gets a boost from the forces of convection which command warm fluids to rise to the top, above the colder section.)

The engine head and block are two pieces which are designed such that, when they are bolted together, holes and passages in one will match those in the

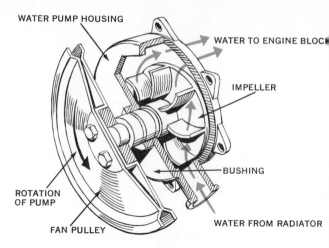

WATER PUMP HOUSING

WATER TO ENGINE BLOCK

IMPELLER

BUSHING

ROTATION OF PUMP

FAN PULLEY

WATER FROM RADIATOR

Cutaway drawing of water pump. The fan pulley is turned by a fan belt (not shown), turning the impeller wheel. Coolant is sucked from the radiator and delivered to the engine.

other. The function of some of these holes is to provide a pathway for coolant flow. Naturally, if there is to be no coolant loss when it transfers from the block to the head, the joint must be tight and the *head gasket* must be without damage. If not, there is little to prevent the coolant from taking a fast detour out through the side of the engine.

THE THERMOSTAT

Once through the junction from the block to the head, the coolant is free to flow, without a care in the world—until it runs smack into a closed *thermostat*.

The thermostat is actually a temperature-controlled water valve placed in the cylinder head at the lower end of the large hose that runs to the top of the radiator. Its long-range function is to keep the temperature of the coolant within a certain range. At this moment it is doing the job by preventing our drop of water from passing through because the water *doesn't contain enough heat.* As the engine warms up, the thermostat gradually opens to permit full circulation of the coolant. During normal engine operation the thermostat may open and close frequently in response to temperature variations. For instance, engine temperature will vary in response to changes in loads imposed on it and in response to outside air temperature and changes in altitude.

Very much like the thermostat that controls the home's heating plant, the cooling system thermostat is sensitive to temperature changes. But, rather than command a furnace to "fire up," this control opens and closes a metal flap in the path of coolant flow.

There are two types of thermostats found on today's cars. The older of these is called the *bellows type.* It was very popular in non-pressurized cooling systems, which will be discussed later in this chapter. The bellows consists of a fine coil of tubing which contains a low-boiling-point liquid that turns to a vapor at a critical temperature. This builds up a pressure, causes the coil to expand and opens the gate for coolant to pass. As coolant temperatures lower, the vapors return to their liquid state, pressure within the coil is reduced, and the valve closes.

The more popular type of thermostat used today is known as the *pellet type.* This unit has a copper-impregnated wax pellet, which actuates a small piston and valve. As the temperature of the coolant increases, the wax expands, pushes on the piston and opens the valve. Cooling causes the pellet to contract, thus closing the valve.

As mentioned earlier, a certain amount of heat is necessary for efficient engine operation. Among other things, this heat helps "burn off" the gallon or more of water formed with every gallon of gas burned. The water is extracted from atmospheric moisture and, when the engine is up to operating temperature, is passed through the exhaust system as vapor. When the engine is cold, some of this water vapor and exhaust gases blow by the clearances between the piston rings and cylinder wall and land in the crankcase where they condense into corrosive acids. Mixed with oil these compounds form sludge which does a fine job gumming up proper engine lubrication, forming sticky varnishes and contributing to loss of engine efficiency and early engine retirement.

Compounding the problem are the fuel-rich mixtures the cold engine thrives on

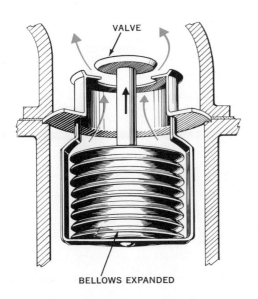

VALVE

BELLOWS EXPANDED

A bellows thermostat. A special liquid inside the brass bellows chamber vaporizes and expands when hot, opening the valve.

while the automatic choke is engaged. Acting on heat signals from the engine, the choke will stay on as long as the low temperature indicates a need for it.

Since most engines are indeed started when they are stone cold, some condensation is unavoidable. However, engineers have made designs to reduce condensation to an absolute minimum. Enter the thermostat and our travelling drop of water.

The name of the game here is, *Heat up your engine as fast as you can.* And to make sure, the thermostat will not allow any coolant out of the engine block until enough, but not too much, heat is built up to satisfy the automatic choke and to cope with atmospheric moisture.

So, if the water pump is the heart of the cooling system, the thermostat is its brain, ever watchful against the twin enemies of engine operation—overheating and overcooling. This is why it is a mistake to believe in the old-time notion that a car does not require a thermostat for summer operation, that it cuts down on circulation and causes overheating. Nonsense! Sludge and over-rich fuel mixtures resulting from overcooling have laid as many engines low as overheating has.

In the early days before thermostats were invented and before they had the reliability they have today, many cars were equipped with a set of "venetian blinds" or shutters in front of the radiator. When the car was started on cold mornings, the driver closed the shutters to ward off any air flow through the radiator. As the engine warmed, the driver had to

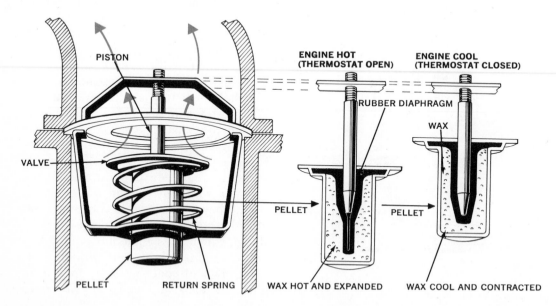

Pellet thermostat. Wax in the copper pellet expands when heated and squeezes a rubber diaphragm against a stationary steel piston. The pellet can only move downward, pulling the valve from its seat. When the pellet cools, the return spring pushes the valve to the seat.

remember to open the shutters gradually — or else steam would be brewed. These blinds have now disappeared on U.S. passenger cars. However, they still can be found on some commercial vehicles operating in the colder climates. On foreign cars the Rolls-Royce had a magnificent set of chrome-clad vertical shutters on their Silver Wraith model which were at first manually controlled and then, in the 1950s, thermostatically operated. The last Rolls shutters were seen in 1959. Volvo had a driver-controlled "window shade" arrangement on their cars up until 1963.

Let's return again to our drop of coolant which has now been routed through a bypass to the water jacket so that it can pick up more heat for another pass at the thermostat.

When the temperature of the coolant in the engine equals the temperature at which the thermostat is set to open (170–180 degrees in most cars) coolant must be allowed to pass through, or else an overheating problem develops. Pass through to where? To the next component in the cooling system, the *radiator*.

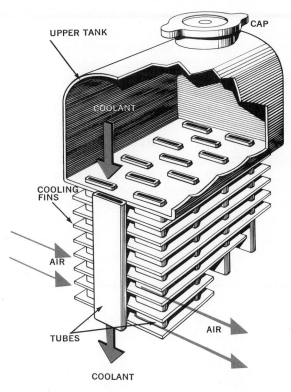

Section of radiator. Coolant entering the upper tank drips through the tubes. The cooling fins draw heat from the coolant and surrender the heat to the outside air.

THE RADIATOR

Almost everyone who drives a car knows about the large, black grill-box under the hood in front of the engine. But not everyone is clear on the simple and passive way the radiator holds the key role of the cooling system. This role is termed passive because the radiator doesn't really do anything. Rather, it allows something to happen. Namely, it permits the coolant to surrender its load of heat to the outside air by radiation — hence its name.

As the water drop passes the open thermostat, it flows upward through the upper radiator hose to the top section of the radiator called the upper tank. There the coolant will gather and drop through one of the many small vertical tubes running to the lower tank. These tubes run straight down the length of the radiator. They are difficult to see because they are situated in a forest of thin metal wafers called cooling fins. The entire radiator midsection is called the radiator *core*.

As the coolant trickles down the tubes, it surrenders its heat to a flow of cool air that drifts from the front of the car towards the rear. Remember what we said earlier: Heat flows from the hot to the less hot. If the car is idling or moving at a slow speed through traffic, the large fan directly behind the radiator sucks cool air through the radiator core. The fan is attached to the water-pump shaft and is driven by the same belt which works the pump. At medium and high speeds the car cuts through enough air to pick up heat from the coolant dropping down the radiator tubes. This enforced draught is known as "ram air." Some cars, especially sport models, have an automatic clutch in the cooling fan which causes it to stop turning when the car attains a certain speed. Since ram air is sufficient for cooling at high engine speeds, performance-minded owners and drivers feel that they are losing engine power unless the fan disengages at a specific speed.

Once the coolant has reached the lower tank of the radiator, it has surrendered a great deal, though not all, of its heat and is ready for another go-'round. Sucked by the action of the water pump, coolant goes up the lower radiator hose, through the pump housing and into the engine block for another pickup and delivery of heat.

Described here is the type of radiator which has been quite popular for the past 50 years—the down-flow type. However, in recent times many cars carry the cross-flow type. This radiator works on exactly the same principle, except that the core tubes run horizontally, rather than up and down. In some cases the upper tank is separated from the core and located elsewhere. These radiators were developed to accommodate the designer's constant need for a lower hood profile. There are no essential engineering differences between the two types of radiators.

PRESSURIZING THE COOLANT

There is an important component we passed up in our journey through the system. Since its role is crucial, we are compelled to examine the radiator pressure cap. The cap's job and origin make up an interesting story.

Like a figurehead on a ship's prow, the old-time radiator was the car's emblem. The radiator's upper and lower tanks were often made of solid brass, and the company emblem graced the head like a jewel. Rare was the occasion when the car owner

Cross-flow radiator. This operates on the same principle as a down-flow radiator. The design allows a substantially lower hood profile.

allowed tarnish to lessen the radiator's gleam. No car cleanup was complete without a good spit-and-polish job on the radiator brass work.

Then in 1930 it happened. The grill appeared on some cars, and the glorious radiator was reduced to a functional component under the hood. The idea caught on and by 1935 all radiators "vanished." From then on the once mighty radiator fought a losing battle with the designers. Hood lines were made lower and lower. As a result radiators got smaller, and coolant capacities decreased.

Meanwhile the popular 4-cylinder engine gave way to the 6; the 6 to the straight-8; then the V-8. Horsepower was constantly on the rise. But the more pistons and power, the more heat. Cooling capacities were dropping in the face of rising power output. There was more heat to carry off, yet radiator size was restricted while water pump efficiency was at its peak.

Operating an engine with the coolant close to the 212-degree boiling point is not only risky, but it is bound to cause subtle and gradual coolant loss through the radiator overflow pipe, which leads to hotter engine operation, which leads to overheating, which leads to trouble.

The answer to preventing boilover at 212 degrees is to raise the boiling point, considering the fact that it was impossible to increase the size of the cooling system. To go beyond the 212 barrier another physical law is utilized. This one says that the boiling point of a liquid can be boosted if the liquid is subject to a pressure which is greater than atmospheric pressure at sea level (14.7 pounds per square inch). The boiling point can be boosted three degrees for every pound of

pressure buildup. This is the same principle behind the kitchen pressure cooker. Through pressure imposed on the contents of the cooker, internal temperatures are raised above the water's normal 212-degree boiling point, and the food cooks much faster.

Without using any elaborate equipment, auto engineers did find a way to pressurize cooling systems. Starting around 1953 on some cars and extending to all makes by 1959, radiators were fitted with a special cap for sealing the system. The whole idea was to allow the heated coolant to produce its own pressure buildup within the confines of the system. The special cap sealed the overflow tube and thus closed the system. When the pressure reaches the designed maximum, a valve in the cap opens to "bleed off" some of the pressure and closes when the safety point is reached.

Taking a typical radiator cap which is rated for a maximum of 14 psi pressure beyond the 14.7 sea level pressure, let's see what actually happens. As the coolant gets hotter, it expands and imposes a

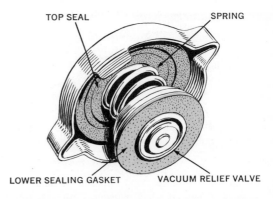

TOP SEAL   SPRING

LOWER SEALING GASKET   VACUUM RELIEF VALVE

A typical radiator pressure cap. The spring is calibrated to exert a precise pressure.

pressure on the entire system. At 14 psi the boiling point is boosted to 254 degrees. This figure is derived from the sea level boiling point of water (212°) plus the three-degree rise for each pound of pressure. Or, for the math buffs: $212 + (14 \times 3) = 254$.

These calculations conform to the laws which govern the conduct of heat. Remember the one which says that the flow rate of heat to cold depends on the difference of temperature between the two objects? So, a super-hot coolant of 254 degrees will give up its heat much more readily at the radiator than coolant of a mere 212 degrees. The hotter it is, the faster it will cool.

As the coolant expands when it is heated, so will it contract when it is cooled. Without the aid of a special relief valve, contracting coolant would create a vacuum in the cooling system. Vacuum is undesirable because of the potential danger of hose collapse and core damage. To avoid this problem, a vacuum relief valve in the radiator pressure cap allows the system to vent after the engine is shut down and coolant temperatures lower.

THE COOLANT'S EFFECT ON THE HEATER

If anyone told you that the car's heater worked off the car's cooling system, you would be tempted to sign him up for a quiet room on that big farm with the high iron fence. Actually your informant wouldn't be institutionalized because the idea works. Using the cooling system to keep you and your passengers warm is very practical. To understand it, all you have to do is apply the magic of relativity.

The term "hot" is descriptive, but it always refers to the relative temperatures of something else. For instance, temperatures at the core of the sun are estimated at 35–50 million degrees Fahrenheit, while the sun's surface is much "colder" at 10,000 degrees. Now this figure is no longer cold when it is compared to the melting point of iron which is a mere 2,795 degrees. Taking relativity a step further, how would a potful of molten iron feel as a foot bath?

Applying the same relativity to the cooling system of the car, the 170-degree temperature found there is quite frigid when compared to the tremendous heat gener-

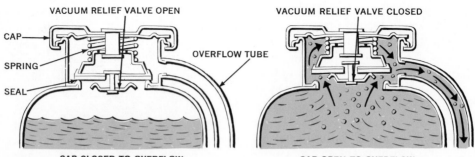

VACUUM RELIEF VALVE OPEN   VACUUM RELIEF VALVE CLOSED

CAP —   OVERFLOW TUBE

SPRING —

SEAL —

CAP CLOSED TO OVERFLOW   CAP OPEN TO OVERFLOW

Pressure cap in operation. Left, the radiator remains sealed as long as pressure remains at or below a specified setting—thus allowing high-temperature operation. Right, when pressure rises above the setting, the seal is pushed back and coolant passes through the overflow tube. When pressure drops, the radiator seals again.

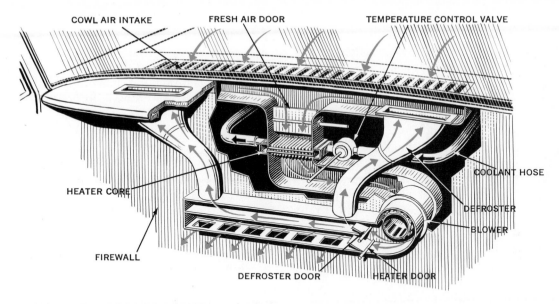

COWL AIR INTAKE   FRESH AIR DOOR   TEMPERATURE CONTROL VALVE

COOLANT HOSE

HEATER CORE

DEFROSTER

BLOWER

FIREWALL

DEFROSTER DOOR   HEATER DOOR

Heater works off the cooling system. Coolant from the engine enters the heater core. Fresh air is forced through the core, warmed and delivered to the passenger compartment. Flaps can direct warmed air to the floor or the windshield. The temperature control valve regulates the flow of coolant to the heater core.

ated by normal engine operation. However, it is at the same time delicious as warm-air temperature drifting around the passenger compartment when the outside air is near zero.

So, 170 degrees is really either hot or cold, depending on whether your reference is to the heating system or cooling system. It all depends on how you look at it, or feel it. Let's see how it works.

HOW THE HEATER WORKS

The heater system operates as a circuit of its own within the cooling system. To explore it, let's pick up another drop of coolant and trace another path, touching all the important bases. But be assured, it's a far less complex trip than the last one.

Starting at the water pump on some cars

or at the engine block in others, we find ourselves following a drop of coolant inside a much smaller hose than found in the main system. This is called the heater hose. Pushed on by pump pressure, we are, in a very short while, at the engine firewall, the metal barrier which separates you from the engine compartment. Mounted to the firewall is the temperature control valve. This unit is designed to control the flow of coolant much like the faucet at your sink controls the flow of fresh water. When you set the heat control knob or lever at the dashboard to "Hot," a maximum flow of coolant drifts through the valve; when the setting is "Warm" or "Off," little or no coolant flows.

By now you may be asking: Coolant will flow to where? The answer is: to a grid-like box with fins called the heater core. This unit looks very much like the big radiator up front, but is located under the dash. On some cars it is mounted to the firewall, but precise location is unimportant in this journey through the heating system. With the valve open, coolant will flow into the core, through it, and out of it. Heat for your comfort is provided by the cold air forced through the fins of the hot core (relative terms, to be sure). Most cars today use a dual system for extracting heat from the heater core by employing an electric heater blower and vents to the outside air.

With the vent doors opened by the driver, outside air is scooped up as the car rolls along. By way of a duct system this air is then directed through the heater core. If the valve is open, the core is hot and liberates heat to the cooler air, which is then deposited as a warm draft on your toes. When the outside air is mild, these same vents can be opened by the driver to admit fresh outside air. But, unless the driver wants the effects of a sauna, the heat valve should be off with no coolant circulating through the heater core.

Let's get back to cold weather conditions. If the car is forced to travel at very slow speeds, not enough scooped air will be available for warmth. In this case the driver can switch on the electric blower. This is a fan that can either pull in air from the outside or recirculate the interior air. In both cases, the fan will force a draft through the heater core.

Continuing our voyage through the heater core, we once again find ourselves in a small rubber return hose that heads back to the engine compartment. Then our journey ends as the coolant spills into the main cooling system at the engine.

From all this it may be easy to understand an old-time truck driver's trick to combat overheating on a long hill, midday in August. When truckers feel the radiator is about to blow steam, they quickly reach for the heater knob and blower switch. The idea is to draw some of the overheated coolant into the heater core so the fan can extract some heat from it, thus taking some of the load off of the main radiator. True, this action leaves the truck cab feeling like a foyer in the house of the Devil, but it prevents the engine from overheating. And the truck continues to roll.

COOLING GEARS

You might be tempted to think that the job of cooling a heat-producing engine and heating a cold passenger compartment is enough of a task for a fairly simple system. But there is still another chore asked of the venerable radiator. This is to handle the heat generated in the automatic transmission fluid by the gears, discs, plates and shafts which make up the transmission.

In Chapter 7 on transmissions we see that the fluid (oil) inside the case serves three functions: (1) as a hydraulic fluid, (2) as a lubricant, and (3) as a coolant. Yes, we are back to the word "coolant" again. Just as the liquid inside the radiator is a coolant for the engine, the oil for the automatic transmission acts as a coolant for its own guts.

We know that for a coolant to be effective, it must act as a medium for the transfer and dissipation of heat. Rather than placing an additional radiator at the transmission, fluid is diverted from the cooling system radiator to the transmission where it constantly absorbs excess heat.

The circular path is quite simple. A steel tube extends from a fitting on the trans-

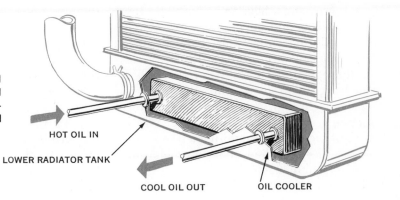

Transmission oil cooler. Hot oil enters the tank submerged in the lower section of the radiator. Cooled oil is then returned to the transmission.

HOT OIL IN

LOWER RADIATOR TANK

COOL OIL OUT

OIL COOLER

mission case to a fitting at the lower radiator tank. Inside the tank is a sealed unit with internal baffles designed to slow up the flow of oil running through it. This unit is called the oil cooler. As transmission fluid passes through the cooler, it gives up heat to the coolant which has just come down through the core tubes. At the other end of the cooler is another fitting to which a steel tube is attached. This time it runs back to the transmission.

In the early days of the automatic transmission, coolant was brought from the radiator to an external oil cooler with a system of water jackets. This bulky unit was located at the transmission base. In a sense, it was the reverse of what is in popular use today.

ANTIFREEZE

Almost all matter will expand when heated and contract when cooled. Water is not an exception. However, water is blessed with a peculiarity. As it is cooled, it shrinks somewhat until it hits about 40 degrees, when ice crystals begin to form. Then it has the nasty habit of expanding. At 32 degrees, water's freezing point, expansion

stops and the water turns to solid ice. But what happens during the expansion period is awesome—sometimes disastrous—and is never to be underestimated. Anyone who has had to live through the experience of burst frozen water pipes or raised concrete slabs knows that even tough and heavy materials offer little opposition to this fierce ballooning process of freezing water.

Neither is the cast-iron cylinder block of the automobile engine a match against the forces of ice expansion. But before we go one step further, let's shatter a myth which has been around for too long. In casually poking around under the hood, you may have noticed metal discs implanted on the walls of the engine. These are quite flat and are about the size of a half-dollar. For some silly reason they got the name *freeze-out plugs.* The name implies that when freezing water in the radiator is in the expanding stage it will seek an "out" via the plug, thus sparing the cylinder block the breakage and the owner the agony. Not true. These openings which are capped with a convex disc are properly called *core plugs,* or sometimes, *welch plugs.*

When the engine is cast from a molten

metal, provisions have to be made for the water jackets and oil passageways which run inside the outer shell of the engine. A special sand is used to outline the mold for these vital avenues. After the liquid metal is cooled to a solid, the sand is removed through these holes, then the openings are capped with a plug. While some of them may pop during a freeze-up, they cannot be relied upon to protect the engine from damage.

Therefore do not listen to those who tell you to relax when the anticipated temperatures for the night will be 20 below and there is only pure water in the car's cooling system. Those "freeze-out" plugs will not save the engine.

Since changing the weather patterns or moving to Florida is too much to ask of car owners, the only practical answer is to add an antifreeze to the water. Enough antifreeze should be added to keep the liquid from freezing at the lowest winter temperatures normally occurring in your region.

In the past, different antifreezes were used. These included solutions of salt, sugar, calcium, magnesium and even oil and kerosene. However, while such additives to water will lower the freezing point

OVERFLOW TUBE   VENT VALVE—CLOSED UNDER PRESSURE

RADIATOR FULL

POLYETHYLENE BOTTLE

Diagram of closed cooling system. Overflow of the radiator is captured. When the engine cools, vacuum created in the bottle sends the fluid back to the radiator.

they do affect the various materials in the cooling system. The salts cause clogging and corrosion of metal parts of the radiator and engine block while the oils attack the rubber hoses and seals.

By the 1930s the home remedies gave way to three popular antifreeze substances. Listed in order of their protective properties they are methyl alcohol, ethylene glycol, and ethyl alcohol. The alcohols are effective—up to a point. True, they are far less expensive than the ethylene glycol, but far more volatile. That is, they evaporate quite readily. This forces the motorist to maintain a constant vigil of the antifreeze strength as the winter drags on. Secondly, alcohol not only lowers the freezing point of the water (which is good) but it also lowers the boiling point (which is bad). For example, water at sea level will boil at 212 degrees and freeze at 32 degrees. When enough alcohol is added to keep the coolant in a liquid state at minus-20 degrees, the boiling point of the mixture will drop to 180 degrees. To keep the coolant from hitting this new, lowered boiling point, cars equipped with alcohol antifreeze must use thermostats which open at lower temperatures, about 160 degrees. The ultimate effect is that engines cannot run at peak thermal efficiency, and the car heater gives no comfort at all on very cold days.

Today most car owners are sworn to the "permanent-type" antifreeze with an ethylene glycol base. This product does not evaporate very readily and has the ability to *raise* the boiling point of the coolant as well as *lower* its freezing point. During World War II when the U.S. Army was involved in the desert campaign in North Africa, ethylene glycol was used in those tanks with water-cooled engines to prevent boilover in much the same manner as the Germans used EG for tanks on the Russian Front to prevent freeze-ups. Another example of the versatility of EG is that it can be used year-'round in the cooling system of cars with airconditioning. Since air flow through the radiator is restricted by a large condenser and the engine compartment is jammed with additional equipment, these cars run much hotter than cars without airconditioning; hence the danger of boilover is greater.

Here's an example of what ethylene glycol can do: A solution protected to minus-20 degrees will boil at 223 degrees, without pressurizing. This is 40 degrees more boiling-point safety than alcohol solutions provide, with the same freezing protection. Another plus for EG is its controlled rate of expansion when heated. With the same minus-20 degree solution installed in a 20-quart capacity cooling system, the overflow loss will be $2\frac{1}{3}$ pints, while methyl alcohol will lose $2\frac{7}{8}$ pints and ethyl $3\frac{2}{3}$ pints due to expansion.

But ethylene glycol has its quirks too. It must be mixed with water to be fully effective. A 100 percent concentration of this compound in the cooling system will freeze more readily than a solution of 60 percent glycol and 40 percent water. The 60-40 combination is considered to be maximum, keeping the coolant in a liquid state down to 70 degrees below zero. Unless you intend to drive on the dark side of the moon, you'll not require better protection than that.

When ethylene glycol antifreeze was first presented to the public by Union Carbide in 1926 and produced by Dow Chemical in the early 1930s it was claimed to be the "permanent-type" answer to freeze-ups. Since 1946, when EG's popularity began to rise sharply, companies making and selling the product have campaigned very strongly to put down this designation—perhaps with some justification.

The story is this: The can of ethylene glycol you buy contains more than just those ingredients which lower the freezing point of water. (For chemists the formula is $C_2H_4(OH)_2$.) Also included in that can are such ingredients as rust inhibitors, rubber parts lubricant and antifoaming chemicals. Though ethylene glycol does not wear out or lose its effectiveness, the additives do. The constant heat imposed on the coolant causes a chemical breakdown of these agents and reduces their effectiveness on the job for which they were designed. Not only is the strength of the additives dissipated; manufacturers claim that additives form corrosive elements in the coolant. It is for this reason, they say, ethylene glycol coolant should be drained and replaced with a fresh fill periodically.

How often? This debate has been raging for years. In the 1940s the recommendation was a fresh fill of glycol every winter with a flush out in the spring. In the early 1950s it was considered good maintenance to fill in the winter and flush the following fall. In 1960, car owners were subjected to the fiasco of the "permanent-permanent" type antifreeze. DuPont with their "Telar," Union Carbide with their "Long-Life Coolant," and Dow with their "Dowgard" all claimed to have the motorist's answer to a dream: an antifreeze which *never* had to be changed. These products never quite made it. Some say they were withdrawn from the market for the sake of the car owners; others credit the stock holders.

Presently, most car manufacturers recommend a coolant change-over every two years. Thus, to be practical, the designation "permanent" is limited. Though it was originally meant to refer to glycol's low evaporation qualities as compared to alcohol, permanent wasn't meant to be "forever."

TODAY AND THE FUTURE

The engineers have no fundamental complaints against the basic system used in water-cooled engines. However, there are a few annoyances they would be glad to be rid of. Namely, oxidation from the atmosphere.

When air mixes with water and iron, the result is rust. When air mixes with heat and chemical additives which guard against corrosion, the result is a change in the qualities of these additives and a subsequent loss of protection. When air mixes with the coolant, the result is foaming.

Based on trends noted in the Renault sealed system and the Cadillac closed system, it seems the push is toward isolating the system against any contamination. Both these systems are designed to prevent evaporative losses, hence they do not require opening for topping off. Thus contamination by air is avoided.

Closed System Cooling. The cooling setup introduced on the 1969 Cadillac is a good example of what may soon be "standard" on most cars. This cooling system uses all the conventional components plus a polyethylene bottle mounted at the same level as the radiator. A rubber tube connects the vacuum vent valve of the radiator cap with the bottle. Another tube vents the

bottle to the atmosphere. As the coolant heats and expands, the overflow is directed into the bottle. The system is not pressurized at this point. It is still vented to the atmosphere. But as the temperature exceeds the setting on the thermostat and the coolant really starts pouring into the bottle, the valve to the bottle closes and the system builds up pressure to suppress the boil—as in a conventional pressurized cooling system. When the system cools after engine shutdown, a vacuum is created which siphons coolant back into the radiator from the bottle. Thus the system is kept full at all times.

Under normal conditions it is unnecessary to remove the radiator cap. If more coolant is required, it can be added through the bottle. According to the engineers, there should be very little coolant loss due to expansion or evaporation. Also since the system is not always pressurized, there is less strain on all soldered joints of the radiator and hoses. Most important, there is a minimum of air (oxygen) in the system which can promote rust, corrosion and depletion of additive strength.

Air Cooling. We spent much time describing a water-cooled system because it is the most widely used method for maintaining engine temperature. However, it is by no means the only way. Another popular method is to cool the engine with air.

Let's go back to that soggy day in August at the opening of this chapter. A hot and humid blanket is draped over your body—skin tight. Got to get rid of that heat! The simplest and most obvious method is to blow it away with a fan. Even a hand-manipulated paper fan can produce a cur-

Air-cooled engine. This type was used on the Chevrolet Corvair. Note the large top fan and the cooling fins.

rent of air that absorbs some heat. But since we are tuned in to the marvels of our age, an electric fan is a more efficient means of blowing the heat from your face.

Air-cooled engines have a large spinning fan which bathes the cylinders and other engine parts with volumes of outside air that flush away the heat.

However, fans can blow away only surface heat. And we know that the greatest concentration of heat in an engine is not on the surface but rather in the cylinder where all the explosions take place. Therefore, the air-cooled engine must be equipped to carry much of this internal heat to the surface. This is done with layers of metal strips called *cooling fins*. They are cast as part of the external section of the cylinder wall and bristle outward. By conduction, heat is drawn away

from the source and accumulates in the air spaces between the fins. Fast-moving fan-driven air then picks up and carries off the heat.

Fans for these engines are driven by belts attached to the crankshaft pulley. Whenever the engine is operating, the fan spins.

Motorcycle and piston-type aircraft engines are usually air-cooled. However, they use slightly different methods for disposing of the heat. The "fan" for the airplane is the propeller, which blows heat from the fins while providing the wind for lifting the craft. The motorcycle has no fan and depends mainly on the force of on-rushing air to cool the engine.

Of course air cooling has its own problems. The main one is that engine temperatures are affected by ambient temperature. All the fan does is move the air. If it is the moist, hot air of summer, engine temperatures will be higher than when the fan is moving the dry, cold air of winter. Another problem is that overall engine temperatures are uneven, depending on how close certain components are to the fan. Or, in the case of the motorcycle, cooling depends on how close certain engine parts are to the outside. Uneven temperatures are a roadblock for that all-important thermal efficiency. Finally, the big gripe against air-cooled engines is that they make more noise. There is no debating of the fact that a water-cooled engine is quieter.

On the plus side, an air-cooled engine is never subject to freeze-ups, and it never requires antifreeze. It has a far more simple system with fewer components. And it poses fewer maintenance problems in the long run.

6
LIGHTING

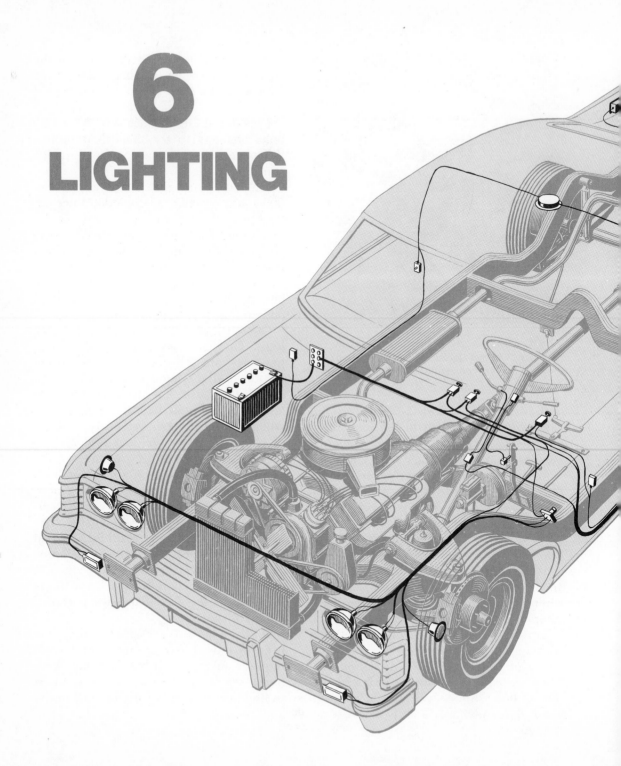

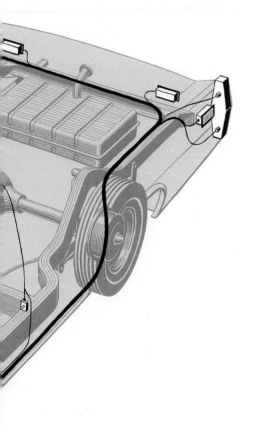

Because vision is wholly dependent upon light, we can flatly state: No light, no sight. Whatever we actually see is a concentration of light rays which emanate from the sighted object and register as an image on the retina of the eye. This image, in turn, is transmitted via the optic nerve to the brain where it is sorted into a message which, in effect, tells us what we are looking at.

With low light there is little reflection, hence little information for the brain to work with. But light does not always have to illuminate an object to serve a function for our sight. Take the ordinary flashlight, for instance. When you walk on a darkened country path, the flashlight illuminates the ground. Yet, this same instrument can be used on a mountaintop to signal another person many miles away. In this instance, illumination of an object is not essential. All that is required is for the observer to see the light.

This distinction — light to see by and light to be seen by — is important in understanding the concepts behind automotive lighting. Since the subject of lighting is so linked to sight, it is well that we spend a little time on the subject of *optics* — the study of the nature and properties of light.

Though we will not here attempt an all inclusive discourse on the nature of light, we should examine a few facts as they relate to automotive lighting, especially the headlamps.

First, what is light? There are a number of theories, but the one most accepted is the *Wave Theory*. According to this concept, light is made up of energy particles travelling at a speed of 186,000 miles per second. In order for our eyes to see light, these energy particles must vibrate, or wave, at a certain number of times per second. This is called *frequency*. If the frequency is low, the waves are so long that they do not produce visible light. Infrared radiation is an example of these "longer-than-light" waves. On the other hand, ultraviolet light has "shorter-than-light" waves and is also invisible. The frequency of visible light lies somewhere between these two.

The method by which a bulb produces light is the heating of a filament with electricity. At the start, the filament gives off long, invisible infrared waves. As it gets hotter, the filament produces shorter waves and emits a red light. Soon the filament gets still hotter and the waves become shorter, producing a yellowish-white light.

One other factor which is worth mentioning, though perhaps it is obvious. Surely, you have noticed that the farther an object is taken from the source of light, the dimmer it will appear. Well, scientists have put this phenomenon into a formula. It is commonly referred to as the "Square

Law." In technical language it says: "Light intensity varies inversely as the square of its distance." This is best illustrated by citing a practical example.

When a light is at Y distance from an object, that object is lit with, say, an intensity of X. If the light is pulled back such that the distance is doubled to 2Y, the intensity of the light on the object will not be reduced by $\frac{1}{2}$ but by $\frac{1}{2} \times \frac{1}{2}$, or to $\frac{1}{4}$X.

This law is vital in considering headlamp design. Then the "Square Law" is applied in the reverse. Every time the distance from the end of the headlight beam to the headlamp is doubled, the light intensity at the source must be multiplied by four to overcome the dimming caused by distance. With this said, let's return to the world of automotive lighting.

Today's automobile has about thirty-five lamps. Some are large and some are quite small. Some have the function of being *luminous*. That is, they emit light for us to see by. Some have the function of *illuminating*. That is, they emit a light to be seen.

Though the automotive lamp functions on the same principle as a household electric bulb, wherein a light is generated by a glowing filament, very little else is similar between the two. All household lamps have a screw-type base which is threaded into a screw-type socket. With few exceptions the auto lamp does not use a threaded base. The configuration of its base is smooth and is called a *bayonet base*.

The name comes from the push-and-twist method used to secure bayonets on rifles. On the side of the smooth base protrude two tiny pins. In some cases, the pins are on an equal line with each other; in others they are offset to make sure the bulb fits in only one way. The socket is just slightly larger than the diameter of the base of the bulb. At the bottom of the socket there is a plastic or fiber disc with a soldered electrical contact in the center. The disc sits on a soft spring which assures a gentle pressure against the disc.

The bulb is inserted into the socket when the two pins are fitted into two small channels along the socket wall. When the bulb bottoms, it is then pushed slightly further to compress the disc spring and twisted slightly to the right. Thus the bulb is held in place. Removal requires the reverse procedure. The bulb is pushed in and twisted to the left for release. Considering the simplicity of headlamp installation, it seems strange that household lamps are not similarly constructed.

Some automotive bulbs are designed to do two jobs. A good example is the tail stop lamp. This bulb has two separate filaments and two contacts at its base. Similarly, the socket contains two contacts which are the termination of two separate wires. When the driver turns on the switch for the headlamps, current flows to one of the filaments in the bulb, and the car shows a lit tail lamp. When the driver depresses the brake, current flows to the other filament, giving the car brighter tail lamps, or stoplights.

SINGLE-WIRE CIRCUIT

Before we examine the individual lighting circuits, keep in mind that there is only one wire for each circuit going to the light sockets. In the household light socket there are two wires—one for electricity to enter and one for return. The one-wire setup on the automobile is no contradiction to the fact that electricity requires a complete circuit to do any work. In the car, the single wire brings in the "juice," while the metal of the bulb base, in contact with the metal of the socket which is in contact with the sheet metal of the car provides the return route. More detail on this type of circuitry is found in Chapter 2, "Electrical System."

VEHICULAR LIGHTING

It is interesting to note that we have used all sorts of vehicles for thousands of years, yet we did not use lighting to any great extent on vehicles until petroleum products were commercially marketed as a light fuel.

Horse-drawn carriages and wagons used candle lamps by the eighteenth century, but vehicular lighting was not in common use until the popular use of the kerosene lantern, starting about 1860. These methods of vehicle lighting had only one function. That is, they created a light to be seen by, rather than a light to see by.

The early horseless carriages either had no lights at all or adapted kerosene lamps from horse-drawn vehicles. This, in spite of the fact that the electric bulb was invented twelve years before the first successful operation of a production car. It took a long time before lighting for illumination found its way to the motor car. Before technology could provide adequate illumination, automotive lighting had many strange phases.

At first, the only lamps on cars were side markers. These were attached to the sides of the vehicle and were, in most cases, modified kerosene lamps. Their glow was visible from the front, sides and from the rear of the vehicle. Around 1900 a kerosene headlight was offered as an accessory by

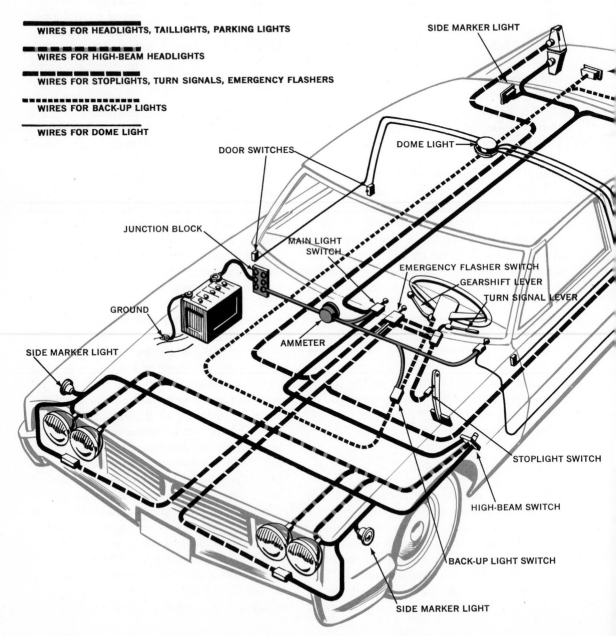

WIRES FOR HEADLIGHTS, TAILLIGHTS, PARKING LIGHTS

WIRES FOR HIGH-BEAM HEADLIGHTS

WIRES FOR STOPLIGHTS, TURN SIGNALS, EMERGENCY FLASHERS

WIRES FOR BACK-UP LIGHTS

WIRES FOR DOME LIGHT

SIDE MARKER LIGHT

DOOR SWITCHES

DOME LIGHT

JUNCTION BLOCK

MAIN LIGHT SWITCH

EMERGENCY FLASHER SWITCH

GEARSHIFT LEVER

TURN SIGNAL LEVER

GROUND

AMMETER

SIDE MARKER LIGHT

STOPLIGHT SWITCH

HIGH-BEAM SWITCH

BACK-UP LIGHT SWITCH

SIDE MARKER LIGHT

122

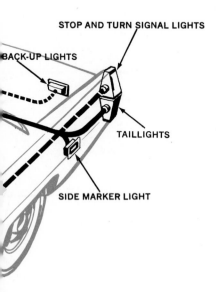

STOP AND TURN SIGNAL LIGHTS

BACK-UP LIGHTS

TAILLIGHTS

SIDE MARKER LIGHT

Overall view of lighting system. Today's cars have over thirty-five lamps for a variety of functions. Future cars will have more lights for a network of warning systems.

the leading lamp maker of the day, R. E. Dietz Company. These lights occasioned a new use for the horseless buggy. They permitted night driving with relative safety. These lamps were capable of casting a 200-foot beam ahead of the car.

Soon after, the kerosene light was replaced by carbide headlamps. This was a cumbersome arrangement. Strapped to the side of the car, on the running board, was a tank containing calcium carbide. Above it was a smaller tank with water. When the motorist found himself on the road at night he would open a valve at the water tank. When the water combined with the calcium carbide, acetylene gas was created. This gas was piped to the head lamps which were about twelve inches in diameter and had a curved glass mirror behind an acetylene burner. The driver would then go to the front of the car, strike a match and light the burners. At frequent intervals the carbide had to be replaced. This was not a pleasant task for the tanks and the gas had a very disagreeable odor.

The next development came in 1904 when it was discovered that a chemical called acetone (what is used as nail polish remover today) absorbs acetylene under pressure the way a sponge absorbs water. Acetone made it possible to sell acetylene gas in cylinders. Car owners did not need the complicated gas-generating apparatus then. All they did was buy tanks of gas which were exchanged for full ones when the present supply was exhausted. The most popular brand of gas was called Prest-O-Lite. It was so popular, in fact, that it became a generic name for headlamp gas. Nevertheless, the motorist still had to get down from the car and strike a match to light the lamps. In 1910 a very fancy car of the day, the Owen, offered an electrical igniting device which allowed the driver to light the lamps without getting out of the car or striking a match.

Electric lamps were still very slow to become popular. By 1912 only ten percent of all cars were so equipped. These lamps contained bulbs with a carbon filament and were very prone to breakage. The big problem was in making a filament that was strong enough to withstand the rigors of automotive use.

Developments then turned toward the metal tungsten, the hardest of all pure metals. However, though tungsten melts at 6,000 degrees Fahrenheit, it is quite brittle. Around 1910 a Dr. W. D. Coolidge evolved a way of making tungsten wire ductile enough to withstand severe vibrations. This was ideal for automotive use. The first electric lights on cars were conversions of the gas lamps. They were powered by dry-cell or wet-cell batteries and were expensive to operate.

With the invention of the electric starter, manufacturers shifted to a storage battery with an electrical generating system. This same system supplied power to the lights. In 1915 Cadillac offered a tilt-beam headlamp on its cars. The light consisted of two bulbs with a curved glass mirror. Because of the high rate of mirror breakage, again from vibrations, the glass mirrors were replaced with a polished metal surface. In 1924 the first dual-filament bulb appeared for high- and low-beam applications. This was an important advance, since it simplified getting the proper focus. Therefore, it was easier to produce a beam that would do its job in the high and low positions.

Even with the development of the two-filament bulb, headlights were still creating problems for the car owner. Dirt

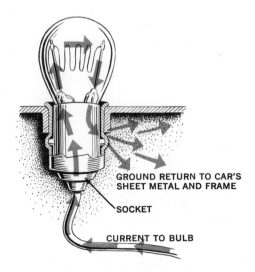

GROUND RETURN TO CAR'S SHEET METAL AND FRAME

SOCKET

CURRENT TO BULB

A typical lamp circuit. Current flows through a single wire, into one end of a filament and out the other. The base of the lamp and socket serve to complete the circuit through metal sections of the car and back to the battery.

and rust kept reducing the efficiency of the polished reflective surface. If the owner took the trouble to clean the reflector, the plating often wore off after a while.

Progress in automotive lighting was not as swift as it was sure. In 1929 the two-filament bulb and reflector were made accurately enough not to require focusing. Prior to this, the car owner had to have the focus of the bulb and reflector checked periodically to assure maximum lighting from the two. Now the setting was permanent and mechanics could change bulbs without upsetting the focus.

The problems of dirt and corrosion remained, however. Yet another problem appeared. There were more than three dozen different types of headlights in the field requiring many different types of care. This produced difficulties in the service industry. In 1937 a committee representing the automobile industry and head lamp manufacturers met to design a standard lighting system which would apply to all cars. By the time the 1940 models rolled off the line they were equipped with the Sealed Beam Headlight system. At last, the dirt and rust conditions were solved. The early units consisted of a light bulb, a bright metal reflector, a gasket and a glass lens. The entire unit was sealed and non-serviceable. The later type, now in wide use, consists of two filaments inside a chamber which is sprayed with bright aluminum paint and fused to a lens. Since the entire unit is sealed and evacuated, a separate bulb is unnecessary. The upper filament glows when the regular headlights are on; the lower filament glows when the high beams are on.

Further developments in head lamps included in 1956 the dual arrangement, or separate lamps for low and high beams. There is some argument as to the value of four lamps. Lighting engineers claim that each pair can be designed for their specific use, rather than having a compromise when only one pair of lamps with wider beams are used for uppers and lowers. Other engineers claim that the design arose merely from a search for a new styling. It is hard to say who is correct since the 4-lamp system began to disappear in 1968.

One other point about headlamp design is that if you think the concealed lamps such as found on Cougar or Toronado are something new, try this: The DeSoto had them back in 1941.

Sealed Beam. The sealed beam headlights of the car are located in special holders called head lamp housings. On some cars, the hardware holding the lamp in place is very easy to remove; on others it is a challenge. In almost all cases, a chrome molding circles the lamp and is held in place with screws. Once access is gained, however, you will find that the head-lamp sealed beam is secured with a special rim having three ears and a like number of screws. The lamp and rim rest on a circular foundation supported by a number of springs. At the top and at the side are adjustment screws. These are very important for aiming the lamp. To raise the light beam, the top screw is turned inward; to lower it, the screw is turned outward. Similarly, adjusting the lamps from left to right is accomplished by loosening or tightening the side screw. Caution: Adjusting the head lamp should not be attempted by the amateur, and certainly not without equipment specifically designed for the purpose.

With the ring removed, the head lamp is completely loose. At the rear end of the glass unit are three prongs which accept a three-hole socket with a like number of wires. One wire leads to a metal surface and provides the electrical ground connection; the second wire supplies the low-beam filament; the third wire is for the high-beam filament.

The wires lead to a junction where the wires from the other head lamp are connected. From the junction, the high- and low-beam wires run to the foot dimmer switch. This switch has no "On" or "Off" position. Rather it acts as a fork in the road, allowing either the high- or the low-beam circuit to operate.

The foot dimmer switch has four wires connected to it. One is a very thin wire which goes to the small light on the dashboard; this reminds you that the high beams are on. Connected to the same terminal is the heavy wire which leads to the high-beam filaments of both lamps. The third wire leads to the low-beam filaments of both lamps. The fourth wire is the feed. It starts at the headlight switch at the instrument panel and provides the current to light the lamps via the dimmer switch.

Light Switch. The light switch is a very complicated device, since it performs so many functions at once. It can be compared with a telephone switchboard. In this case, the "incoming call" is the flow of current from the battery. The "extensions" to where the current is routed are many and varied.

When the switch is set on the first notch, current flows to the parking lights, taillights, side markers and dashboard lamps. When the switch is set to another notch the headlamps are illuminated. On cars prior to 1971, the parking lamps go out when the switch is pulled all the way. However, cars made after that year are required to maintain the parking lights while the headlamps are on.

In addition to serving all of these circuits, the light switch on many cars also has a rheostat for gradually dimming the dash lights, an extra switch for turning on the interior light, and a circuit breaker for protecting the headlight circuit.

Where the dashboard dimmer is incorporated into the light switch, turning the knob does the trick. To turn on the interior light, the knob has to be turned in the other direction. Some cars have installed a separate switch for dimming and/or interior lights.

The circuit breaker is a very vital link in the lighting setup. It is unlike the circuit breakers used in many homes. These break the flow of electricity when there is a short circuit or other defect which pulls a great deal of current. Then the circuit remains "broken" until the breaker is reset manually. The headlight breaker operates on a heat principle. In the event of a defect in the wiring and the drawing of current far greater than what the breaker was designed to handle, the circuit is shut down. After a few seconds, when it has a chance to cool, the circuit is reconnected, and the lights go on again. If the defect is still in the line, the lights go off—then on. This continues until the defect is corrected. This type of breaker is far more reliable than a fuse which will "pop" more readily than a breaker.

Parking and Tail Lamps. This circuit is less complex than that of the head lamps. However, both the parking and the tail lamps use the double-filament bulbs described previously. That is, though there are two filaments inside the same bulb, each has a separate job to do, each has its own wiring.

For the parking lamps there is a wire coming off one filament from the left lamp and one from the right. They are both joined by a connector such that a single wire runs from the light switch. The same setup is found with the tail lamps. Inside the light switch there are tabs which make sure that both the parking and tail circuits are activated at the same time. Incidentally, the lamps which illuminate the dashboard are also tied to the park-tail circuit *and* the head lamp circuit. So, when either system is turned on, the dash lights are activated.

Turn Signals. This is a somewhat more complicated circuit involving many wires and units. Generally, the lights are grouped left front with left rear and right front with right rear. Let's follow the circuit of one set—the right side.

Starting at the turn-signal filament of the rear bulb, there is a wire which runs all the way up front to the turn signal switch located under the steering wheel. This is coupled with the contact point of the wire coming from the right-front turn-signal filament.

When the lever is pushed to indicate a right turn, both contacts are covered by the "hot" contact coming from the flasher. In turn, the flasher is fed from the fuse located at the fuse panel. Until the 1968 cars, that's all there was to it. However, after the advent of the emergency 4-way flasher, this circuit lost its simplicity. Now, before the wire enters the turn-signal switch it goes to a big connector which accumulates the wires from all of the turn-signal filaments. A main wire runs from this connector to the emergency flasher which is fed by its own fuse. When the emergency system is off, signalling takes place as described. When the emergency system is turned on, all four signal lights are activated by the current which is shunted away from the regular system to the 4-way system. This is why moving the turn-signal lever while the emergency system is on produces no extra flashing.

The flasher itself is an interesting device. It is very similar to the heat-controlled switch which comprises the headlight circuit breaker. Inside the little tin can are two contacts. When electricity is flowing through the flasher, the contacts close and the circuit is complete. In a few seconds, the contacts heat up. Since they are made of a special bi-metal which bends when heated, the contacts separate. This breaks the circuit and the flow of electricity is interrupted. In a short while the

contacts cool and are drawn together by a spring. The circuit is then completed and the cycle starts all over.

Stop Lamps. Stop lamps imply that there is a separate set of lamps which indicate when the driver is stopping. This was so at one time, but no longer. Now the same filament that does the job of providing the flashes for the turn signals also glows when the driver presses down on the brake pedal.

Heart of this circuit is the switch. There was a time when a hydraulic switch was used. This was screwed into the brake line. It consisted of a housing with a threaded base and two terminals for wires. Inside the housing is a small metal bar just below the opening at the base. When the driver depresses the brake pedal, hydraulic fluid under pressure goes through the opening and pushes the small metal bar upwards. Thus the two contacts are bridged. Since one of the wires on the terminal comes from the battery and the other goes to the stop lamps, a complete circuit is made when the contacts are united by the metal bar.

Since the 1960s a different switch has been used. This is a simple mechanical device located near the brake pedal. When the pedal is relaxed, a button on the switch is depressed. Thus, the circuit is kept in an open position. Any forward motion of the pedal will cause the button to come out, thereby closing the circuit and making the stop lamps light up.

Courtesy Light (dome light). Most cars have a light located in the center of the ceiling. The light can be turned on by two different methods, either by turning the light switch knob or by opening the door. In the latter case, a spring-loaded push button installed

HEAD LAMP HISTORY

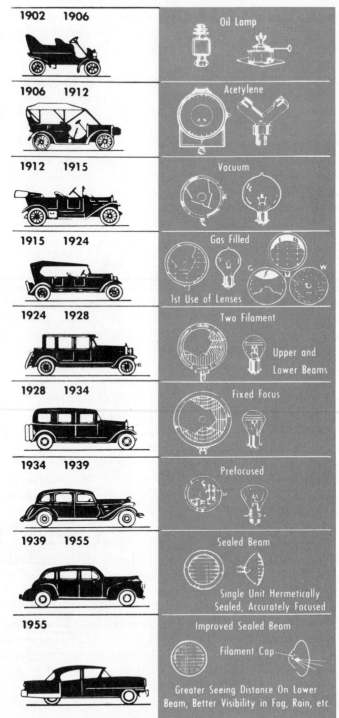

1902 1906	Oil Lamp
1906 1912	Acetylene
1912 1915	Vacuum
1915 1924	Gas Filled — 1st Use of Lenses
1924 1928	Two Filament — Upper and Lower Beams
1928 1934	Fixed Focus
1934 1939	Prefocused
1939 1955	Sealed Beam — Single Unit Hermetically Sealed, Accurately Focused
1955	Improved Sealed Beam — Filament Cap — Greater Seeing Distance On Lower Beam, Better Visibility in Fog, Rain, etc.

in the door post, completes the circuit when the button is released. The peculiar thing about this switch is that it is a "ground switch." That is, instead of the switch's allowing a "hot" wire to complete a circuit, with the grounding taking place at the lamps, this switch permits grounding while the circuit is constantly energized. In this manner it becomes unnecessary to run a hot wire all the way to the dome light and back down again to the switch.

New Lighting. Just when everyone was convinced that we had gone as far as we could go in lighting technology, a very new idea emerged. In lighting, two new ideas can be found on late-model cars. The first has the fancy title of *Electroluminescent Lighting.* This mode of illumination does not cast a light to see by. Instead it provides a light that makes objects, such as dashboard instruments, visible.

Electroluminescent lighting employs no filaments or gases. It is composed of laminated layers of material which produce a glow when an alternating current is applied. In electrical language the "lamp" is a condenser. The gauge that lights up for reading consists of a steel plate, a ceramic

layer with a phosphorescent surface like that found on watch dials, a transparent conducting layer, and a protective glass coating. When the A.C. voltage is applied between the steel plate and the transparent conducting layer, it excites the ceramic nonconducting layer, causing it to glow.

To provide the required electrical current, the system uses a transistor oscillator which converts the 12 volt D.C. to 200 volts A.C. at 250 cycles per second. (House current is 110 volts A.C. at 60 cycles.)

The other new lighting development is called *fiber optics,* which employs special plastic tubes that carry light from a source to another location, much the way water is carried in a pipe. The light source is usually one bulb. Running from this source is a series of pipes, each one terminating at an instrument or gauge. When the bulb is on, light is directed to the ends of each of the pipes, which serve much like the spray heads on a fountain.

Some cars use the light tubes to monitor all the lamps in the rear of the car. Each of the rear bulbs has a tube running to a console located on the rear window shelf. If one of the bulbs is not functioning, the driver will see an unilluminated spot on the console and take note.

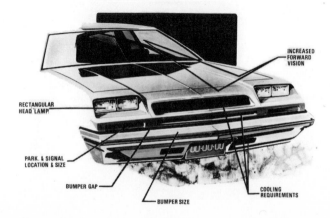

Modern head lamps. With less height than the conventional round sealed beam, these rectangular head lamps allow more space for bumpers, which tend to be larger due to impact standards. These lamps also allow an increase in the downward slope of the hood to give the driver a closer look at the road.

7
TRANSMISSION

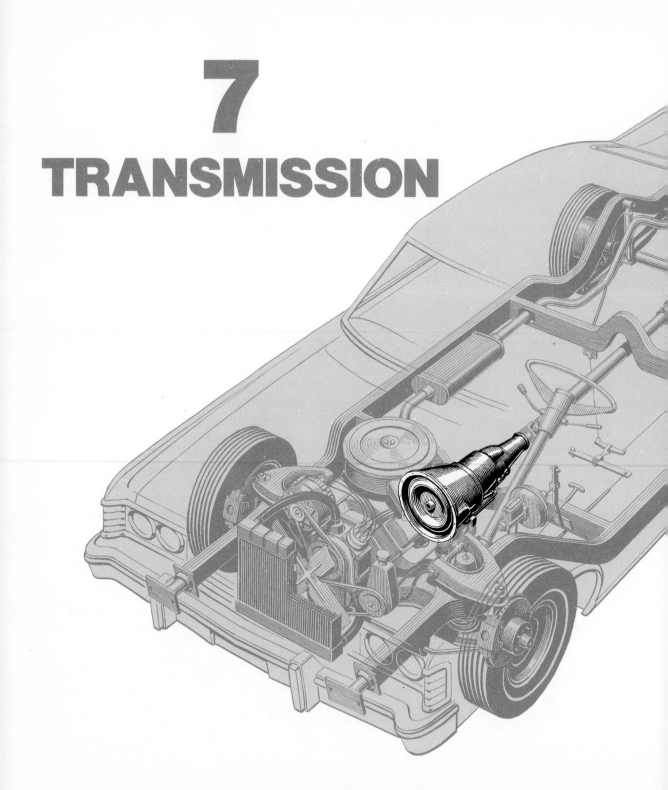

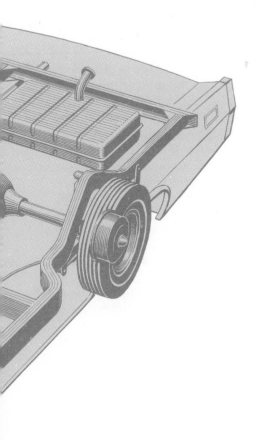

When the engine operates, many simultaneous actions occur. Carburetor parts are busy opening and closing to deliver the right amount of fuel. Ignition parts are twirling, loading and unloading to ignite the spark at the right time. Pistons are driven up and down to keep the crankshaft turning. Though all the action seems to be spread out and disjointed, it actually comes to focus on one vital engine part— the flywheel. From here the turning force, called *torque,* is aimed through the necessary stages which lead, finally, to the turning of the wheels.

From the flywheel, the first big step is the transfer of torque to the transmission. There it will be matched with various gear combinations that best suit the speed, load and power requirements of the driver at any particular moment during car operation. If the car has an automatic transmission, the relay of energy and selection of gears is through the movement and pressures of hydraulic fluid. However, if the car has a manual transmission the process starts with a small problem. In order for the driver to get out of one gear combination and into another the gears must be either stationary or turning slowly. To make this happen the driver must be able to disengage the power flow from the engine in order to select the proper gears, then engage it again. The *clutch* is the mechanism for this job.

It may very well be asked, Is a clutch mechanism still necessary if the vehicle has no transmission and operates in one gear? The answer is, Yes! As a matter of fact, there was no such vehicle as an automobile until the clutch and transmission were invented. The internal combustion engine came into full flower in 1865 through the work of Dr. Otto. The wagon has been with us since the dawn of history. But, a truly self-propelled vehicle (an automobile) under the full control of the driver was not possible until the clutch and transmission provided the means of disconnecting and connecting engine torque and the mechanical means of increasing engine torque. These were not developed until 1890. Prior to this time, experimenters got gasoline buggies under way in a very curious manner, not without its humorous side. In these cars, the engine crankshaft was coupled directly to the drive wheels. To get going, a strong person held up one end of the vehicle containing the drive wheels while another person would spin the wheels until the engine started. The driver then entered the buggy, the wheels were then lowered to the ground and the "car" moved on its own. To stop, the brake was applied until the engine stalled. Not a very convenient way to travel!

THE CLUTCH

The clutch used in the modern-day car has only six main pieces. It works on the principle of extreme friction. That is, the power from the flywheel to the transmission is carried by parts which are held together by such powerful pressures that the movement of one forces a movement of another.

Pressure is applied by a series of springs and is controlled by the driver through the clutch pedal and the linkage. When the pedal is depressed there is no spring pressure and no friction in the clutch components — hence, no transfer of torque. As the clutch pedal is released, spring pressure bears down and friction causes a transfer of torque. The clutch is built to permit the gradual application of engine power. This assures a smooth engagement of the moving engine element with the stationary transmission elements.

Two Groups of Clutch Parts. The principal parts of the clutch can be divided into two groups — the driving members and the driven members. The former consist of two flat machined surfaces. One of them is the rear face of the flywheel. The other is an assembly called the *pressure plate*. The main piece of the pressure plate is a flat, heavy ring which is fitted into a steel case on a bed of springs. The unit is designed with three steel levers, called fingers. One end of each of the levers is hooked into a groove in the iron ring. The center of each of the levers has a pivot pin going through it. The other end of the levers sticks onto the center of the pressure plate assembly. They protrude in such a manner as to divide the circle into three equal parts. When the lever ends are depressed, the flat ring is retracted, crushing the springs around its rim. When the fingers are released, spring pressure forces the flat ring outward. Some pressure plates are designed with a flexible steel dish, called a diaphragm plate, rather than with the

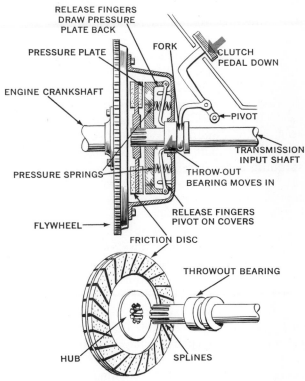

RELEASE FINGERS
DRAW PRESSURE
PLATE BACK

PRESSURE PLATE

FORK

CLUTCH
PEDAL DOWN

ENGINE CRANKSHAFT

PIVOT

TRANSMISSION
INPUT SHAFT

PRESSURE SPRINGS

THROW-OUT
BEARING MOVES IN

RELEASE FINGERS
PIVOT ON COVERS

FLYWHEEL

FRICTION DISC

THROWOUT BEARING

HUB

SPLINES

The clutch assembly. When the driver depresses the clutch pedal, the throw-out bearing is forced into the pressure plate in such a manner that the friction disc is released. There is no connection now between the crankshaft and the transmission input shaft. When the clutch pedal is released, the pressure plate presses the disc against the flywheel. Since the disc is splined to the transmission shaft, motion given to the disc by the flywheel is tramsmitted to the transmission.

springs and levers. Pushing on the center of the plate produces the same results as pushing the fingers. Releasing the pressure on the center of the plate forces the ring outward. In either case, the pressure plate assembly is bolted to the flywheel with the ring facing the machined surface of the wheel.

One of the driven members is a flat disc made of spring steel. Both sides of the disc are covered with segments of frictional

material similar to that used on brake shoes. The frictional material extends about three inches toward the center. The hub of the disc contains a series of springs which will be explained shortly. The center of the disc has a round opening with notches all around its rim. This is known as a *splined hub*. The purpose of the spline is to allow a shaft with similar splines to mate with the hub. The result is that the shaft and friction disc must rotate together, but the disc can slide lengthwise along the splines of the shaft. The clutch disc fits between the pressure plate and the flywheel.

The other driven member is the splined shaft which has one end anchored inside the front of the transmission. It is called by many names, but the most descriptive is the *transmission input shaft*. This shaft has a smooth tip, a splined center and a gear on its rearmost end. The gear is not seen since it is inside the transmission case.

The fifth member of the team is neither driving nor driven. It is a heavy round bearing which is positioned at the pressure plate fingers. The part is called the *throw-out bearing*. Holding lightly to the bearing is a steel lever called the *throw-out fork*. The two fingers of the fork embrace the bearing; the center of the lever rests on a pivot point; and the far end of the lever is attached to the linkage which leads to the clutch pedal.

Installed, the clutch assembly looks like this: First, there is the polished face of the flywheel. Up against this face is side 1 of the friction disc. Contacting side 2 of the disc is the pressure plate which is pressing very hard on the disc. The cover of the pressure plate is bolted to the flywheel. Resting on the fingers of the pressure plate is the throw-out bearing with the fork holding it in place. Finally, running through the center of the throw-out bearing, through the center of the pressure plate, through the center of the disc and coming to rest in a small opening called the *pilot hole* in the dead center of the crankshaft is the transmission input shaft. The shaft does not touch the bearing or the pressure plate. It is not influenced by the turning of the crankshaft either because the pilot hole is smooth, as is the front tip of the shaft. The only influence on the shaft—whether it turns or not—is the friction disc with its splined center.

Clutch in Operation. Let's get the car started and moving to see what is happening. The driver shifts to neutral, turns the key and the engine starts. With no pressure on the clutch pedal, the clutch is said to be "engaged." The flywheel is turning; the pressure plate bolted to it is turning; the disc between the two is turning because the pressure of the plate against the flywheel is in full force. If the disc turns, it means that the transmission input shaft is turning, since the two are splined together. The car does not move because the gear attached to the input shaft is not affecting any of the gears that will turn the transmission output shaft.

The driver then pushes the clutch pedal inward. The linkage attached to the pedal follows a path until it starts pushing on the throw-out fork. This form is on a pivot; as one end is pushed rearward the other end moves forward. The fork then pushes on the throw-out bearing, which in turn leans on the fingers in the pressure plate. As the bearing applies its pressure against the fingers, it starts to spin at the same speed as the pressure plate is spinning. That's the whole idea of this bearing. It allows a non-revolving part like the fork to depress

the pressure plate fingers which are spinning.

As the fingers are depressed, they relieve the pressure of the iron ring against the disc. When the clutch pedal is fully depressed, the iron ring of the pressure plate has moved back creating a space big enough (.015 inch) to have the disc slide a little on the shaft so that is is free of any spinning parts. The flywheel is still spinning because the engine is operating. The pressure plate is still spinning because it is bolted to the flywheel. The throw-out bearing is spinning because it is up against the pressure plate fingers. The only parts which are not spinning now are the disc and the transmission input shaft. The clutch is said to be "disengaged."

The driver now places the gear selector in first gear for the highest torque multiplication. (What actually happens in the transmission will be explained later.) Now the gear of the input shaft is connected via a hardware circuit to other gears which will produce a turning of the transmission output gear. The driver then slowly releases the clutch pedal. The shift fork is pulled back by a strong spring. Pressure of the throw-out bearing against the fingers of the pressure plate begins to relax and the springs in the plate can resume its pressure against the flat ring. In a short while, the flat ring has the disc in a squeeze. The part of the disc with the friction pads starts to spin a fraction of a second before the hub of the disc and the shaft. The little springs in the hub take up the shock. When the disc starts spinning at the same speed as the flywheel, enough power is transmitted to the gear of the input shaft to start the other gears turning, and the car moves forward.

The unsung hero of the clutch system is the linkage. All the levers, links and rods connecting the clutch pedal with the throw-out fork not only allow the driver to "reach" the throw-out bearing from his seat, they also give him a mechanical advantage.

Spring force at the pressure plate is very strong. It has to be if the disc is to spin without slipping. Spring pressure is so strong that it is impossible for even a strong person to depress the pressure plate fingers by hand. Therefore, the linkage has a great deal of leverage designed into it. In addition, the strong pullback spring assures the return of the pedal.

Another Way: Hydraulics. Where clutch linkage would be very complicated and difficult to integrate into the total layout under the hood a hydraulic system is used. This system is somewhat like the one used to actuate the brakes. Immediately behind the clutch pedal there is a unit called the *clutch master cylinder*. Think of it as a big plunger. Down below, near the throw-out fork is a unit called the *clutch slave cylinder*. Think of it as a small plunger. Connecting the two units is a short run of hydraulic tubing. The two cylinders and the tubing are filled with regular hydraulic brake fluid. When the driver depresses the clutch pedal, he actuates the big plunger which transmits hydraulic pressure to the small plunger. A rod is forced out of the slave cylinder and pushes against the throw-out fork. Release of the pedal relaxes the pressure while the pullback spring puts the fork in its neutral position. The tubing rules out all necessity for linkage and maintains a high mechanical advantage.

The Clutch and Free Play. If a newly assembled car were placed in gear and made to travel for 100,000 miles — without a stop —

there would be virtually no wear on the clutch disc. Friction between the flywheel and pressure plate against the disc is said to be 100 percent. Wear of the friction material takes place at the engagement stage while the clutch pedal is being released. As the disc material wears, it gets thinner. The pressure plate ring wants to "follow" it. However, there are limitations. At a certain point the ring will not be able to "reach" the disc and there will be less than 100 percent contact. Slippage will then occur when there is no pressure on the pedal. This accelerates disc wear. After a while so much slippage occurs that there is no transfer of torque from the flywheel, to the disc, to the transmission. Then the disc is replaced.

To make up for wear, the clutch pedal can be adjusted. The last link to the fork is a threaded shaft. A certain standard is set for how long this shaft is to be. This can be ascertained by testing for the amount of free play in the clutch pedal. The free play can be felt by the ease with which the clutch pedal travels before the throw-out bearing is flush against the pressure plate fingers.

As the disc wears and the metal ring follows, it pushes the fingers backwards against the bearing, reducing the free play. Periodically, the free play must be reestablished according to the distance set by the car maker. The rod is turned and made shorter. With the proper amount of free play in the pedal, the clutch can then operate to fully engage and disengage.

TRANSMISSIONS — THE TORQUE MULTIPLIERS

It has already been noted that a buggy and an engine alone "do not an automobile make." The gasoline internal-combustion engine simply does not have the muscle to get a car moving from a dead stop or get it up a long grade without a drastic loss of speed. Of course, there is enough power to get the vehicle up to 90 or 100 miles per hour—once the car gets rolling. But, overcoming the static inertia of a car requires a little help.

The answer, of course, is the use of gears. By routing the engine torque through a combination of gears it is possible to multiply the engine's turning power to satisfy the needs of the driver under various conditions. The matching of engine torque with the requirements specified by the driver takes place in a very confined metal case located immediately behind the clutch assembly. We call it the transmission, but the British name of "gearbox" is more descriptive. For the moment we will concentrate on the *manual* transmission, so called because the driver selects the gears by using his hand to shift. After the manual transmission, we will discuss the automatic.

The easiest way to understand the principle behind gears is to disregard the fact that they are round wheels with teeth. Instead, consider them as a series of levers planted on a wheel. Apply to this the well-known principle that a longer lever can do more work than a shorter one. But don't forget that a longer lever must pay the price by travelling a greater distance.

Gearing is a complex aspect of mechanical engineering. But with the awareness of a few basic laws, much of what happens at the transmission can be understood.

Law 1. Gears are generally distinguished as *driving* gears and *driven* gears, regardless of size. The driving gear is usually on a shaft which is attached to some source of power. The driven gear picks up this turning force and, in turn, imparts it to its own shaft. In the car's starter system, the small pinion gear on the starter motor is the driving gear while the larger ring gear on the flywheel is the driven gear.

Law 2. The driving gear will rotate the driven gear in an opposite direction. If the

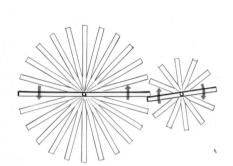 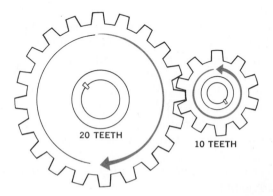

20 TEETH   10 TEETH

A gear is a lever which rotates. In each of the above two drawings, one member is powered; the other is not. The larger the lever, or gear, the greater the capacity for work. In gears, the "lever ends" are called teeth. If the gear with ten teeth is the driving gear, the result is high power and low speed. If the gear with twenty teeth is the driving gear, the result is low power and high speed.

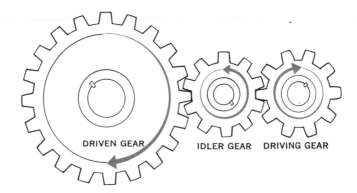

Idler gear. When only two gears are used, the driving gear and the driven gear will always turn in opposite directions. To get them to spin in the same direction, an idler gear is interposed. The idler gear does nothing more than cause the two important gears to turn in the same direction.

DRIVEN GEAR   IDLER GEAR   DRIVING GEAR

driving pinion gear of the starter is set up to turn clockwise, then the driven flywheel will turn counterclockwise. In order that the driven gear turn in the same direction, a small *idler* gear is interposed between the two principal gears. The idler gear has no function other than to affect the direction in which the driven gear turns.

Law 3. If the driving gear is smaller than the driven gear, the advantage is torque multiplication. If the driving gear is larger than the driven gear, the advantage is speed.

This final point brings up the matter of gear ratios. Ratio is an engineer's shorthand for describing the relative differences of size of two gears meshed together. If the driving gear has ten teeth and the driven gear has twenty teeth the ratio is said to be two-to-one (2:1). Such a combination says this:

1) Torque of the driving gear is doubled at the driven gear. Using levers for a moment, when the driven gear is turned, a long lever is activated by a short lever. In this case, the larger lever will have twice as much turning force (torque) as the smaller one.

2) Speed of the driving gear is halved at the driven gear. Now we are dealing with distance. The driving gear is half the size

of the driven gear. Therefore, when it completes one full turn of its own, all it has succeeded in doing is turning the driven gear a half turn. This may be stated another way: A driving gear will cause a driven gear to travel a distance identical to its own in one revolution. In this case (2:1 ratio) the full distance around for the smaller gear is equal to only one half that of the larger. This 2:1 ratio would apply if the gear tooth combinations were, say, 50 and 100 or 25 and 50.

The Gearbox. A common transmission has three forward gears and one reverse gear. In rounded numbers the ratio in first and reverse gears is 3:1; in second gear, 2:1; in third gear, 1:1. This last situation means that the gear speed of the crankshaft is the same as the speed of the transmission output shaft. Naturally, if the speeds are equal, there is no torque multiplication. But when the car is going fast enough to allow shifting to third-speed gear, no increase of engine torque is necessary. That is why third gear is called *direct drive*.

To examine gear ratios at work let's examine some of the simple arithmetic for a typical first-speed gear. A certain engine will develop 144 lb./ft. of torque when the crankshaft has attained a speed of 2,000

TYPICAL 3-SPEED MANUAL TRANSMISSION

When the driver shifts gears, shifting positions of gears of various sizes, he can have either high power and low speed (1st gear), low power and high speed (3rd gear) or a compromise of the two (2nd gear).

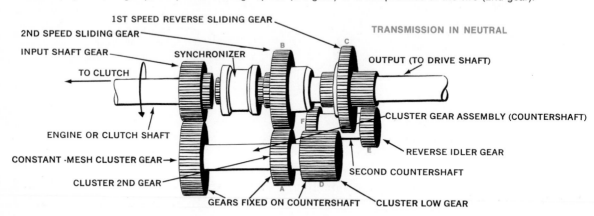

1ST SPEED REVERSE SLIDING GEAR

2ND SPEED SLIDING GEAR

INPUT SHAFT GEAR

SYNCHRONIZER

TO CLUTCH

TRANSMISSION IN NEUTRAL

OUTPUT (TO DRIVE SHAFT)

CLUSTER GEAR ASSEMBLY (COUNTERSHAFT)

ENGINE OR CLUTCH SHAFT

REVERSE IDLER GEAR

CONSTANT -MESH CLUSTER GEAR→

SECOND COUNTERSHAFT

CLUSTER 2ND GEAR

GEARS FIXED ON COUNTERSHAFT

CLUSTER LOW GEAR

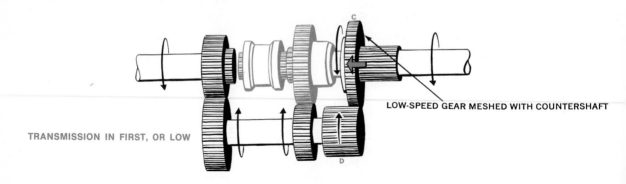

LOW-SPEED GEAR MESHED WITH COUNTERSHAFT

TRANSMISSION IN FIRST, OR LOW

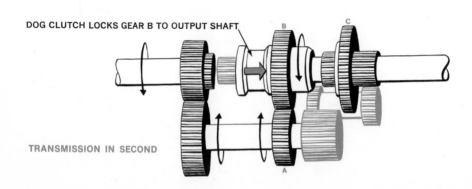

DOG CLUTCH LOCKS GEAR B TO OUTPUT SHAFT

TRANSMISSION IN SECOND

138

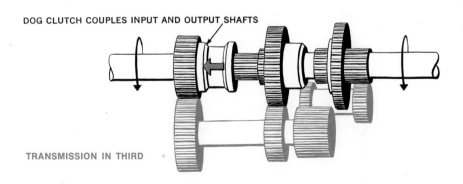

DOG CLUTCH COUPLES INPUT AND OUTPUT SHAFTS

TRANSMISSION IN THIRD

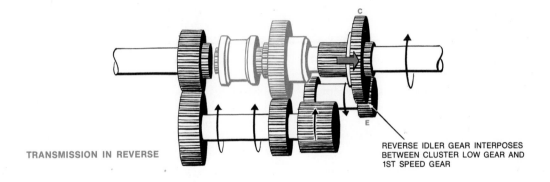

TRANSMISSION IN REVERSE

REVERSE IDLER GEAR INTERPOSES
BETWEEN CLUSTER LOW GEAR AND
1ST SPEED GEAR

THIS MEMBER SLIDES ON SPLINES

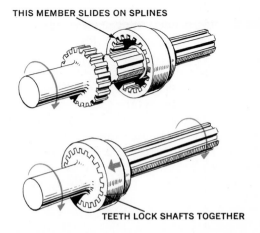

Constant-mesh transmission. Here certain gears remain in mesh at all times. They are engaged by sliding clutches.

TEETH LOCK SHAFTS TOGETHER

rpm. The ratio for the first-speed gear in this car is 3.02:1. The engine torque (144) is *multiplied* by the ratio 3.02. We now have 435 lb./ft. of torque coming out of the transmission—an increase. But in order to gain torque, we must be willing to sacrifice some speed. Therefore, the input speed (2,000 rpm) must now be *divided* by the ratio 3.02. Output rpm is reduced to 662—a decrease. Perhaps now you can see why a car's speed has definite limits until it is in direct drive. (Further speed reduction is made when the torque enters the differential in the rear of the car. This is covered in Chapter 8, "Drive Line.")

Transmission Construction. The typical 3-speed transmission case is made of cast iron or aluminum. Packed into a very tight area are eight gears, four shafts, a synchronizing device, bearings and a means of moving, or shifting the gears into and out of position.

Upon first glance at the parts in the gearbox there is an appearance of chaos. Yet, order does prevail. Basically the parts are lined up in two rows, one above the other. The lower row is called the *cluster gear assembly*. Actually it is a solid piece of metal which has three gears of diminishing sizes cut into it. The largest is at the front of the unit and is called the *constant mesh cluster gear*. It gets this name from the fact that it is always in mesh with the input shaft gear above it.

To the rear is the slightly smaller cluster second gear. Behind that is the yet smaller cluster low gear. The final gear of the cluster assembly is the reverse idler drive gear. The drive gear is also in constant mesh with the small reverse idler gear which spins on a shaft of its own. Again, the idler gear serves to change direction.

On the top row, the first gear is the one that is part of the input shaft. This is the same shaft which is splined to the friction disc of the clutch. As mentioned, the input shaft gear is in constant mesh with the largest gear of the cluster assembly below it. Beyond the input shaft there is a complete break; then comes the beginning of the output shaft. This shaft is splined. Riding on this spline is a synchronizer unit which facilitates shifting from second to third gear while the car is in motion. Also there are two gears. The first is called the second-speed sliding gear, the other is the first-reverse sliding gear.

Completing the hardware are small levers for shifting the 2-3 gear and the first-reverse gear. These levers have a Y shape and are designed to fit over special collars machined into the two gears. The long end of the lever goes to the outside of the transmission case where linkage is attached to allow the driver to shift the gears by moving the lever under the steering wheel. If the car has a floor-mounted shift lever, no linkage is used.

In Operation. The path of power within the transmission changes for the different speed positions chosen by the driver. The interaction of the gears can be seen more clearly when the paths of power are traced for each position.

First or low gear. The driver depresses the clutch pedal and the clutch disc stops turning. Therefore the input-shaft gear stops turning; the cluster gear assembly stops turning. By using the shift lever, the driver moves the first-reverse gear forward to engage the cluster low gear. When the clutch pedal is let out, the disc begins to turn; the input-shaft gear turns; the cluster gear assembly turns; the cluster low gear begins to drive the first-reverse gear which is splined to the output shaft. High-torque and low-speed power is delivered from the transmission.

Second Speed. At a certain point the driver depresses the clutch pedal. The input shaft is no longer powered by the clutch. Now, the rotation of the rear wheels is actually driving the output shaft and all the gears previously mentioned. Prior to the shift to second speed, the linkage forces the first-reverse gear out of mesh and into a neutral position. The 2-3 gear is pushed rearward to engage the cluster second gear. When the clutch is released the path of power now resumes from the engine all the way through the cluster assembly. But this time, power comes up at the second-speed gear and then through the output shaft.

Third Speed. The 2-3 gear is now brought all the way forward to lock with the input shaft gear. Now the power no longer is shunted to the cluster gear assembly. Though it is still turning, power flows in a direct line from the input gear, to the 2-3 gear, to the output shaft.

Reverse. The first-reverse gear is shifted rearward of its hold position to engage the reverse idler gear. By interposing this small gear, the direction of the first-reverse gear is changed and the direction of the output shaft is changed, causing the car to back up.

Neutral. At this stage no gears are in mesh except those designed for constant engagement. Power flows from the input shaft gear to the cluster assembly with nothing happening at the output shaft.

Keeping the Transmission Quiet. Just described were the workings of a very basic transmission. However, one more problem has to be solved before shifting can take place quietly and without damage to the teeth of the gears.

As mentioned before, when the rear wheels are in motion the output shaft is forced to turn. This is true even with the engine off and the car rolling downhill in neutral. This creates a problem for the 2-3 gear. On one side, the input shaft has slowed down or stopped because the clutch is disengaged. On the other side the 2-3 gear spins because it is splined to the output shaft and the rear wheels are turning the output shaft. In order for gears to mesh silently and without damage, it is necessary that the two gears are either at a full stop or are turning at the same speed.

Almost all transmissions are equipped with a synchronizing device which is designed to match the speeds of both gear sets. Traditionally the device operates only for the shift from second to third. First and reverse are usually selected when the car is at a full stop. Lately however, with the popularity of 4-speed transmissions, synchronizers are used between all forward gears—hence the advertising slogan, "fully-synchronized." Under these conditions the driver can downshift to first while the car is moving. For illustrative purposes, let's stay with the 3-speed transmission with a synch unit between second and third.

When the driver shifts to second the synchromizer sleeve actually moves to the rear, toward the constant mesh second gear. Remember, this gear turns from the windup given the car in first speed. As the sleeve moves, a wedging action occurs. The moving output shaft starts turning the entire synch unit, and the input gear starts to spin. Soon the speeds of both shafts are equalized. With a little more movement of the clutch sleeve, splines of the synchronizer unit engage the second gear completing the shift.

On the shift to third, a similar action

occurs toward the front of the transmission, at the input shaft gear. The motion of the synchronizer can be summarized in three distinct steps. First comes the wedging action of the ring and hub; then the equalization of speed; then the lock into the second or third speed. This motion may be hard to visualize, but it is indeed essential.

The synchronizer has been around since it was first used on the 1928 Cadillac. Prior to this time the transmission was nicknamed the "crash box." The driver had to feel his way with the gearshift lever as to when the moment was right for making the shift. There were times, however, when he miscalculated and grimaced to the sounds of broken transmission gear teeth.

The Rolling Start. Knowledge of the basic gear system in the transmission makes it easy to understand how a car with a manual transmission can be started when rolled down a hill or pushed. With the gearshift in second gear, the turning of the rear wheels will start turning the output shaft, then the input shaft, then the clutch disc, which then turns the flywheel and crankshaft. The crankshaft activates the pistons as if getting power from the starter motor. This rolling start is often employed to overcome weaknesses in the electric starting system.

Helpers. Inside the manual transmission are many bearings and bushings which support gears and shafts. They are forced to work under severe circumstances. They must not only keep the gears and shaft turning with a minimum of friction, but they must also take a great deal of stress from the passing of engine torque to the output shaft. To ensure lubrication to the bearings, the gear box should be at all times filled with a heavy oil.

AUTOMATIC TRANSMISSION

The automatic transmission was to the automobile what the invention of the printing press was to the Renaissance. With one technological sweep, operating a car became possible for almost everyone. The "automatic" eliminated worries of shifting, clutching, and stalling. Now full attention could be given to steering and braking.

The main purpose of a transmission is to provide suitable gear ratios between the engine and the rear wheels. In the manual transmission, the driver shifts to the gear deemed appropriate for a specific condition. In the automatic transmission, gears or gear combinations are selected and shifted automatically.

The idea of driving without manually shifting the gears came early. A non-shifting unit first appeared in the 1904 Sturtevant. It was strictly a mechanical affair without the use of hydraulics. An automatic transmission making full use of oil pressures first appeared on 1937 Buicks and Oldsmobiles. In 1939, when General Motors first introduced their "Hydra-Matic," the race started in earnest. Every car maker threw his research and development department into overtime to come up with a comparable unit.

Today there are 50 different types of automatic transmissions found on a variety of U.S. and import cars. Going through the characteristics and operation of each would be beyond the scope of this book. However, all types of automatic transmissions employ similar combinations of parts and operation principles. Let examine the basics.

A Box with Brains. If your regular driving routine includes driving on crowded streets and roads, you know how convenient the automatic transmission is. Rather than depressing the clutch pedal, moving the shift lever and releasing the pedal — often several times within a city block — the automatic does its own decision-making and chooses its own gears.

You might ask, How can any piece of machinery be so smart that it can determine what gear ratios to use, how much power to apply, and how fast to go? The truth is that the automatic transmission is not so much a master as it is a servant. You the driver give all the orders via the gas pedal; the transmission carries them out.

The decision-making and parts operation depend on hydraulics — or essentially the application of engine power on a liquid (oil) that transmits pressure for motion and torque. While hydraulics is more fully discussed in Chapter 10, "Brake System," let's take a look at two important hydraulic principles as they relate to the automatic transmission.

Pressure can be transmitted and multiplied by a liquid. With liquid confined within an enclosed system, one without air, pressure applied at one end of the system can be transmitted to any point in the system — without any loss of pressure. This was mentioned earlier in this chapter in the discussion of the hydraulic clutch. Pressure at the clutch pedal is transmitted directly to the clutch fork through hydraulic lines rather than through linkage.

Motion can be transmitted by a liquid. Responding to the pressure transmitted to any or many points in the system, mechanical devices can be set into motion. One example of this is found in the hydraulic clutch. Another is in the action of the wheel cylinder as it moves the brake

shoes. Engineers use the term "servo action" to describe the application of a small force to bring about an action of much greater force.

The Automatic's Four Parts. There are four basic, but broad, areas common to all automatic transmissions. They are: the fluid coupling between the engine and transmission; the brake bands, clutches and servo mechanisms; the planetary gear sets; the hydraulic circuits.

Some of these parts and units have curious sounding names that do not appear in other systems of the car. However, after we examine these parts in their simplest form, you will see that they are not so new after all. Many of the principles already discussed in other systems of the car are similar to those of the automatic gearbox.

Basically, operation of the automatic transmission resembles the operation of the manual transmission. Power is taken from the engine through the input shaft, applied through a series of gears and, eventually, imparted on the output shaft. Hydraulics enters the picture in two ways: first, in the coupling of engine power with transmission action; second, in effecting the various shifts from low to high and reverse gears. These points will be detailed shortly. Now let's look at the first link between the engine and transmission.

Fluid Coupling or Torque Converter. The early automatics had a large, heavy unit attached to the flywheel called the *fluid coupling.* From the outside it looks like a large doughnut. But it is not as simple. The coupling actually consists of two "slices." One is called the *impeller* or *pump* and is the driving member. The other is called the turbine and is the driven member. Some car makers call them the driving torus and the driven torus. But, to simplify, let's call them the pump and turbine. Both halves are contained in a leakproof housing which is filled with oil and bolted to the flywheel. The pump is attached to the engine crankshaft, and the turbine has the transmission input shaft splined to it.

Operation. To appreciate how the coupling operates, how one half influences the other half, you should picture two electric fans facing each other at about six inches apart. One is plugged into the electrical receptacle; the other is not. Switch on the powered fan and allow it to come up to full speed. In a short while the blades of the second fan will start turning. The direct air stream from the first fan powers the second one.

The fluid coupling operates in a similar manner. There is no physical connection between the pump and the turbine. The

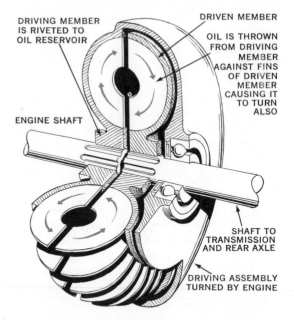

DRIVING MEMBER IS RIVETED TO OIL RESERVOIR

DRIVEN MEMBER

OIL IS THROWN FROM DRIVING MEMBER AGAINST FINS OF DRIVEN MEMBER CAUSING IT TO TURN ALSO

ENGINE SHAFT

SHAFT TO TRANSMISSION AND REAR AXLE

DRIVING ASSEMBLY TURNED BY ENGINE

Transferring motion without actual contact. Just as the powered fan, below, can turn the blades of the fan not plugged in, by churning the air in front of it, the driving member of the fluid coupling, above, can turn the driven member by churning the oil within it.

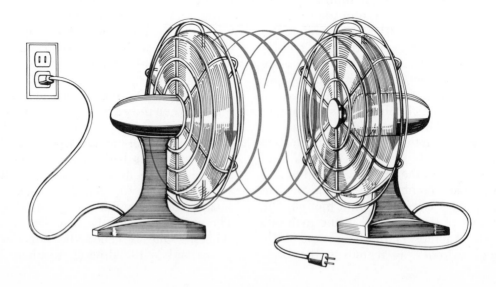

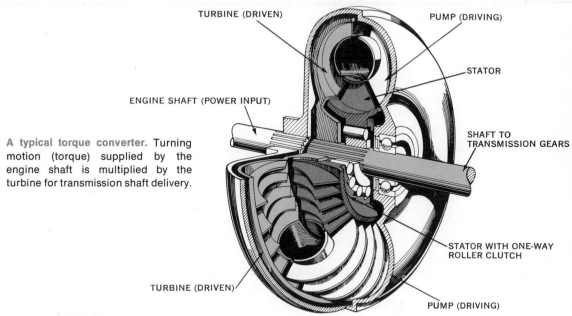

TURBINE (DRIVEN)　　　PUMP (DRIVING)

STATOR

ENGINE SHAFT (POWER INPUT)

SHAFT TO
TRANSMISSION GEARS

A typical torque converter. Turning motion (torque) supplied by the engine shaft is multiplied by the turbine for transmission shaft delivery.

STATOR WITH ONE-WAY
ROLLER CLUTCH

TURBINE (DRIVEN)　　　PUMP (DRIVING)

3 OIL FLOWS FROM *STATOR*
  (WITH A CHANGE IN DIRECTION) BACK TO THE PUMP

2 OIL FLOWS FROM *TURBINE* TO STATOR

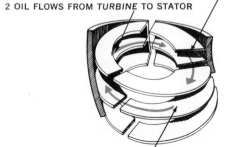

1 OIL FLOWS FROM *PUMP* TO TURBINE

Oil flow in torque converter.

medium between the two is oil rather than air. As the pump is rotated by the flywheel, the pump sets oil into motion which rotates the turbine.

To better picture what is inside the fluid coupling, imagine a grapefruit sliced through the middle. Let's call one half A,

the other B. Carefully remove the fruit from both halves making sure to leave the fibrous separators intact. With both pieces "clean" match them very closely, without allowing them to touch, such that the halves appear to form a whole grapefruit. The grapefruit separators resemble the vanes inside the fluid coupling. As piece A is turned by the crankshaft its vanes churn up the oil and direct it against the vanes of piece B.

The fluid coupling has many advantages and disadvantages. On the plus side it enables the engine to idle while the transmission is in gear. It prevents lurching while the gears are shifting. Its greatest disadvantage is the amount of slippage which occurs as the pump "winds up" enough oil to drive the turbine. Also, when the fluid leaves the turbine after striking it, the fluid is directed back into the sides of the pump vanes in such a manner as to slow up the pump and cause power loss.

Coupling Improved. During the middle 1950s a new type of coupling appeared. It was called, for good reason, a *torque converter.* This unit improved the fluid coupling with the addition of a stationary set of blades placed between the pump and the turbine. This third element is called a *stator,* which changes the direction of the flow of oil after it has passed the turbine. The stator returns the oil to the pump vanes such that the oil gives the pump a boost. This boost helps raise engine torque.

Thus the turning force of the flywheel is doubled. However, multiplication gradually tapers off as turbine speed slowly approaches pump speed. At a certain point the turbine and pump are rotating at the same speed and the unit operates as a simple coupling with no torque multiplication.

An important part of the stator is the one-way clutch in the hub which permits the stator to rotate in only one direction—the direction of pump rotation. The clutch locks the stator to prevent any backward rotation. With this in mind, let's trace the power flow through the various ranges of transmission operation.

From a standstill: When the driver depresses the gas pedal and makes the engine race, the pump rotates rapidly and directs a high velocity of oil flow against the turbine vanes. The turbine absorbs the energy from the oil and also starts to rotate. Oil leaving the turbine is directed against the stator which, in turn, redirects the high velocity oil to the pump. It is

the force of this redirected oil to the pump that provides multiplication of engine torque.

As speed picks up: Soon the speed of the turbine approaches that of the pump. Meanwhile, torque multiplication falls off gradually until it is at a point where there is a one-to-one relation between the pump and turbine. Up until this point the oil leaving the turbine has been striking the front face of the stator vanes—that is, the face of the stator which is facing the flywheel. Because of the one-way clutch, the stator absorbs the force of the oil but remains stationary.

Cruising speed: When the car is cruising, the pump and turbine are spinning at the same speed. The oil that comes off the turbine now strikes the back face of the stator. Thus the stator turns in the same direction as the pump. The entire unit with its three elements turn now as an efficient fluid coupling.

Throughout the years various converter designs have appeared on a number of cars. The three-member unit just described is found on late-model Powerglide (Chevrolet) and Fordomatic (Ford). A four-member unit consists of a pump, a stator, and a first and a second turbine; this was found on the Ultramatic (Packard), Fluid Torque Drive (Chrysler), and Twin Turbine and Variable Pitch Turbine (Buick). Some cars have even used a five-member converter which the engineers felt was an improvement. These were on the early Powerglide (Chevrolet) and Dynaflow (Buick). The five-member unit consists of a primary pump, turbine, primary stator, secondary stator and secondary pump.

In all cases the idea behind the converters is basically the same. That is, they control the flow of oil to give the maxi-

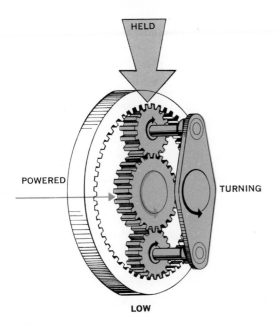

HELD

POWERED

TURNING

LOW

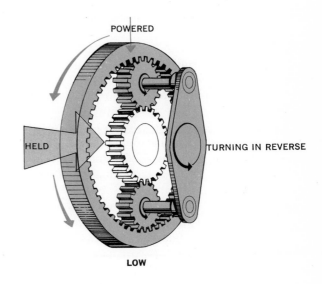

POWERED

HELD

TURNING IN REVERSE

LOW

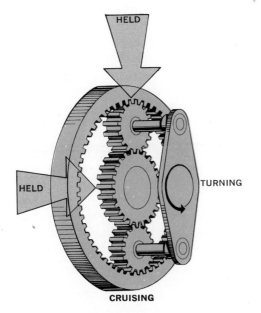

HELD

HELD

TURNING

CRUISING

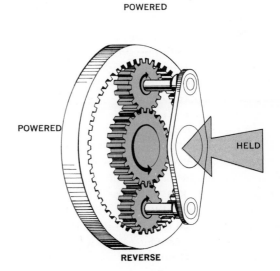

POWERED

POWERED

HELD

REVERSE

Planetary gears at work. By locking and/or releasing certain gears of the planetary assembly, it is possible to achieve a variety of ratios for operating the car at different speeds.

mum amount of torque in starting and the minimum amount of resistance when the car has reached cruising speeds.

The Gears. In an odd way a torque converter is a type of automatic transmission in itself. From a standing start, it can more than double engine torque. Then at cruising, when torque multiplication is no longer necessary, the energy delivered by the pump and received by the turbine is at a 1:1 ratio. However this is not enough for the full range of power needs for today's driver.

Most people tend to picture gears as being fixed or sliding, each rotating around its own axis. Conventional examples would be the timing gears attached to the crankshaft and camshaft in front of the engine. Ratio is determined by the relative sizes of the driving and the driven gears. Yet, their only motion is *rotation,* each about its own axis. For a variety of reasons this setup does not prevail in the typical automatic transmission. Within its core are one or two sets of gears called *planetary gears.* These operate on an entirely different concept. They *revolve* as well as *rotate* and offer a wider variety of ratios than the fixed gear does.

The name "planetary" illustrates the manner in which the gears rotate in relation to each other. This gear train imitates the action of our solar system. The center gear is called the *sun gear.* The gears which revolve about the sun gear are called *planet gears.* Surrounding the planets is a gear called either the *internal* or *ring gear.* The latter is a more apt term since it isn't confused with the sun gear at the center of the set. The ring gear is a ring with teeth machined all around its inner circumference. This ring completely surrounds the sun and planet assembly, and meshes with the planet gears.

The idea for a planetary gear set was first conceived by James Watt in about 1760. He wanted to develop a machine without crank, and protected his invention with a patent. Watt observed that he could get interesting ratios from gears in mesh when one was fixed and the other was free to revolve.

In the illustrations on page 147, the two planetary gears rotate and revolve (like planets) around a sun gear. When the sun gear travels 90 degrees and rotates 90 degrees, the planetary gears turn 180 degrees. When the sun gear is 180 degrees around and rotated 180 degrees, the planetaries have already rotated a full 360 degrees. Since mesh of the teeth is strictly one-to-one, how can this difference occur? The secret is that the actions of rotation and revolution by the planetary gears are cumulative. Therefore, rotation will be reflected in the planetary gear set as a double value. The load applied to the assembly is distributed over several gears so that more power can be transmitted in less space. Operation is always smooth because gears are always in mesh. There are no shifting noises and there is no tooth damage due to partial engagement. Planetary gears were used in the Ford Model A manual transmission.

Gear combinations. There are three basic functions required of the automatic transmission. The first is high torque with a decrease in speed, which is called "breakaway" by the engineers. The second is low torque with an increase in engine speed, called "cruising." Finally there is reverse. A typical planetary gear set can afford these functions by holding some gears and releasing others.

Let's first take a look at the design. Connected to the sun gear is the input shaft. The forward end of this shaft is located inside the torque converter and is splined to the turbine. The planet gears are contained within a housing called the *planet carrier*. Part of this housing is the output shaft.

Increasing power while decreasing speed: There are two ways to do this: 1) Hold the ring gear stationary and apply the power from the turbine to the sun gear. This forces the planet gears to "walk around" the ring gear carrying the planet carrier with them in the same direction that the sun gear rotates. As a result the planet carrier rotates at a speed somewhat less than the speed of the engine-driven sun gear. 2) Hold the sun gear stationary and apply power to the ring gear. In this situation rotation of the ring gear also causes the planet gears to rotate on their own little pins and also "walk around" the sun gear and rotate around the planet carrier at a speed somewhat less than that of the engine-driven ring gear. In both situations the planet carrier acts as a power-increasing, speed-reducing unit.

Reversing direction of rotation: In order to reverse the direction of rotation with a planetary gear set, it is necessary to reverse the holding process, apply power to the sun gear, and lock the planet carrier. With the sun gear spinning and the carrier locked, the planetary gears will start spinning on their pins—going nowhere. In this manner they serve as idler gears and transmit the turning force to the ring gear. Earlier in this chapter in the discussion of manual transmissions, reverse speed was obtained by interposing an idler gear between the cluster shaft gear and first-speed gear. The same principles apply in an automatic transmission: The planetary gears act as idlers, causing the ring gear to turn in an opposite direction to that of the engine-driven sun gear. In this mode the planetary gear set functions as a speed-reducing, direction-reversing unit.

Thus you can see that a *planetary gear train functions as a reduction unit when any one of its three members is held stationary and power is applied to either the sun or ring gear.*

So far only two basic gear functions have been covered—low and reverse. These involved the locking of any *one* of the three members. The third basic function—cruising—occurs when any *two* members of the team are held stationary. Let's lock up the sun gear and the ring gear. In this case, the planetary action is stopped and the gear set will revolve as a solid unit. This is the same as direct-drive on a manual transmission. Torque is transmitted through the planetary set, but it is neither increased nor decreased. Here's a chart that reviews the functions:

Speed	Sun Gear	Planet Carrier Gears	Ring Gear
Low	Powered	Turning	Held
Low	Held	Turning	Powered
Reverse	Powered	Held	Powered
Cruising	Held	Turning	Held

Now we can add the statement: *A planetary gear train functions as a direct drive unit when two members are locked or held.*

The one function not yet mentioned is neutral. In this case none of the members of the planetary set is held. Thus the turbine can go around because the engine is idling, but the sun gear attached to it is

TRANSMISSION/CLUTCH WITH GEAR OPTIONS

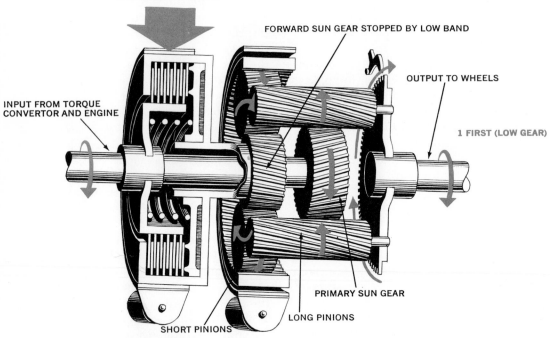

LOW BAND IS APPLIED

FORWARD SUN GEAR STOPPED BY LOW BAND

OUTPUT TO WHEELS

INPUT FROM TORQUE CONVERTOR AND ENGINE

1 FIRST (LOW GEAR)

PRIMARY SUN GEAR

LONG PINIONS

SHORT PINIONS

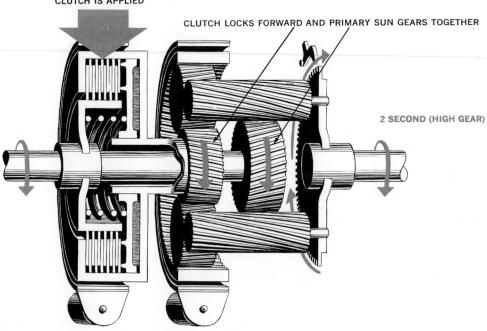

CLUTCH IS APPLIED

CLUTCH LOCKS FORWARD AND PRIMARY SUN GEARS TOGETHER

2 SECOND (HIGH GEAR)

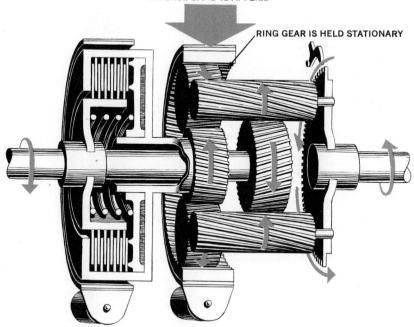

REVERSE BAND IS APPLIED

RING GEAR IS HELD STATIONARY

3 REVERSE

NO CLUTCH OR BANDS APPLIED:
THE GEARS TURN
WITH NO POWER
OUTPUT

PARKING PAWL APPLIED

4 NEUTRAL & PARK

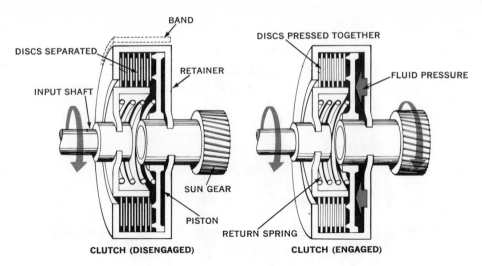

Automatic transmission clutch package. The clutch discs are pressed together by oil pressure. They can release or hold the shaft and gears.

spinning and not transmitting any torque to the planet carrier. For "Park" position there is a slight modification. Here the gears are in a "neutral" mode, but a small lever drops and engages a tooth on a disc which is splined to the planet carrier. This locks the output shaft and prevents the car from rolling when it is parked.

This is a simple arrangement with only one planetary gear unit. Many transmissions today have two and sometimes three planetary units. Having each of the units contain different gear ratios gives this transmission a wide range of forward gears. Operation is basically the same in those units with more than one planetary train.

Bands and Clutches. Throughout the discussion of planetary units, we stressed that they operate in held and unheld situations, depending on the speed or torque required by the driver. The devices which hold and release are called bands or clutches.

The band is a steel open circle with

friction material on the inside rim. It is positioned around a smooth drum which may serve as a base for a ring gear. The open section of the band spreads out to form two lips. In its unapplied position the band is fairly loose and permits the drum to turn without interference. When it is the correct time for the ring gear to be held, the lips close and the circle around the drum tightens. This is very much like the band brakes that were used on the wheels of old-time cars or on the parking brakes of more modern cars.

The clutch operates in a different manner. It consists of a steel retainer, which looks like a bowl with a central hole and a tight fitting piston which fits into the bowl. On top of the piston is a heavy spring and a series, usually six or eight pairs, of discs and steel plates. Each disc has friction material; the plates do not. Finally, pressed into the bowl on top are the sun gear and a large snap ring.

The hole in the center of the clutch retainer is splined to the input shaft. The

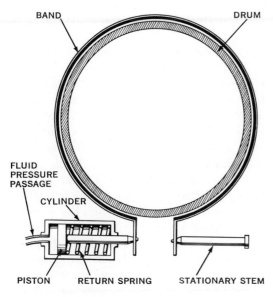

BAND   DRUM

FLUID
PRESSURE
PASSAGE
    CYLINDER

PISTON   RETURN SPRING   STATIONARY STEM

A typical transmission band. Oil pressure acting on the piston can cause the band to contract
to hold the drum. The band releases when
fluid pressure on the piston lessens.

piston is attached to the sun gear itself. Therefore, the clutch has but one function —to lock the planetary sun gear to the input shaft. The piston itself is operated hydraulically to engage the clutch. When the clutch is engaged, the piston retainer (the bowl) is locked to the hub by means of pressure which compresses all the discs and plates. Since the planetary sun gear is attached to the piston retainer, a firm connection is formed between the clutch hub and the sun gear when the discs and the plates are pressed together. When there is no pressure applied to the clutch pack, the sun gear is independent. Thus when the band is applied to the ring gear, the planetary is in "Low." When the clutch is applied in addition, the planetary is in "High." When neither the clutch nor the band is applied, the unit can de-

liver no power and the function is "Neutral."

Hydraulic Pressure. Both the band and the clutch are actuated by hydraulic pressure. The band uses a simple device called a *servo*. This unit is essentially a small cylinder with a piston and a stem coming off the piston. It acts very much like the wheel cylinder for the brakes. The stem reaches to contact one of the lips of the band; a stationary stem contacts the other band lip. Between the piston and the bottom of the cylinder is a spring.

At the appropriate time, pressurized fluid pushes against the piston, overcomes spring pressure and moves the stem. This pushes the lip on the band toward the other lip and the band contacts. Thus the ring gear is held. To release the band, hydraulic pressure is applied to the other side of the piston. With the aid of the spring, the reverse pressure pulls the stem from the band lip and the ring gear is released.

It is interesting to note that the hydraulic method is a modern extension of a more basic system used on the planetary transmissions found on the model T Fords. In these old cars the band was applied and released through a cable operated by the driver by means of a special foot pedal. On very early automatics, electrical solenoids and magnets using iron filings were employed. However, all car makers now agree that pressurized fluid is the most practical means of actuating the band.

The activation of the clutch is also accomplished with hydraulics. In this case, the fluid is forced against the piston at the bottom of the clutch retainer. This forces the clutch discs against the ring and sun gears, causing them to lock. When the pressure is released, the large spring in the retainer pushes the piston back and releases the clutch discs.

The Hydraulic System. In order to operate the band and clutch hydraulically so that the gears "shift" automatically, a number of important basic components are necessary. The total number of valves and controls varies with the individual makes of cars. However, all systems must contain the following five foundation pieces:

1) *Oil pump*—to maintain a constant pressure

2) *Pressure regulator*—to maintain a constant pressure

3) *Manual valve*—to turn oil pressure on or off

4) *Shift valve*—to direct oil to the servo or clutch

5) *Governor*—to deliver oil pressure according to vehicle speed

Let's take a closer look at each of these components and get more acquainted with the functions they serve.

The *oil pump* is driven by the car engine. This pump resembles the pump which supplies the engine components. A line runs from the pump to the oil pan of the transmission. Its job is to keep a constant supply of pressurized fluid in the transmission's system.

The *pressure regulator* is a simple opening in the oil duct near the pump. It has a spring-loaded door. The regulator is a type of safety valve which opens when the oil pressure is too high and allows some oil to drain back to the pump to relieve the pressure. As the pressure reduces, the spring closes the regulator valve and allows the pressure to build up. The action of closing to increase pressure and opening to relieve pressure goes on continually while the transmission is in operation.

The *manual valve* is the unit which is shifted when the driver shifts the gear selector lever. Inserted in the main oil line from the oil pump, the manual valve acts as a traffic cop. When the gear selector is placed in Neutral, the oil is routed in such a manner that neither the band nor the clutch will receive any fluid. When the selector is put into Drive, circuits called galleries are open for the activation of the band and clutch. When the selector is put into Low only the band will be activated. When reverse is desired the oil will flow to hold the planet carrier so that the sun gear can spin in one direction and the ring gear can spin in another.

The *shift valve* is an additional traffic control that directs the oil to apply the band or clutch. The valve is spring loaded to give rapid and smooth operation.

The *governor* assures that the shifts take place at the proper time with relation to vehicle speed. The governor is located on the output shaft of the transmission and operates by centrifugal force to deliver oil pressure that varies with vehicle speed. When the vehicle is at a standstill there can be no governor pressure because the transmission output shaft is stationary. As the vehicle starts to move, the governor activates and regulates the oil pressure upward. The increase in pressure continues as vehicle speed increases. Governor oil pressure is directed at the shift valve and controls the switch from low- to high-gear operation.

There is one other valve that is noteworthy in the shifting process. This is the *throttle valve*. The shift valves and the governor are not very sophisticated. According to the way they are set up, shifts

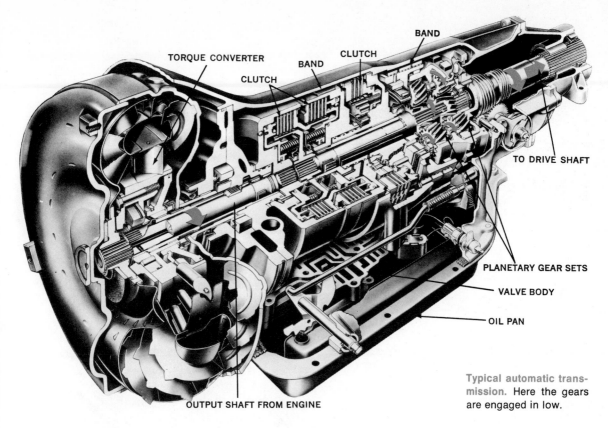

TORQUE CONVERTER · CLUTCH · BAND · CLUTCH · BAND

TO DRIVE SHAFT

PLANETARY GEAR SETS

VALVE BODY

OIL PAN

OUTPUT SHAFT FROM ENGINE

Typical automatic transmission. Here the gears are engaged in low.

will occur at the same vehicle speed, with the governor calling the shots. This arrangement is not always to the driver's advantage because shifts at different speeds are often desirable, such as when accelerating from a stop light or up a hill.

In these instances, a throttle valve assembly is used to delay the shifts. This valve is so called because it is tied into the carburetor linkage and causes the oil pressure to vary with the carburetor throttle opening. This oil pressure is called "throttle pressure," and it works to increase shift-valve spring pressure. Therefore, higher vehicle speeds and governor pressure will be required to accomplish each shift. To accelerate slowly, the accelerator pedal is depressed gradually. Shifts will then occur at low vehicle speeds. During rapid acceleration, the gas pedal is almost fully depressed. Because the

throttle valve opening is wide, the shifts will not take place until the vehicle reaches a higher speed. Thus the throttle valve holds back the shift until the proper time.

AUTOMATICS: IN PARTING

The usual automatic transmission is, of course, more complicated than we've shown in our discussion. First, most of them today have front and rear planetary units. That is, they have two gear sets with two bands and two clutches. Second, it takes many more intricate valves to meet the driver's every demand, as shown in the accompanying photo. In this chapter, we've stripped down the automatic transmission while purposely disregarding many intricate parts which tend to complicate discussion of basic operation.

155

8
DRIVE LINE

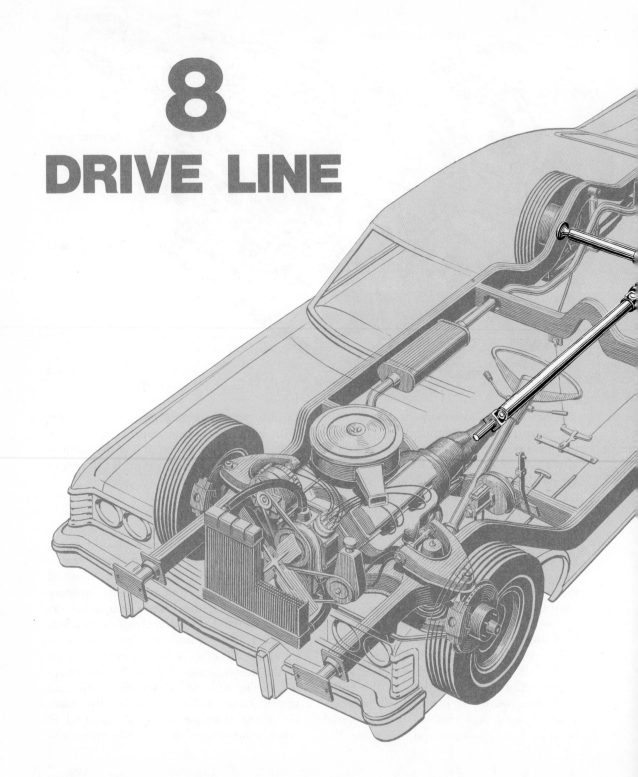

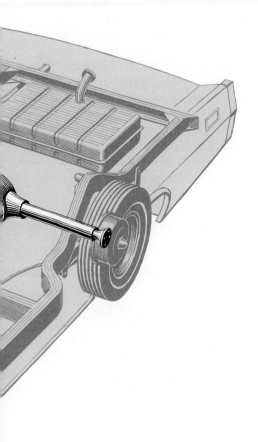

In the conventional automobile, the power is created up front (engine); multiplied in the center (transmission); and put to work in the rear (rear axle). This transport of power creates problems of its own. (The unconventional cars, such as those with front wheel drive and those with rear engines will be discussed at the end of this chapter.)

From the previous chapters, we already know that engine power is expressed in a turning flywheel. The developed torque is sent to the transmission for boosting via the clutch on cars with a manual transmission or via a torque converter on cars with an automatic transmission. The multiplied torque is expressed in a turning output shaft. The problem now is to bridge the five- or six-foot gap from the transmission to the rear axle.

In the early days of the automobile, a chain and sprocket was used, resembling a bicycle mechanism. But this system has shortcomings. Chains stretch and fall off sprocket wheels. Chains must be constantly lubricated and adjusted. Chains are noisy and, today, would not survive the loads of heavy, high-powered cars.

DRIVE SHAFT

Around 1902 some cars began carrying power to the rear wheels by means of the time-honored shaft. Long before the automobile, the shaft was used to make a power source "reach" a point where it was needed. In some of the old photographs of factories, wheels with leather straps appear over each machine. All the wheels were fastened to a common shaft which ran the length of the plant and was attached to a source of power.

Running a shaft for stationary use gives no special problems since the height or the angle of the shaft remains the same from the engine to the machine it runs. In an automobile, there are special problems.

1) The transmission output shaft and the rear axle input shaft are often at two different heights from the ground. This means the shaft must be positioned at an angle.

2) When one of the rear wheels strikes a hump in the road or drops into a hole,

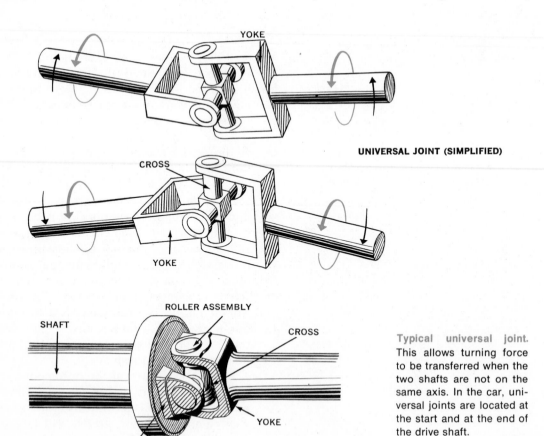

YOKE

UNIVERSAL JOINT (SIMPLIFIED)

CROSS

YOKE

ROLLER ASSEMBLY

SHAFT

CROSS

YOKE

YOKE

Typical universal joint. This allows turning force to be transferred when the two shafts are not on the same axis. In the car, universal joints are located at the start and at the end of the drive shaft.

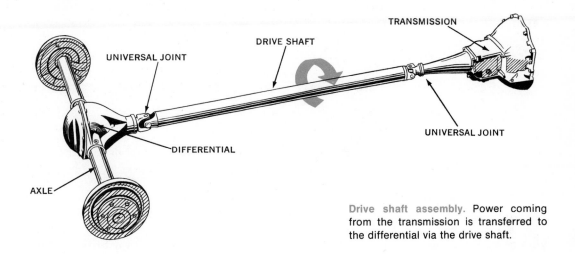

Drive shaft assembly. Power coming from the transmission is transferred to the differential via the drive shaft.

the alignment of the rear axle with the car frame shifts. As the car moves, the angles of the parts that carry power to the wheels are constantly changing.

Both of these problems are solved by use of a flexible connector called a *universal joint*. The device permits a driving shaft to turn a driven shaft at an angle which is constantly changing and twisting. To demonstrate how a U-joint works you can "construct" one with your fingers. Using your left thumb and index finger, form a circle. This represents the driven shaft. Do the same with your right hand, but form the circle inside the first one. This represents the driving shaft. Slowly start twisting your right hand and notice how the left one must follow. Now, without breaking the connection, turn your left hand so it is palm upwards; hold your right hand palm downwards. Twist with your right. The left still follows though it is not on the same plane. No matter at what angle you hold your left, power will always be transferred through this crude universal joint.

The Typical Joint. To provide the utmost in flexibility a typical car has two universal joints. One is between the transmission output shaft and the drive shaft toward the front of the vehicle; the other is between the drive shaft and the axle input shaft at the vehicle's rear.

A typical U-joint is known as the cross and roller type. The core of the unit is a steel cross. Its center is flat, but the ends of the four points are machined round to a specific size. Fitted to north-south points of the cross is a yoke. This is a Y-shaped section of pipe which is also attached to the transmission output shaft. It fits there as a spline. That is, the inside of the pipe has notches which are made to fit grooves on the outside of the transmission shaft. The spline arrangement enables the pipe to slide forward and back. The rearmost pipe section branches into the Y and has the holes which fit over the cross ends.

The front part of the drive shaft also has two branches of a Y with holes. These fit to the east-west ends of the cross. So far the fits of the holes to the cross ends are

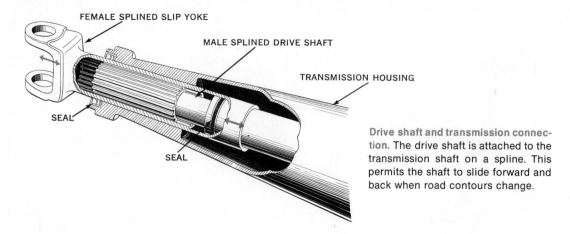

FEMALE SPLINED SLIP YOKE

MALE SPLINED DRIVE SHAFT

TRANSMISSION HOUSING

SEAL

SEAL

Drive shaft and transmission connection. The drive shaft is attached to the transmission shaft on a spline. This permits the shaft to slide forward and back when road contours change.

very loose since the holes are much larger. To make the assembly snug and to provide a frictionless movement, four caps are used. Each one is made of steel and looks like a screw-on bottle cap. Their insides are ringed with a series of roller bearings. The rollers are so thin that they are called needle bearings. The total size of the cap's inside with the bearings is a shade larger than the cross ends. The total size of the cap's outside is a shade smaller than the holes in the yoke and the drive shaft. When the caps are pressed on the four cross ends, a snug joint is formed which can tilt a few degrees left, right, up and down, yet transfer torque.

At the back end of the drive shaft a similar assembly exists. The holes of the shaft continue to hold the east-west positions of the cross, and the holes of the rear axle input shaft hold the north-south positions. Of course the compass points change as the shaft revolves. We mention them here merely as reference points.

Changes in Length. When the car is in motion, the distance between the axle and the transmission changes as the rear wheels bob up and down. In going from

the extreme low position to the extreme up position, as when the wheels go into a deep hole or over a large bump, the rear axle travels in an arc. Both extreme positions bring the axle closer to the transmission, while the midway point carries the axle farthest from the transmission.

This is the reason the yoke on the transmission shaft is splined. As the car goes over the bumps and into the holes, the yoke is free to slide in and out as it spins, allowing changes in the length of the drive line.

Double Shaft. Long cars require longer drive shafts. However, a longer shaft increase the likelihood of unwanted vibrations and the tendency of the shaft to whip as it turns. On a number of cars the problem is solved by a two-piece shaft. Three U-joints, like those described above, are used. The run is from the transmission to the first U-joint, to the front drive shaft. The far end of this front shaft rests in a center support which is bolted to the car frame. Just rear of the support, the shaft is splined to the second U-joint. Then comes the rear shaft running from this joint to the rear axle where the third U-joint is located. On these models there is no spline at the transmission yoke. Fore and aft movement is taken up at the spline of the two shafts at the center support.

The Shaft. The *drive shaft* is sometimes called the propeller shaft. It is usually a hollow pipe which is fat enough to carry the torque to the rear without twisting or bending. It is made of fine quality steel and is carefully balanced at the factory so that it spins with a minimum of vibration.

On some cars the shaft is a solid rod located inside a solid, non-turning pipe. The design is called *torque-tube drive* and was quite popular on General Motors' cars. The difference between this design and the more popular drive discussed thus far will be detailed later in Chapter 9, "Suspension."

One newcomer to the drive-shaft scene is a flexible cable found on the Pontiac Tempest. Like the rod, the cable is in-stalled inside a tube. It has a great deal of flexibility as it turns. The "shaft" con-sists of many strands of steel wire which are twisted together to form a cable.

THE REAR AXLE ASSEMBLY

By this time the term "torque" should be more than familiar. Born in the engine, multiplied in the transmission, transferred at an angle by the U-joints and drive shaft, torque has yet to accomplish its mission — something to move the car. We are almost at that point, but torque still needs some processing.

The most important problem now is that the turning force is wrong for moving the car forward or back. It has been wrong ever since it came from the flywheel. For illustration purposes, imagine that you are standing in front of your car (when it is parked, of course). Extend your right arm straight in front of you and rotate it in a small clockwise circle. Now, extend

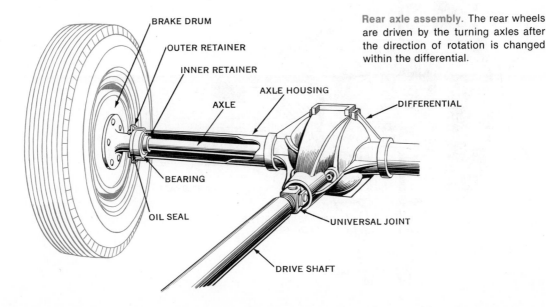

BRAKE DRUM
OUTER RETAINER
INNER RETAINER
AXLE HOUSING
AXLE
DIFFERENTIAL
BEARING
OIL SEAL
UNIVERSAL JOINT
DRIVE SHAFT

Rear axle assembly. The rear wheels are driven by the turning axles after the direction of rotation is changed within the differential.

your left arm straight out to your side and rotate it in a counterclockwise direction. Your right arm represents the direction of movement of the flywheel, transmission output shaft, drive shaft and rear axle input shaft—all going the same way. Your left arm represents the direction of movement of the rear axle, wheel and tire.

Obviously the units your arms represent turn in planes at a right angle to one another. Thus a reorientation of torque must have taken place somewhere. It did—just inside the *rear axle housing.* This housing with its many internal parts has a number of important jobs. First, as noted, it must reorient the torque. Then it must deliver the torque to the rear wheels via the axle

shafts, which it must also support. It also provides the base for the rear brakes.

The typical housing is known as a banjo housing. It resembles two of these stringed instruments joined at the body with their necks 180 degrees apart. Bolted to the center of the banjo facing the front is a large housing called the *differential carrier.* Protruding from the center of the carrier and bolted to the rear universal joint is the *pinion shaft,* sometimes called the rear-axle input shaft. It gets its name from the fact that the other end of the shaft has a cone-shaped gear. Gears having this shape are called pinions. The pinion gear is meshed with a large gear called a *ring gear.* This one is shaped like a large

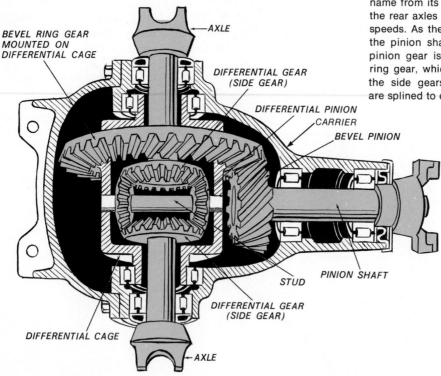

BEVEL RING GEAR
MOUNTED ON
DIFFERENTIAL CAGE

—AXLE

DIFFERENTIAL GEAR
(SIDE GEAR)

DIFFERENTIAL PINION
CARRIER

BEVEL PINION

PINION SHAFT

STUD

DIFFERENTIAL GEAR
(SIDE GEAR)

DIFFERENTIAL CAGE

—AXLE

The differential. This gets its name from its capacity to permit the rear axles to turn at different speeds. As the drive shaft turns, the pinion shaft is rotated. The pinion gear is meshed with the ring gear, which is meshed with the side gears. The rear axles are splined to each side gear.

dinner plate. The "table" side is quite smooth. The "eating" side of the plate has gear teeth cut into it. The teeth on the ring and pinion gears are cut at a 45-degree angle and may still be referred to by some as *hypoid gears*. In operating position the ring gear is stood on its edge as it meshes with the pinion.

The thin edge of the gear faces the front and back of the car, while the flat sides are left and right. In this mode the shaft turning clockwise can make the ring turn forward. The plane of motion is changed a full 90 degrees. However, the pinion shaft is not held exactly at right angles to the ring gear. The centerline of the shaft does not match the centerline of the ring. Here engineers take advantage of the angled cut of the teeth (Hypoid) by placing the meshing point well below the centerline of the ring. This allows a lower profile for the drive shaft and reduces the size of the tunnel on the floor of the car.

Ratio Again. The horizontal motion of the drive shaft will be translated to vertical motion at the ring gear. But the degree of rotary travel of the gear and the shaft will differ. A full turn of one will not produce a full turn of the other. The simple explanation is that the ring gear and the pinion do not have the same number of teeth.

Gear ratios for these parts have very odd numbers. 3.09-to-1 or 2.56-to-1 may be fairly typical ratios. The odd numbers are designed to prolong life of the teeth and to prevent damage in case of a slight imperfection on two matching teeth. If the ratios were even, such as 3:1 or 2:1, then a certain tooth on the pinion would contact the same tooth on the ring gear every three or two revolutions. However,

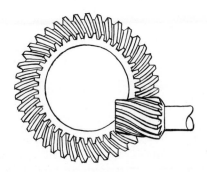

Hypoid gears. The small pinion is positioned below the centerline of the rear-axle ring gear. This allows a lower drive-shaft profile and a lower hump in the floor pan.

a ratio of 3.09:1 or 2.56:1 means the one pinion tooth will contact a specific ring tooth only once every 309 turns or 256 turns.

The ratio at the ring and pinion has an effect on the speed of the rear wheels in relation to drive shaft speed. If a rear axle ratio on a certain car is 4.10, it means that the pinion will have to turn 4.1 times to produce a single revolution of the ring. This accomplishes a torque multiplication — above and beyond the multiplication given the engine torque in the transmission. If the ratio were less than 4.1, say 2.5, less torque multiplication would occur. When the car is designed, engineers try to prescribe a gear ratio which is a compromise between power and speed. But the people who race cars in competition often revise the ratios by replacing the gear set. The person who is interested only in power for a 1/4-mile drag race will "lower" the ratio by installing a 4.10 or a 4.59:1 gear set. The person who wants to win long distance races or wants peak fuel economy will "raise" the ratio by using a 2.01 or a 2.59:1 gear set.

THE AXLE

So far, we have a spinning drive shaft and pinion shaft. The pinion gear causes the ring gear to turn, and the plane of rotation shifts 90 degrees. Now the gear spins in the direction the car will travel. All this action takes place in the differential carrier at the center of the banjo housing.

To link up the spinning ring gear with the rear tires, it would be best to jump across and trace the path of power from the outside to the inside.

The tire is secured to a wheel and the wheel is turned by an axle shaft. The axle is made of fine steel and is solid. Its length is roughly half that of the car's width. On all conventional cars, the part of the axle that is closer to the center of the car, the inside end, has splines. The design of the outside end of the axle is one of two popular styles.

Tapered Axle. Here the outside end of the axle narrows down to a point. Cut into the taper is a groove ¼-inch wide and ⅛-inch deep and about three inches long. The brake drum which fits on the axle has a matching taper in its hub and a similar slot. When the drum is installed the two slots are lined up and a square piece of steel, ¼ × ¼ × 3 inches, called a key is inserted into the two matching grooves. A large nut holds the drum to the axle. Now when the axle turns, it puts pressure against the key and forces the drum to turn with it. The rear wheel is bolted to the drum. Power is then transferred from the axle to the tire.

Flange-type Axle. The outside end of the axle suddenly flares out to a dish-shaped flange about five inches in diameter. The face of the brake drum has five holes. The flange is also equipped with five threaded studs. The drum is mounted on the studs as is the wheel. Both are secured with tire nuts. Thus the turning axle influences the wheel directly. In both cases, the axle shaft fits inside the long axle housing, the neck of the banjo.

Some cars, such as Corvette, have a somewhat different rear axle design. In these cases, there is no rear axle housing just a differential carrier. Protruding from the right and left sides of the carrier are two universal joints. Attached to them are axle drive shafts. This design gives the utmost in flexibility. Each rear wheel can rise or drop independently of the other. Such design is easily identified by its exposed axle shafts with universal joints of their own.

Now let's go back to the ring gear and set up a reception for the splined end of the axle. Bolted to the flat side of the ring gear is a steel box called the *differential case*. Inside the case are four gears arranged in a square. The fore and aft pieces are called *pinion gears*, again, because the gears are cone shaped. They are rather small and have a smooth center. A steel bar connects the center of one with the center of the other. The other two gears are called the *side gears*. The teeth of both side gears are in contact with the teeth of both pinion gears. The centers of the side gears are splined.

When the axle shafts are installed, they are fitted inside the splined center of the side gears. Now, finally, the path of power is complete. The drive shaft turns the main pinion shaft, which is in mesh with the ring gear. The differential case is bolted to the ring gear, so it turns along with it. The side gears are inside the differential case, so they turn as well. The rear axle shafts are splined to the side gears, so they turn, the rear wheels turn, the car moves.

TAKING THE CORNERS

If a car would only travel in a straight line, the rear axle assembly would be much simpler. The fact is that the car not only needs to turn corners; it weaves as it travels straight ahead. Every time the car digresses from the straight-ahead, the speeds of the two rear axles differ. In an extreme case, as when turning a corner, the outside wheels must speed up while the inside wheels slow down. The principle is the same as with a column of marching people. When marching straight, all persons take the same size step, keeping the column straight. When rounding a corner for a 90-degree turn, the person on the inside must take much shorter steps, almost mark time, while the person on the outside of the turn must increase stride since he must cover a greater distance. Inside and outside people adjust to keep rank and file in line.

The front wheels of a conventional car or the rear wheels of a car like a Toronado (Front-Wheel drive) do not need special provisions for making a turn. The left and right wheels are independent of each other and rotate on what are known as "dead" axles. That is, no power is transmitted by these axles, and they can turn at independent speeds. However, the wheels that propel the conventional car are fed by "live" axles. Power is transmitted to both of them by a single ring gear. The axles rotate at different speeds, yet they must drive the vehicle as if they were a single unit.

Now it should be clear why the box bolted to the ring gear is called the *differential.* It permits a different speed rate for each axle. When the car is travelling in a straight line, the gears in the differential case are stationary in relation to each other. Torque is delivered from the ring gear to the differential case and to the small pinion gears via the steel shaft between them. The teeth of the pinion gears are, in a sense, locked against the side gear teeth causing the side gears and axles to rotate.

When the car turns a corner, the side gear of the outside wheel starts to turn faster. This causes the pinion gears in the case to rotate as the case revolves. The small pinion gear teeth "walk" around the side gear teeth, pushing one side gear faster and allowing the other to turn at the same rate as the inside wheel. The average speed of both side gears, shafts and wheels is always equal to the speed of the ring gear. There is no torque multiplication or other mechanical advantage when the car turns a corner.

SLIPPAGE

There is one basic fault in this differential system. If one of the wheels loses traction by slipping on ice or mud, the other wheel will remain stationary. Almost everybody who has driven a car under slippery conditions has experienced this phenomenon. The side with the least traction gets all the power; the other side gets none. Internally, the small pinion gears are racing around in the differential case, giving all the torque to one wheel.

The slippage problem was first solved on the 1955 Packard. Since then manufacturers have offered, as an option, a

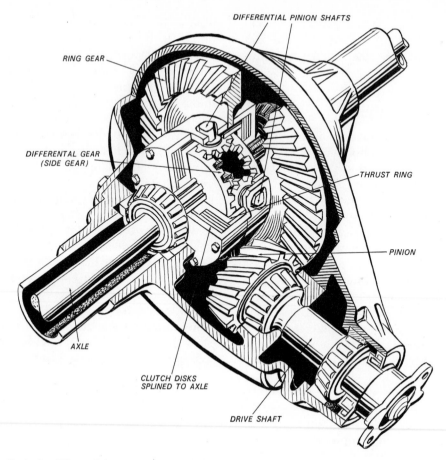

DIFFERENTIAL PINION SHAFTS

RING GEAR

DIFFERENTAL GEAR
(SIDE GEAR)

THRUST RING

PINION

AXLE

CLUTCH DISKS
SPLINED TO AXLE

DRIVE SHAFT

The limited-slip differential. This permits the turning force to be transferred to the wheel that has the most traction. Thus, this differential allows getting out of a snow bank without excessive wheel spinning.

special-traction differential. By the use of small friction clutch plates or a tapered cone clutch inside the differential unit, it is possible to transfer torque to the non-slipping wheel. The clutch plates or the cone clutch goes into action as soon as one of the wheels starts to spin. These clutches assure power to the opposite axle.

This special-traction differential is a vast improvement over the standard one.

In addition to providing optimum traction under slippery conditions, it also assures a fast-acceleration getaway, since it keeps either wheel from spinning at initial takeoff.

UNCONVENTIONAL SYSTEMS

Thus far, we have considered the drive line of only the conventional car—with the engine up front and the drive wheels in the rear. But, this is not the only route the drive line can take. The two major variants are the vehicles with front-wheel drive (FWD) and those with the engine in the rear. The former is found on the Oldsmobile Toronado, and the latter is found on the Volkswagen.

In both cases, the engine is located near the drive wheels. But here too there is need to multiply engine torque and assure differential action in the drive wheels. The solution is found in the use of a *transaxle*.

This unit takes over the function of both the transmission and the rear axle. It contains all the gears for selection of the necessary gear ratios. The very end of the transmission shaft has a pinion and ring gear set inside the transmission case, complete with a differential case. The only

protrusions are two axle shafts from either side of the unit.

The transaxle has two distinct advantages. It eliminates the drive shaft. It also keeps most of the car's weight over the drive wheels, thus improving traction.

REDUCING FRICTION

Some of the biggest and most hardy bearings are used in the differential carrier and axle housing. This is the section of the car to which all torque production is directed. The main pinion shaft has a heavy bearing; the ring gear and differential case have bearings; the axle rotates on bearings. Lubrication is provided by a heavy oil which constantly bathes all parts.

This completes the entire train of power from the engine to the rear wheels.

9
SUSPENSION

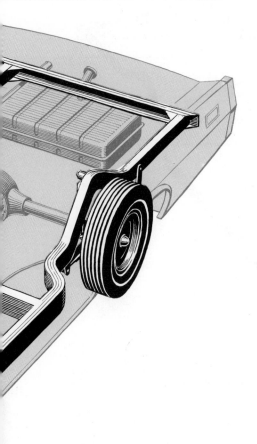

ooking at the vehicle as a complete unit, it is possible to assign its parts to either of two assemblies—the chassis or the body. The chassis includes all the units necessary for the proper operation of the car, such as engine, transmission, steering system, suspension, axles and wheels. The body provides accommodations for the passengers and any additional loads.

CHASSIS

Considering the chassis, we can divide it too into two basic systems—the frame and the suspension. The frame is supported by the axles and wheels. Between the frame and each axle a suspension system allows the wheels to move up and down and prevents road shock from being transferred to the body. Cars today are built on either of two basic frames: the *unit-body* (or *integral*) *frame* and the more conventional *parallel frame.*

169

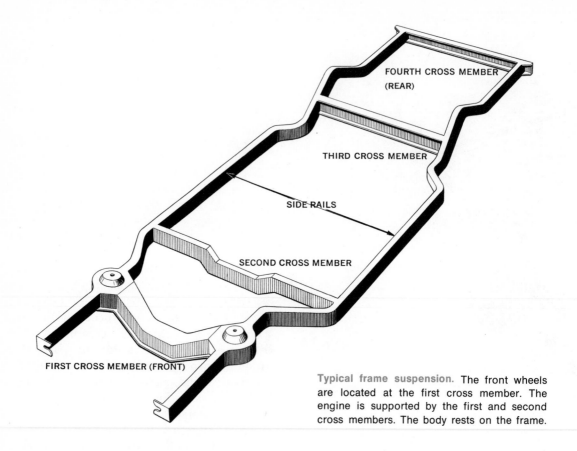

FOURTH CROSS MEMBER (REAR)

THIRD CROSS MEMBER

SIDE RAILS

SECOND CROSS MEMBER

FIRST CROSS MEMBER (FRONT)

Typical frame suspension. The front wheels are located at the first cross member. The engine is supported by the first and second cross members. The body rests on the frame.

Unit-body Frame. The car body is secured directly to this frame. The front section of the frame has short steel rails that support the engine. The back has short rails that support the rear suspension. The center of the unit-body frame is strengthened to support itself. Construction can be compared to some money-saving methods for building houses. Rather than pour a solid foundation that extends from the front to the rear of the house, contractors use piers along both the front and rear and then bridge the expanse with extra-heavy beams to the piers. The best that can be said about unit-body frame in the automo-

bile is that it saves the car maker money. Claims that it is stronger or superior to the full-frame construction are not substantiated by collision reports.

Parallel Frame. Here the body of the car is provided with a separate foundation. The parallel frame is made of box-shaped steel and is rigid enough to carry the body firmly while resisting all the twists and bends applied to the car. Its major parts are the *side members,* which run the length of the car, and the *cross members,* which run the width of the car. A typical frame has four cross members. The front one usually supports the suspension. The second stiffens the frame and provides a base for the support of the back end of the engine and transmission. The third is about three-fourths of the way back and gives the front and rear springs solid support. This third cross member is very important since the vehicle is propelled at this point. We will discuss this later in the chapter when we look at the rear suspension. The fourth cross member is at the very rear of the two side rails and provides support for the fuel tank, trunk and bumper.

SPRINGS

Unlike a house a car is built to move. Movement means vibration, rough spots in the road and rocking from stop-and-go driving. If no provisions were made to absorb all the bumps and vibrations, riding in today's car would be as uncomfortable as riding in yesterday's chariot. In those days the designers had no solution for road shock. As the wheels hit the bumps, the shock was transferred to the axle, which was bolted to the platform upon which the driver stood. To minimize the jolts to his upper body, the charioteer absorbed much of the action by flexing his knees. The engineering solution came many centuries later as carriage and coach builders found ways to build the coach such that the up and down wheel action was intercepted, absorbed and dissipated by springs. This is still the function of today's suspension springs. When the spring is interposed between

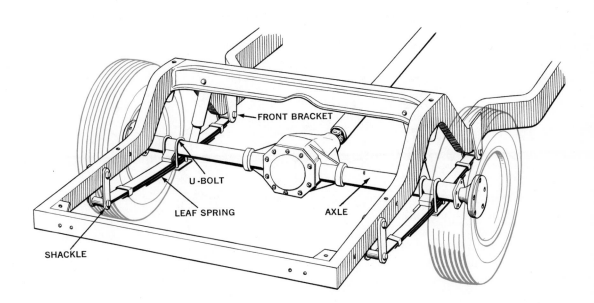

Rear leaf spring suspension. The stress points of body weight are on the front and rear ends of each leaf spring—at the shackle and front bracket.

the chassis and the axle it can minimize the transfer of motion by giving and re-covering.

The earliest springs were wooden rails made of willow and yew. These woods have a lot of "give" and resiliency. They were installed in the coach, anchored at one end like a diving board. The longer the rail, the greater its bounce and ability to intercept road shocks. By the time the automobile was developed, steel springs had been in use on horse-drawn carriages and wagons for more than 100 years. The early cars generally copied the carriages by using a flat spring between the axle and the body that ran the width of the car. Installed, it looked like an upside-down U.

Auto springs have changed somewhat since the early days. Today there are three basic springs used in the front and rear suspension.

Leaf Springs. These get their name from the use of a pack of flat steel strips, called leaves. Each strip is gradually shorter than the one above it. The entire pack is held together by a center bolt which runs through the center of each leaf and is held with a nut. The top strip is called the main leaf, and its ends curl up to form an eye. Both eyes are used to anchor the spring. Small bands, called rebound clips are fixed to the stack of leaves a short distance from the eyes. These serve to keep the leaves from pivoting sideways when the spring is flexed up and down. As the springs work, there is a sliding friction between the leaves. Here neoprene pads are inserted to

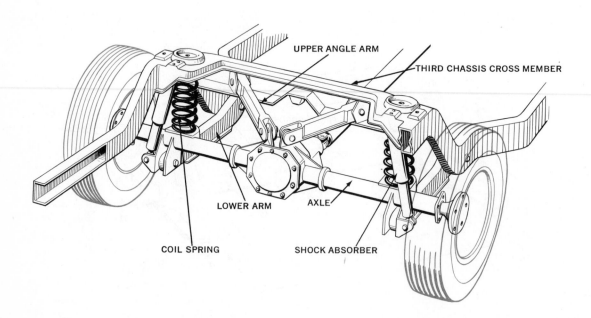

UPPER ANGLE ARM

THIRD CHASSIS CROSS MEMBER

LOWER ARM   AXLE

COIL SPRING   SHOCK ABSORBER

Rear coil spring suspension. The lower arms pivot up and down, allowing the springs to compress and expand in response to irregular road surfaces.

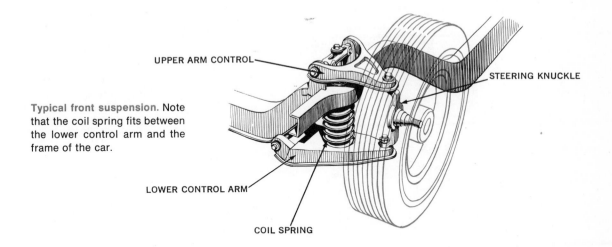

UPPER ARM CONTROL

STEERING KNUCKLE

Typical front suspension. Note that the coil spring fits between the lower control arm and the frame of the car.

LOWER CONTROL ARM

COIL SPRING

prevent excess wear and noise. Some cars use a single leaf rather than a group of leaves, but the purpose and the effect are the same.

Coil Springs. This spring is found in almost every piece of moving equipment from wrist watches to railroad cars. Basically, a coil spring consists of a steel rod which has been wound around a uniform cylinder to form a helix. The coil is then heated, tempered and given proper tension. Almost all of today's cars use coil springs in the front suspension. These springs are employed in the rear suspension as well, but not to the same extent as in the front.

Torsion Bar. This type of spring is a relative newcomer. It is even more simple than the coil spring. It utilizes a stout bar made of spring steel. One end of the bar is securely anchored while the other end is free to twist. If the load is placed on the free end so that the bar twists, the load will cause springing action. The torsion bar

acts much like your forearm when your elbow is held rigidly and your wrist turns left and right. The only difference is that the torsion bar is a spring and will seek its original position and resist movement.

Spring Ratings. When you get to know them, springs are interesting. In the suspension system springs have a very basic function; they can be considered as keepers of the status quo. The construction fundamental for a car is to attach the body to the frame — rigidly. Both are then bolted to front and rear axles. In between the frame-and-body assembly and the axle is one spring for each wheel. The springs are flexible and always return to a neutral position. Thus they maintain the status of the frame/body for any given load. But, before the system can really do its job, some problems of design need attention.

When engineers design a car, they must select special springs for the suspension. A spring for a sub-compact simply cannot

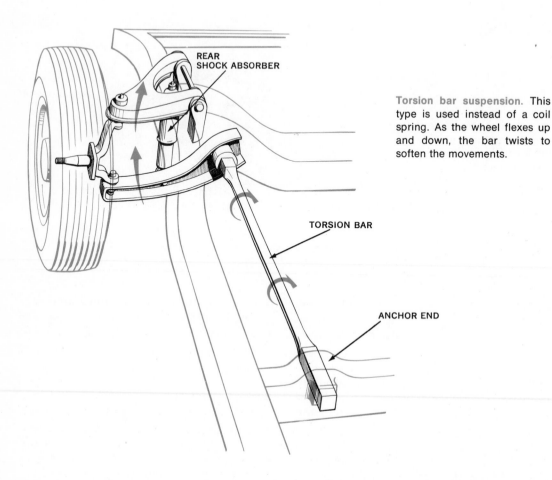

REAR
SHOCK ABSORBER

Torsion bar suspension. This
type is used instead of a coil
spring. As the wheel flexes up
and down, the bar twists to
soften the movements.

TORSION BAR

ANCHOR END

support the weight of a limousine. The "limo" spring installed in the sub-compact will have no give at all. The amount of springing allowed for a particular car is carefully calculated by the engineers. They use a formula called the *spring rate* to determine how stiff the springs should be. This rating tells them how many pounds it takes to make a spring deflect one inch. The stiffer the spring, the greater the spring rate.

An oscillation is the natural movement of a spring when a load has been thrust upon it and removed. Oscillation causes the "boinnng" sound when you tweek a flat spring. When a car rides on a flat surface or stands still, the spring is in a neutral position. When one wheel climbs up a steep bump, the spring there will "wind-up." That is, it will go into a compression stage and store the energy. When the wheel begins its sudden descent, the

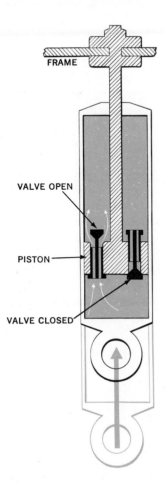

FRAME

VALVE OPEN

PISTON

VALVE CLOSED

Typical shock absorber. Up and down movement of the body is controlled by the restricted flow of oil through the piston.

Swing axle construction. This design is used on cars with transaxles at the rear wheels. Inboard universal joints allow the axles to swing up and down as the tire bounces along the road.

spring unwinds and releases that stored energy. In so doing, the spring will not stop in its neutral position but go past it. This is called rebound. During rebound, the spring gathers energy of extension. This rebound energy is less than that of original compression, but it is enough to make the spring want to pop back rather quickly. As it does, the spring again compresses beyond the neutral point but with less stored energy than accompanied rebound. The spring will continue to compress and extend with gradually diminishing motion until it comes to rest. These oscillations are taken into account when a specific spring is prescribed for a vehicle.

SHOCK CONTROLS

Spring oscillation is considered in the overall design, but it is tolerated only to a limited extent. If all the springs are allowed to compress and rebound as they wish while the car is in motion, every ride in that car will feel like a trip through high seas in a dinghy. For control over the oscillations, the spring is connected to a device which will retard but not eliminate the up and down movements. This device

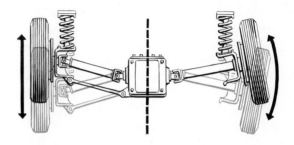

is ineptly called a *shock absorber*. The English seem to have a better name for it. Their cars are equipped with *spring dampeners*. That's exactly what a shock absorber does; it dampens the movements of the springs. The springs themselves absorb the shock.

The modern shock absorber works on a hydraulic principle. By regulating the rate of flow of a fluid from one chamber to the other, it is possible to regulate the motion of the shock absorber. In appearance the unit resembles two large pipes which fit into each other. The upper and lower ends of the pipes are shaped for attaching the shock from the solid chassis to the moving spring.

When the wheel climbs up a bump, the spring compresses and the shock telescopes, exercising control over the amount and speed of spring compression. Inside the shock, the telescoping causes a piston to plunge within a tube of oil. Built into the bottom of the piston are small valve openings which open in opposite directions. Regardless of the pressure imposed by the top section of the shock, the piston can descend only as fast as the oil flows through one of the fixed valves and out the top of the position. It is very much like locking two fluid-filled hypodermic syringes nose to nose. Pushing one plunger will transfer all the fluid to the other syringe and drive its plunger away from the nose. However, the speed at which the fluid transfers depends more on the size of the opening than on the pressure applied.

When the spring and the shock absorber have fully compressed, rebound will occur. However, during rebound the

piston is pulled up and hydraulic flow inside the shock is down through the top and out the bottom of the piston. The result is that the spring may oscillate only once or twice. If the jolt from the road is particularly severe, there may be an extra dip in the spring, but the shocks will make the spring action smoother.

The telescoping shock absorber used today on most of the cars is called an "airplane" shock because it was first introduced on aircraft in the early 1930s. However, the idea of controlling the actions of the spring is not a new one. The early cars had "snubbers." These were springs coiled in a flat circle, much like the mainspring of a clock. They were attached to the car spring in such a manner that the snubber unwound when the

Shock absorber. The top end is always attached to the car frame; lower end is attached to a moving arm at each wheel. This type accepts pressurized air through the nipple near the top to compensate for heavy car loads.

spring compressed and wound up when the spring rebounded. Thus they afforded some control. In the late 1920s some cars had a hydraulic shock absorber which was incorporated with the arms of the front suspension. The arms of the suspension acted as levers for a hydraulic pump. As the arms went up and down, fluid transferred from one chamber to another at a controlled rate. This absorber was called "knee-action" because it was similar to the action of man's legs when he stood while riding over a bumpy surface. The major problem with the knee action shocks was that the entire front suspension had to be dismantled if the shock needed replacement or repair. The airplane shock is self-contained and can be replaced without disturbing any other suspension components.

FRONT AND REAR

Now let's take a look at how the frame/body is suspended over the axles. Suspension systems vary in style, but certain fundamentals must hold. For instance, the spring and its shock absorber are always interposed between the frame and the axle. Since the rear suspension is far more simple than the front, let's examine it first.

The Rear Suspension. There are two basic types of rear suspensions in use on most cars today. One has leaf springs running parallel to the side members; the other has coil springs. Opinion is split as to which style is better.

The leaf spring is called semi-elliptical, since it resembles half an ellipse before it is installed. Once installed, the springs are pressed almost straight under the car's weight. Each of the leaf springs has three installation points. The front eye of the spring fits into a special bracket welded to the chassis about two feet in front of the rear axle housing. With the eye in place a heavy bolt is run through the spring eye and bracket. Thus, this section of the spring is held rigidly.

Leading to the rear, the spring is slung under the rear axle housing. There, it is firmly secured with two large U-bolts and nuts. The rear of the spring requires a special bracket because a semi-elliptical leaf spring shortens when no load is on it and lengthens when a load is imposed. Therefore, the rear anchoring point of the spring must adjust to the varying lengths that occur when the car is in motion. This rear bracket is called the *spring shackle*. The top leg fits into a hole in the chassis. The lower leg fits into the spring eye. Now the lower section can pivot. When the rear wheel drops into a hole, the axle drops also, making the spring shorten and appear more elliptical. The shackle will follow this shortening and will swing toward the front. When the rear wheel climbs a bump, the axle will rise in relation to the frame. The spring will become straighter and will lengthen. The shackle will then swing to the rear to follow the end of the spring.

The main advantage of the leaf spring is that it lends stability to the car against side-to-side forces. This is important in making a turn, when the side forces push the most. The very length of the spring acts as a lever against these side forces. To help keep the car level during fast acceleration and sudden stops, some cars have springs that are installed off-center. This puts the rear axle slightly ahead of the spring's center so that the result is a shorter arm between the front spring anchor and the axle and a longer arm between the axle and the spring shackle.

The coil-spring rear suspension is quite different, in that much more hardware is required. The coil spring is squeezed between the rear axle housing and the chassis above it. Any up-and-down movement of rear axle will be absorbed by the compression and rebound of the coil springs. For up-and-down movements this system is sufficient. However, by itself, this system has no provisions for handling side thrusts.

To give the needed stability, support arms are employed. In one typical design, two steel arms run from the rear axle to the third chassis cross member. In addition, two more arms are installed at an angle from the differential housing branching outward to the third cross member.

A departure from these two suspension systems is found on cars such as the Corvette, which use flexible axle shafts. With this swing-axle a transverse leaf spring is used. That is, only one spring is used and is positioned across the width of the car. Side stability is provided by two arms extending frontward from the backing plate of the wheels to the frame. These are called *trailing arms.*

Naturally, shock absorbers are used on all cars, regardless of the suspension style. The typical anchoring points for the shocks are the chassis on top and rear axle on the bottom. In the case of cars with a swing axle, the lower section of the shock is attached to the trailing arms.

Pushing the Car. With the various rear suspensions clarified, we can now plot exactly how the car is moved ahead. (Again, we are discussing only the conventional front-engine, rear-wheel drive automobile.)

Consider the action at the rear axle. Torque is delivered to the rear wheels via the differential and the rear axle. Torque is spent where the rear tire touches the ground. The wheel turns and pushes the car ahead. The car's forward progress and the location of stress points are determined by the type of rear suspension and the type of drive shaft arrangement.

In Chapter 8, we discussed the drive line's regular, exposed drive shaft with its two universal joints and the concealed shaft which runs within a long tunnel from the transmission to the differential. The exposed shaft is called Hotchkiss drive; the concealed shaft is called torque-tube drive. If the car has Hotchkiss drive with a leaf spring, the turning wheel against the road transfers the force back to the axle housing. In turn, the axle housing pushes on the leaf spring. The thrust is then transferred to the front bracket of the spring. The car is pushed from this point.

Should the rear axle be a Hotchkiss drive with coil springs, the forward motion is taken up by the support arms. The precise point is the spot where the arm contacts the chassis at the third crossmember.

If the car has torque-tube drive, the springs may be either coil or leaf. The exact point of push is at the very rear of the transmission. As the tires exert torque, the force is transferred through the hollow tube which houses the concealed shaft and is bolted to the rear of the transmission.

The Front Suspension. The front axle of a modern car is not an axle at all. At least, it is not in the same sense as the rear assembly. The rear has a solid axle housing extending to each of the wheels; the front does not. The entire rear section of the car is affected by a bump under one wheel; in the front only one side is affected.

The front of the car reacts differently because its construction is different. The front has an *independent suspension*. This means that, within limits, each wheel can react to the road differently. One side can go into a slight road depression while the other goes over a slight bump, yet the stability of the body will be affected only slightly. With the solid axle, a bump in the road under one wheel will cause a tilt of the entire axle and a swaying car body.

Prior to the 1930s, the front of the car was supported by a solid axle, usually in the shape of an I beam. In turn, the axle was supported by the front wheels. As will be described in Chapter 11, "Steering," each front wheel was mounted on a steering knuckle which was attached to the axle end with a long king pin so that it was free to pivot. Either two longitudinal leaf springs or one transverse leaf spring was installed between the chasis and the axle. With a few tie-rods for steering, the front end was complete. This simple construction did little more than hold up the front end of the car.

Independent suspension is a bit more complex but it gives a better ride. Each side contains a set of four parts. These are the lower control arm, the upper control arm, the spring and the steering knuckle support. In the more modern suspension which has ball joints, the support is eliminated.

The popular name for the lower control arm is A frame. The wide part of the A is secured to the underside of the chassis front so the narrow portion points to the front wheel. The A is not rigidly bolted to the chassis but is designed to pivot up and down. Modern cars use rubber bushings which allow A frame movement. Early cars used threaded metal bushings.

The upper control arm is sometimes called the little A frame. It has a slight resemblance to the lower arm but is much shorter. It is secured to the top section of the chassis front so that it too can pivot up and down.

In the older style independent suspension, the steering knuckle support connects the outer ends of the upper and lower control arms. The support has a hole bored through it to accept the C shape of the steering knuckle; a king pin through the support and the knuckle unites the two pieces. Thus the knuckle is allowed to pivot when the wheels are steered.

The newer style uses ball joints. Essentially, a ball joint is a tight-fitting cup over a steel ball. It can pivot up and down as well as left and right. Suspension ball joints are used at the outer points of the lower and upper arms. Here the steering knuckle has arms long enough to extend to the upper and lower ball joints.

The final piece, the spring, is placed between the chassis and the lower control arm. On some cars the spring is placed between the body and the upper arm, but

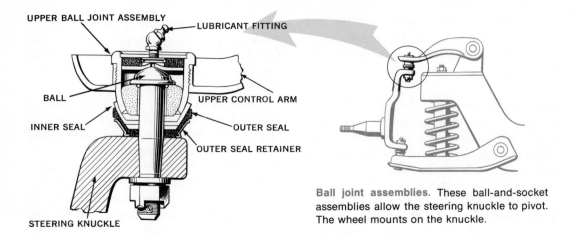

UPPER BALL JOINT ASSEMBLY

LUBRICANT FITTING

BALL

UPPER CONTROL ARM

INNER SEAL

OUTER SEAL

OUTER SEAL RETAINER

STEERING KNUCKLE

Ball joint assemblies. These ball-and-socket assemblies allow the steering knuckle to pivot. The wheel mounts on the knuckle.

the effects are the same. The spring establishes a resistance to up and down motion.

If the system is equipped with torsion bars instead of springs, another configuration is used. The torsion bar is laid parallel to the side members of the chassis. The rear of the bar is secured solidly to a bracket welded to the side member. The front of the bar is attached to the lower control arm. Any flexing of the arm will load the bar, as if compressing a coil spring.

Looking at the front suspension now, we have an odd-shaped box at each wheel. The vertical members are the chassis and the wheel; the horizontal members are the upper and lower arms. If the wheel goes over a bump, the horizontal members will incline upward. A small hole will incline the members downward. Action at one wheel, has no effect on the opposite one.

The only time when one wheel relates to the other is during a turn. In, let's say, a full left turn, the car's weight shifts to the right side. In the front suspension, the

right spring will compress and the left spring will rebound, both from their neutral positions. With the front in this posture, steering and handling of the car becomes difficult. To reduce the amount of dipping and stretching to a minimum, both sides are linked with a common brace called a *stabilizer bar*. This bar resembles a very wide and shallow U and is attached to the front face of the lower control arm on each side. To appreciate how the bar works, take about ten inches of coat hanger wire and form a shallow U about six inches wide at the mouth. Now, by holding the two short vertical bars, you can simulate the car going over a washboard road, each wheel taking the bumps evenly. In this case the U will bounce with no distortion or twisting. A downward pressure on one bar and an upward pressure on the other simulates what happens to the stabilizer bar when the car is in a turn. Both sides of the bar will resist and want to return to neutral position. It is this resistance which prevents excessive dipping to one side of the suspension during turns. In reality, a certain amount of dipping and stretching does occur, but the stabilizer bar keeps it to a minumum.

THE WHEELS

Almost every mechanical device, gear, shaft and bearing in the car is destined to turn the wheels to move the car. Throughout its 7,000-year history, the simple wheel has undergone continued refinement. Even the last 80 years of automobiles have produced vast changes in the wheel. The evolution includes the use of very large, bicycle-type wheels with wire spokes, wooden spoked artillery-type wheels, and solid-disc steel wheels. These styles lasted well into the 1930s, even after the advent of the dished steel wheel.

Today all cars use the dished wheel, except special cars which still use heavy wire spokes. The modern wheel is made of two pieces. It has a center section with four or five holes, for mounting the wheel on a drum, and a rim section which is welded to the center piece. When stood on its edge, the wheel has a soft shape of a V. This is called a drop-center wheel and it is capable of holding a tire with an airtight seal.

The wheel is mounted to a drum with either nuts or bolts called lugs. At the rear of the car, the drum is mounted to the axle. At the front, the drum has a special hub which includes two tapered bearings. These are designed to match the taper of the front wheel spindle. When the hub is joined to the spindle, the bearings greatly reduce friction, allowing the drum and wheel to spin freely.

THE TIRES

If the wheels are the feet of the car, the tires are its shoes. The tire has undergone more changes than any other part of the car. And the quality of today's cheapest tire is far better than yesterday's most expensive one. In the old days every car carried two or more spares. No family outing was complete without one or two flats. Every motorist had a patch kit and an intimate knowledge of the procedures for dismounting and repairing a tire. Today, it is quite possible to travel 10,000 miles without a single flat. While it is true that roads are in better shape, so is the quality of the tires.

The tire is a most familiar object, yet few realize that it has specific areas with names for them. The *bead* is the rim of the inner circle. It is that part of the tire which grips the wheel and provides the air seal. The bead also fights the centrifugal force which wants to spin the tire off its rim. The *cord body* consists of layers of rubber impregnated fabric. The layers, called *plies,* are bonded together into a solid unit. The *tread* is that part of the tire which comes directly in contact with the road surface. It has a varying zigzag pattern of grooves and ribs. The ribs provide the traction for gripping the road surface; the grooves provide an easy escape for water runoff. Some tires have small cuts, called *sipes,* molded into the ribs. These sipes open up as the tire flexes on the road to give extra gripping action, particularly on wet roads. The *sidewalls* are part of the tire body and are made of a formula which gives great flexibility.

Raw Products in Tires. The tire is made of three basic materials: rubber, fabric, and steel wire. The rubber, both synthetic and natural, is mixed with various compounds to meet each manufacturer's requirements for traction, wear and resistance to damage. It is then rolled into sheets and cut to length. This rubber will become the tread of the tire. The fabric is the backbone of the tire. In the past, simple cotton cord was used. Today, the tire makers choose from rayon, nylon, polyester or fiberglass. One brand (Michelin-X) uses a thin cord made of steel. Each tire uses about 3000 yards of cord.

The cords are laid out side by side, all running in the same direction. Then they are dipped in a gum rubber, heated and dried under tension. With the cords frozen in place, rubber is applied to both sides of the sheet which is then cut into specific widths and angles. The strips are then rolled in layers. Each ply has the cords running at a different angle.

When the plies are rolled, a strip of tread rubber is applied as a final layer. Then the steel wire is incorporated into the edges of the roll on both sides to form the bead. At this point the pack doesn't look like a tire at all. It resembles a rolled mattress. This roll is placed, long side up, in a tire mold where it is subjected to high temperatures and pressure. All the rubber materials bond and shape to form the tire in its finished form.

Different Constructions. Today there are three basic types of construction for tires. Debate will forever rage over which is superior. All of them are good for the service they are designed to give. The names of the tires refer to the arrangement of the tire cords.

Conventional Bias Construction. Here there are two, four or more overlapping plies of rubber-coated fabric with the cords alternating in direction with each ply. The cords run at an angle (bias) from the front bead to the back bead. Tires have been made in this way for the past 50 years. The advantages of the bias ply are low-cost dependability and good mileage.

Belted Bias Construction. The foundation of the tire is the conventional bias plies. Then, two broad belts cover the plies, just under the tread rubber. The belts are not attached to the beads as are the ply cords. Advantages include increased mileage, very good traction and a resistance to punctures and cuts.

Radial Ply Construction. The cords of these tires do not run on the bias. They run in a straight line, across the face of the tire from bead to bead. Directly over the plies and under the tread are two or more belts with cords running on the bias. These are called stabilizer belts as they hold firmly the tread area of the tire. The radial tire's advantages are a greater tread contact with the road; less tread flexing due to the stabilizer belts; resistance to bruises; and savings in gasoline due to the reduction on rolling resistance.

Tire Size. There was a time when automobile tire sizes were fairly easy to interpret. If the size on the tire said 7.75×14, it meant the following: The tire was $7^3/4$ inches wide measured from the edge of one sidewall, across the tread to the edge of the other sidewall. The second figure said the tire is for mounting on a wheel with a 14-inch diameter. An 8.50×15 tire has an $8^1/2$-inch cross section, mounted on a 15-inch wheel.

Recently, a new breed of tire has brought a new set of tire sizes. This is the wide-oval tire. The new design makes the tire fatter and lower. Contained within the size is the relationship of the tire's height to its width. Thus you may see stamped on

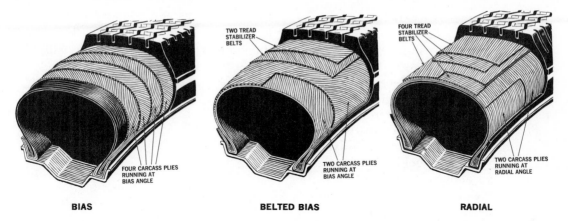

BIAS   BELTED BIAS   RADIAL

Three types of tire construction. The bias ply has each layer of cord running at an angle to the axis of the tire. The belted bias has the same construction, but the plies are covered with two belts of rubber running around the outside rim of the tire. The radial type has the cords running at a right angle to the axis of the tire and is capped with stabilizer belts.

the tire the following size: GR 70-15. The G is the load carrying capacity established by the tire industry. G equals 1620 pounds of load at an inflation of 32 pounds per square inch of air pressure. A tire with an F will sustain a load of 1280 pounds at 24 per square inch inflation. The load-carrying capacity increases as the letters go up the alphabet. The R in the size says it is a radial tire. The 70 says that the tire's height is 70 percent of its width. In tire language this is called the *aspect ratio*. Other popular ARs are the 78 series (height is 78 percent of the width) and the 83 series (height 83 percent of the width). Finally, the 15 in the size says the tire is mounted on a 15-inch rim.

According to the latest U.S. Government standards, size is not the only information which must appear on a tire. The following must be embossed on the sidewalls of each tire in terms the consumer understands:

1) *Size.* Let's say it is a GR 70-15

2) *Load and Inflation.* The significance of the G must be spelled out as above.

3) *Construction Type.* Explains the R as being of radial-ply construction.

4) *Manufacturer's Number.* Every tire maker is assigned a number by the Department of Transportation.

5) *Load Range.* The letter B says the tire has a 4-ply rating; C has a 6-ply rating; D an 8-ply rating. This may not be the same as the actual number of plies, for two actual plies may be equal to the strength of four plies.

6) *Ply Material.* Spells out the exact number of plies in the tire and the cord material under the tread and under the sidewalls.

Tuning the Tire. Consider that the wheel and the tire are products of factory production. As a result, if the weight mass is not evenly distributed, the imbalance will show up

183

when the wheel is spinning. And during rapid rotation imperfections will be exaggerated.

There are two regions on the tire where distribution of weight affects tire balance. These are around the circumference and on both sides of the center line. If the weight is not distributed correctly around the circumference, there will always be a heavy spot. If the wheel is raised from the ground and allowed to rotate freely, the heavy spot will always come to rest on the bottom. In actual operation of the car this imbalance will produce what is called *wheel tramp*. That is, every time the heavy spot comes around to contact the road, it actually slams to the pavement. Though the amount of imbalance may amount only to an ounce or two, the "tramping" force of a fast-rotating wheel may be several hundred pounds.

This wheel is said to lack *static balance*. It gets its name from the fact the test of the wheel balance is done when the wheel is at rest, static.

The other kind of tire balance describes the weight distribution between the inner face of the tire and wheel and the outer face. If the tire is in balance, the center line of the weight mass coincides with the center line of the wheel.

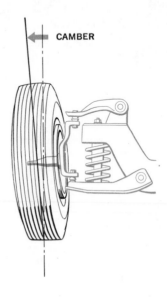

Camber is the angle of tilt the wheel has toward or away from the frame, as measured from the top of the wheel.

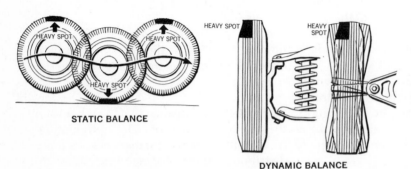

STATIC BALANCE

DYNAMIC BALANCE

Two types of wheel balance. Static balance is affected by heavy spots around the rim of the tire; dynamic balance concerns heavy spots on the inner or outer rims of the tire.

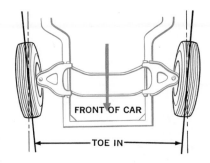

Toe-in is the angle of the front wheels tilted toward the car frame when the car is at rest. In motion, the wheels tend to run in a straight ahead position.

If one tire face is heavier than the other, centrifugal force will try to transfer the weight to the opposite face every half turn of the wheel. The result is that the wheel will wobble or *shimmy*. Again, the amount of imbalance will be exaggerated with the motion of the wheel. This wheel is said to lack *dynamic balance*. The name indicates that the condition can only be revealed by a moving or dynamic wheel.

Both static and dynamic imbalance are corrected by placing lead weights on the rim of the wheel. The weights are installed opposite the heavy sides.

FRONT-WHEEL ALIGNMENT

Designing a front suspension for a car is not as easy as, say, nailing down a baby carriage axle for a soap box racer. In addition to the quality of materials and the machining of all parts, there is the problem of relating each part to the others. Placement of front suspension parts has a great deal to do with car behavior and tire wear. Front-wheel *alignment* involves the angular relationship of all front-end com-

ponents with the wheels and the car frame.

There are five main factors to consider in alignment. The grand object of these various alignment factors is to put the center line of the front tires in flush contact with the road. With the wheels aligned, tire and front component wear are kept to a minimum, and the car handles well. There are many factors that conspire against maintaining alignment. Road surface, road contour, steering, and weight load are but a few. Unless alignment is correct, the result is severe tire scuffing, dragging and slipping as well as severe strain on all front end components.

Alignment Factors. *Camber.* The word usually refers to a bend or a curve. Regarding wheel alignment, *camber* refers to the inward or outward tilt of each wheel when measured at the top. Camber can be either a "bow-legged" or "knock-kneed" posi-

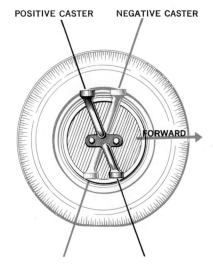

Caster is the angle at which the steering knuckle is forward or back. It affects steering.

tion. If the wheel is tilted outward, camber is said to be positive. If the tilt is inward, camber is negative. The tilt from vertical is measured at the top of the wheel in degrees, with the fully vertical line tabbed as zero. Wheels are given some positive camber primarily to support a greater part of the vehicle's weight on the inner wheel bearing, which is the larger of the two. Also, positive camber offsets the tendency of the wheels to tilt inward when the loaded car gets rolling. Camber makes the wheels roll as if they were cones. The pull is to the outside, away from the vehicle. Too much camber will cause severe slippage at the inner part of the tire tread. It is vital that the camber be equal at each wheel, for the car will pull toward the side with the greater camber.

Toe-in. Here the front wheels are set so that the front portions of the wheels are closer together than the rear portions. *Toe-in* is much like walking "pigeon-toed." The amount of toe-in is measured in fractions of an inch and is regulated by the length of the tie rods, which are adjustable. Toe-in is necessary for two reasons. First, it compensates for the camber which causes the wheels to toe outward. Toe-in tends to make the wheels roll toward each other. Second, even if the wheels had no camber at all, the steering linkage tends to pull the wheels outward when the car moves forward. In compensation the wheels are set slightly inward. When the car is in motion, the wheels point straight ahead.

Caster. This describes the number of degrees that the ball joints are tilted forward or backward from their vertical positions when viewed from the side. If the tilt is backward, caster is designated as positive; a forward tilt is termed nega-

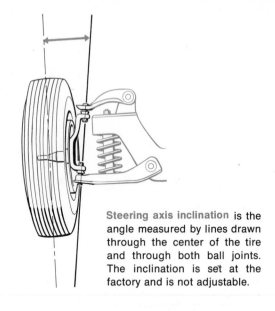

Steering axis inclination is the angle measured by lines drawn through the center of the tire and through both ball joints. The inclination is set at the factory and is not adjustable.

tive caster. Think about the action of a furniture caster. No matter in which direction the furniture is shifted, the caster will always swivel to the rear of the direction traveled. The downward load of the piece of furniture is not directly over the axle of the caster wheel, but in front of it. Thus, with the weight on the forward part of the wheel, the remainder of the wheel will swivel to the unloaded, or rearward side. In most cases a little positive (rearward) caster is desirable since this will place the car load directly in front of the vertical center line of the wheel, like the furniture caster. Thus steering will be easier. The front forks of a bicycle have negative caster. Unequal or negative caster causes the vehicle to wander and retards the rapid return of the steering wheel after completing a turn. Excessive caster keeps the wheels in a straight-ahead position but makes turning a corner or veering from the straight-ahead very difficult.

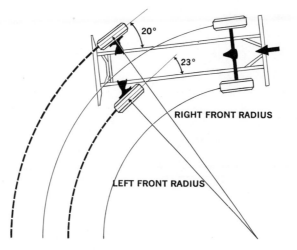

20°

23°

RIGHT FRONT RADIUS

LEFT FRONT RADIUS

Toe-out on turns permits the inside wheel to turn at a steeper angle than the outside wheel. Without this provision, the tires will scrub the road surface as they turn.

Steering Axis Inclination. This refers to an upper ball joint that is a trifle more inboard than the lower ball joint. When a line is extended from the upper joint, through the lower one, and to the road surface, the line will meet the road directly under the heavy end of the tapered spindle which holds the wheel. The amount of tilt is the steering axis inclination and is measured in degrees. This inclination is important. While driving, perhaps you have noticed after turning a corner that if you loosen the grip on the steering wheel the front wheels will automatically spring back to the straight-ahead position. Due to the steering axis inclination, the spindle will always swing in an arc—upwards—when you turn the steering wheel. This lifts the entire front of the car. As a result, when you release your grip on the steering wheel, the car's weight straightens the wheels. This is much like hanging a door with the top hinge farther from the door stops than the lower one. If the door is unlatched, it will swing open under its own weight.

Toe-out on Turns. When a car makes a sharp turn, the angles of the two front wheels must differ. The wheel on the inside must turn in a smaller arc than the wheel on the outside. If it is otherwise, the tires will be torn to shreds after only a few turns. The inner wheel will steer about 23 degrees while the outer wheel will steer about 20 degrees when making a turn.

The car maker determines how much the wheels or ball joints are tilted. Each car model has its own specifications. Caster, camber, and toe-in are adjustable and must be reset periodically. Steering axis inclination and toe-out on turns are built in as a permanent design feature. But they must be checked after the car has been involved in a serious collision. Often the only way to get these factors back into alignment is by replacing the parts.

10
BRAKE SYSTEM

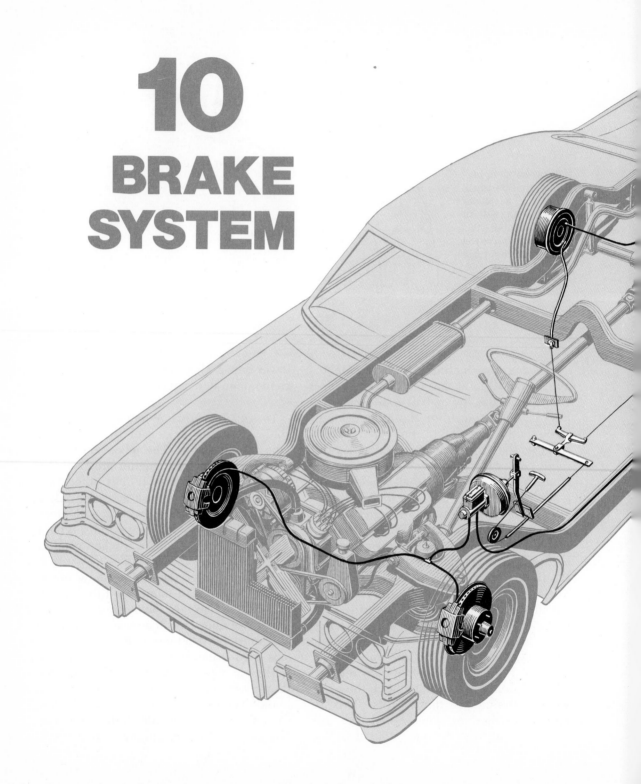

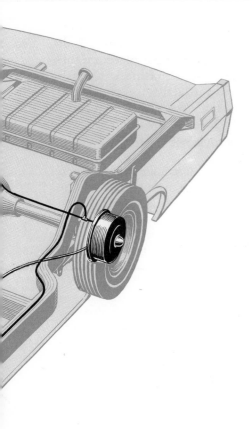

To apply the brakes on old wagons and stagecoaches a direct lever was used. It pushed a brake shoe against the wheel rim. The force of the brake shoe against the rim was in direct proportion to the force applied to the lever. To apply the brakes on old automobiles, a brake lever was installed outside the car, but the braking process remained indirect. The driver, in pulling the lever, actually pulled on steel cables which were attached to the brakes at the rear wheels.

By about 1912, some cars appeared with foot pedals and brakes on all four wheels. However, the cable setup remained. Brake application was mechanical. The force of the driver's foot was transferred to cables and the brake shoes. The last mechanical brakes appeared in the 1937 Ford.

Applying the brakes by the cable method was less than ideal. Besides the fact that the driver's effort on the brake pedal was not boosted to any extent, there were other problems. When the brakes were applied, the cables and linkage all moved the same distance. If the brake shoes on one wheel happened to be a little more worn than the others, they would provide less braking power than the other three sets of shoes. This caused a braking pull, with the car veering toward the side with the better brakes. Another problem was that when one wheel passed over a bump, it caused the brake cable at that wheel to tighten. If the brakes had to be applied at that moment, premature braking would occur, causing the car to veer in the direction of the affected wheel.

In 1918 Malcolm Loughead and some associates formed the Lockheed Brake Company and began using liquid force to develop a new concept in braking. In 1920 the first four-wheel hydraulic brake system appeared on an American-made vehicle — the Duesenberg.

PASCAL'S LAW: HYDRAULICS

A seventeenth-century French mathematician and philosopher, Blaise Pascal, formulated the principle on which hydraulic brakes operate. By experimentation, he found that "pressure applied to an enclosed fluid is distributed equally and undiminished in all directions."

Here is an example that shows the meaning of Pascal's law. Imagine a special type of hypodermic syringe, which, in addition to an opening at the bottom, has four additional openings along the side of the cylinder. When the cylinder is filled with water and the glass plunger is depressed, liquid will spurt from all the openings. If we put a pressure gauge at each opening, the readings will be identical — regardless of the distance each opening is from the plunger. There is no pressure loss at the point farthest from

the piston; there is no pressure increase at the point nearest the piston.

Here is another example of hydraulics: We have a U-shaped, 1-inch tube half filled with a liquid, and we place a tight-fitting piston in one leg of the U to push the liquid down exactly 1 inch at 100 pounds of pressure. We will then observe that the liquid level in the other leg will rise exactly 1 inch and a pressure check will read 100.

Suppose we try a similar experiment, attaching a nozzle to a piston-type syringe. The nozzle attachment has four 1-inch tubes, all filled with a liquid, all interconnected. As the piston applies pressure, the oil levels in each of the tubes rise

Primitive braking device for a wagon. When the lever is pushed forward the brake shoe rubs against the wheel rim.

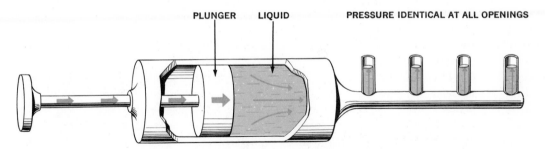

PLUNGER   LIQUID   PRESSURE IDENTICAL AT ALL OPENINGS

Illustration of hydraulic principle. Pressure remains the same at each opening when the plunger is pushed.

equally. (If the piston cylinder were the same diameter as each of the tubes and the piston were driven 1 inch at, say, 100 pounds of pressure, the piston would cause the oil in each tube to exert 100 pounds of pressure also. However, the level in each tube would rise only ¼ inch because the volume of oil displaced would be shared equally by the four tubes.)

In this case there is a duplication of effort, but no multiplication. However, if we use a U-shaped tube whose one leg is 1 square inch in area and the other is 4 square inches, we can multiply effort. When the piston in the smaller tube is pushed down a distance of 1 inch at 100 pounds, the piston in the larger tube will rise only ¼ inch, but the total upward pressure will be 400 pounds. Distance is lost, but effort is increased. The 100-pounds-per-square-inch pressure applied to the smaller tube had to be distributed over an area of 4 inches, hence the distance moved by the larger piston was only ¼ inch. However, the force of 100 pounds was applied to each of the 4 inches in the larger tube, hence we got a multiplication of effort, or 400 pounds per square inch.

There are many examples of how hydraulics extends our muscle power. The garage jack is familar to anyone who has ever visited a gas station. When the mechanic places the jack under the car and starts pumping, he is sending a special fluid from a small cylinder to a large one. For every pound of effort he applies to the handle, the result is multiplied, based on the comparative sizes of the cylinders in the jack. But, did you ever notice how many pumps of the handle it takes to raise the car a few inches?

BRAKE FLUID

The fluid used in the automobile brake system is a vegetable-base oil. According to Pascal, the fluid need not be oil. It can be water, alcohol, beer, or mother's beef broth, but a special oil is used in cars to take care of some unique requirements:

First, a brake fluid must have a very high boiling point, owing to the tremendous amount of heat generated by normal braking. If the fluid is subject to boiling, it will form a vapor and will no longer be-

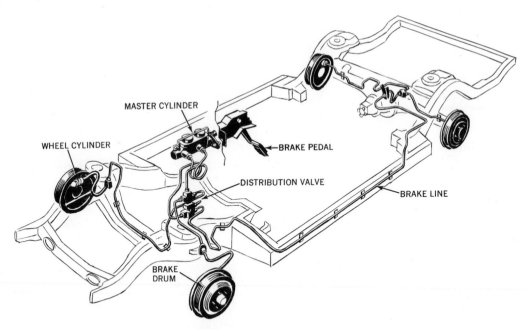

MASTER CYLINDER

WHEEL CYLINDER

BRAKE PEDAL

DISTRIBUTION VALVE

BRAKE LINE

BRAKE DRUM

The car's braking system. Pressure at the brake pedal creates pressure in the master cylinder and is distributed to all four wheels equally.

have according to the laws of hydraulics.

The second qualification for a brake fluid is that it must have a very low freezing point. Obviously, if the fluid freezes, the brakes become inoperative.

Third, the oil in the fluid must be compatible with rubber. Mineral oil, the type that comes from the ground and is used for engine lubrication, attacks and destroys rubber. A vegetable-base oil, such as that extracted from peanuts, castor beans, bananas, or coconuts, is compatible with rubber. Automotive brake fluid has a castor oil base.

Finally, the brake fluid must not decompose readily and leave a residue. Though oil does tend to get gummy as it grows old, a quality brake fluid has certain additives which not only prevent

this, but absorb moisture to inhibit rusting or freezing in the system.

Though there were many top brands of brake fluid now on the market, they are all governed by specifications set up by the Society of Automotive Engineers. Any brake fluid you use in your car should meet specs SAE 70-R1. This statement is on the can label.

Another essential consideration in any hydraulic system is the exclusion of air. Air is compressible; a liquid is not. If air finds its way into the system, the driver's effort on the brake pedal is wasted on compressing the air rather than on applying pressure to the fluid. What about air-brake systems on trucks? On those vehicles, the air is already compacted and can be compressed no further. In this state, the air performs as a liquid, and pressure can be transmitted through it.

Keep in mind that the hydraulic system is closed to the atmosphere. During routine service of the brake system, it is sometimes necessary to "open" the system to replace certain hydraulic parts. After the repairs are completed, the mechanic then must go through a procedure of "bleeding" the system of air.

THE PARTS OF A BRAKE SYSTEM

The present-day automobile has an entire network for putting these hydraulic principles to work in applying the brakes. Essentially it resembles the four-tube nozzle fed by the piston-type syringe described earlier in this chapter. The first tube, in this case, is a unit called the master cylinder; the other four tubes correspond to units at each wheel and are called the wheel cylinders. At the end of the brake pedal is a piston rod. This rod is semi-exposed. One half can be seen poking through the firewall, while the other half is in the master cylinder. Attached to the rod is the master-cylinder piston which

slides in the polished cylinder. At the far end of the barrel is a metal tube which eventually carries the pressure to each of the four wheels.

At each of the wheels is a strong steel disc known as a backing plate. Mounted on this plate are the brake shoes and another metal container called the wheel cylinder. Inside the wheel cylinder is a piston and a piston rod, which is attached to the shoes of the brake. The entire system is filled with brake fluid.

When the driver applies the brakes by depressing the pedal, the piston inside the master cylinder is pushed forward, exerting pressure on the brake fluid. This pressure is instantly transmitted through the brake lines to the pistons inside the wheel cylinders. As the pistons are forced outward they push small rods, which push on the brakes, which contact the wheel drums, and cause friction.

When the driver releases the brake pedal, strong springs cause the brake shoes to retract and pull toward the center of the drum. This forces the wheel-cylinder pistons to retract, pushing the fluid the other way, toward the master cylinder. As

Typical brake master cylinder. When the push rod is forced into the cylinder, the piston seals off the lower chamber, creating hydraulic pressure. The pressure is then transmitted to the wheels via the outlet tube. When the brake pedal is released, fluid returns to the master cylinder.

CAP

COMPENSATING PORT

RESERVOIR

INTAKE PORT

CHECK VALVE

DUST COVER

PUSH ROD FROM PEDAL

TUBE TO WHEEL CYLINDERS   RETURN SPRING   PISTON

PRIMARY CUP   SECONDARY CUP

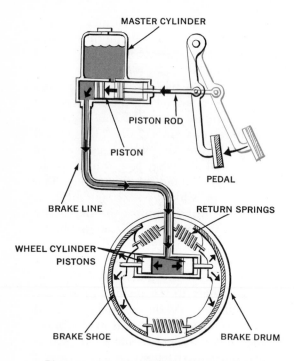

MASTER CYLINDER

PISTON ROD

PISTON

PEDAL

BRAKE LINE

RETURN SPRINGS

WHEEL CYLINDER
PISTONS

BRAKE SHOE

BRAKE DRUM

Diagram of braking system. Pressure from the master cylinder is sent to the wheel cylinder. Wheel cylinder pistons push outward against the brake shoes.

thing was to use a second "wheel," the drum.

Actually, the term "drum" is somewhat misleading. A brake drum looks more like a deep dish with a hole in the center for mounting on the axle. In the early days of the car, the drum was made of pressed steel—that is, one piece of metal was placed over a die and pressed into a dish shape. This type was light in weight but it had a low coefficient of friction, meaning that a lot of brake pressure was needed to stop the vehicle. But, cars were slow then; thus stopping was an easy task. The steel in this drum was fairly thin but dense in molecular structure. As a consequence it had a tendency to distort under severe braking, and it dissipated heat slowly.

In the late 1920s a drum of cast iron appeared. It is still in wide use today. This one is thicker than steel drums and better resists distortion. And because cast iron

the master-cylinder piston retracts, the excess fluid is pumped into the large reservoir above the barrel and remains there until the next application.

The Drums. The part to which the wheel is bolted is the drum. It is often called the "second wheel," but its sole purpose is to provide a surface for the brakes to contact.

As mentioned, horse-drawn wagons never used drums. Braking took place at the wheel rims. With the advent of the rubber tire, it was no longer practical to stop the vehicle by exerting pressure against the rubber rims. The next best

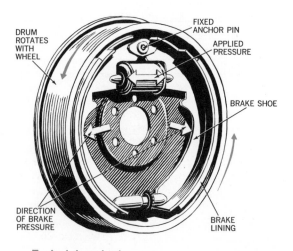

DRUM ROTATES WITH WHEEL

FIXED ANCHOR PIN

APPLIED PRESSURE

BRAKE SHOE

DIRECTION OF BRAKE PRESSURE

BRAKE LINING

Typical drum brake.

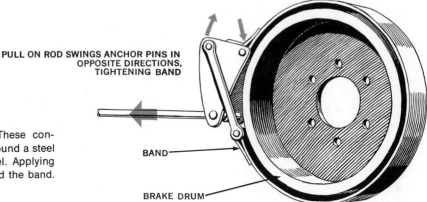

PULL ON ROD SWINGS ANCHOR PINS IN
OPPOSITE DIRECTIONS,
TIGHTENING BAND

BAND

BRAKE DRUM

Old-style brakes. These consisted of a band around a steel drum at each wheel. Applying the brakes tightened the band.

is less dense than steel, it has a greater ability to absorb heat.

In the 1940s some cars and trucks adopted combination iron and steel drums. The rim was an iron ring riveted or welded to a flat steel disc. The combination design had a great deal of rigidity and good heat absorption. A variant of this design was the all-steel drum with an iron ring fused to the inside.

In the latest drum innovation, the outer surface is made of cast aluminum and the "business" surface of cast iron. The aluminum and the outside fins provide additional heat absorption.

Since 1900, brake drums have appeared in three designs. The early type accommodated the external contracting brakes. Its braking surface was on the outside of the dish rim. A design used later was the internal-external type, with two braking surfaces—the inside for the regular brakes, the outside for a parking brake band. Present-day drums are exclusively of the internal expanding type.

Brake Linings. In the drum brake, the part contacting the drum surface is the brake lining. The purpose of the brake lining is to create the friction against the brake drum to convert the moving energy of the vehicle into heat energy. Engineers and car owners agree that brake linings should possess the following qualities: (1) long-wearing, (2) high in friction potency, or in coefficient of friction, (3) easily replaceable, (4) wet resistant, (5) non-injurious to brake drums, (6) free from odors, (7) quiet in operation—no squeal.

Regarding coefficient of friction, here at the linings is where it matters. Materials used in brake linings which have a low coefficient of friction, that offer little resistance to the rubbing action, require excessive pressure to make the car stop within safe limits. On the other hand, a high coefficient (or high resistance to rubbing), will produce "grabby" brakes. However, selection of friction material is not just a matter of finding the ideal compromise formula for linings and using it on all cars. The linings must suit the individual vehicle. A Grand Prix race car requires linings which must sustain high-speed stops and slowdowns and therefore would be much too hard for that little old lady with the four cylinder, two-door coupe for Sunday drives. Reverse the situation: If the linings ideal in a light car were used on a racer, the driver would have to drag his foot to stop the car after the second turn.

There are three types of lining now in general use. The first is known as *woven lining*. Its materials are usually made of asbestos fibers, cotton, and metallic particles such as brass, lead, or zinc alloys. The combination is mixed with a compound which will hold it all together and then compressed to the proper width and thickness. Depending on the formula, these linings are available in high, medium and low coefficients of friction.

The second type is known as *rigid molded linings*. These consist of asbestos fiber, powdered sulphur, crushed shells of certain nuts and powdered raw rubber. A bonding agent is then added. The mixture,

now in a plastic state, is injected into molds. Then pressure is applied to the mold to remove all air and to compact the mass. A certain amount of heat hardens the material, which is then removed from the mold and machined to its final size. The rigid molded lining is considered the universal type for general purpose vehicles because it possesses good resistance to heat.

The final type of lining is known as the *dry-mix molded lining*. As the name suggests the ingredients are mixed dry, placed into a mold and subjected to extreme heat. This process transforms the mix into an extremely hard mass. This lining is generally used on trucks with air or vacuum boosters since it has a low coefficient of friction.

Brake Shoes. Brake linings are attached to brake shoes. The brake shoe has no sole, but it does have a toe and heel. The shoe is an all-metal semicircular part of the brake which provides the foundation for the lining. The part to which the lining is

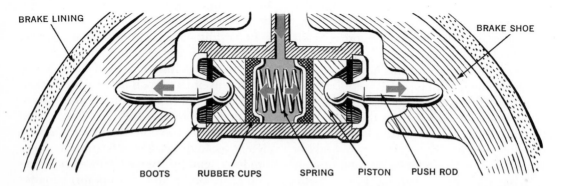

Typical wheel cylinder. Hydraulic pressure enters through tube in center of the cylinder. Pressure is then dispersed to both directions against the push rod, forcing brakes outward.

attached is called the shoe table. The supporting rib, which runs at right angles to the table, is called the shoe web. The web is full of various holes and indentations to allow mounting the shoe to the steel backing plate and to allow actuation by the wheel cylinder push rods.

Throughout the years there have been many methods for attaching the lining to the shoes. A popular method still in use, though not as popular as it once was, is riveting. In this case the lining is pre-drilled with countersunk holes and is placed on the shoe table's matching holes. Rivets are then inserted and crimped. The head of the rivet is well below the lining surface. However, when the lining wears "down to the rivet," it is time to replace the lining. Though rivets are made of brass and the drum of cast iron, some damage still can occur with repeated contact of the two.

Around 1950 a new method for attaching linings came into use. It is called bonding. In this case, the lining is placed on the shoe table, which is coated with a special adhesive. The entire assembly is clamped and then put into a 450-degree oven. After baking the lining is permanently bonded to the shoe.

For attachment of heavy-duty shoes two other methods are employed. One utilizes nuts and bolts, in the same manner as rivets. The other method uses clips which grip the lining at the sides and hold it to the edge of the table.

Brake Designs. Since the basic brake components at the wheel are the drum, linings, shoes, wheel cylinder and assorted hardware, it is interesting that there were about 100 different designs and configurations used from the past to the present day.

However, it would be academic to review each variant and each major style. All the brake styles on today's passenger cars can be placed in three major groups. These are the *non-servo*, the *servo* and the *disc*.

On non-servo brakes, each shoe acts independently. There is no multiplication of brake effort, as accompanies the servo type. Typical is the type known as Lockheed brakes which were popular on all cars up to the 1930s, and on Chrysler Corporation cars up to the 1960s. A typical configuration included two shoes with a single pullback spring linking them. At the lower end, at the heel, each shoe is secured to an anchor. The shoes are free to pivot but are otherwise held rigidly. At the upper end, at the toe, there is a link to the wheel cylinder. In the center, behind each web, is an irregularly shaped metal disc called the adjusting cam. When the lining wears down, the cam is turned with a wrench to set the shoes closer to the drum.

With this type of independent construction, an interesting phenomenon takes place. On each of the wheels, the brake shoe that is closer to the front of the car, called the primary shoe, will wear faster than the shoe that is toward the rear, the secondary shoe. This difference results because the front shoe is not rejected by the motion of the revolving drum. The front shoe holds its position. However, the rear shoe is situated so that the turning drum tries to push the shoe back toward the cylinder. To compensate for this action, some brake designs include what is called a step-bore wheel cylinder. This makes the diameter of the cylinder opening at the rear shoe larger than the opening at the front. The effect is a greater hydraulic pressure backing the rear shoe, making the rear shoe work like the forward one.

Another way to make up for the work difference of the two shoes is to use two wheel cylinders; one is located at the top of the backing plate and actuates the front shoe; the other is located at the bottom and actuates the rear shoe. This assembly has a small metal tube, which connects each of the "half" cylinders, and two pullback springs, rather than one. As mentioned, there are many variants to this non-servo-type brake design.

Self-energizers. A servo-type brake is quite different from the non-servo in design and in the way it stops the car. To begin with, both shoes are linked together so that they

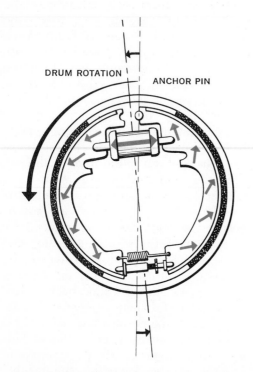

DRUM ROTATION

ANCHOR PIN

Servo Action. To help stop the car, the brake shoes float around with the direction of drum rotation. The effect is that the brakes lock more securely to the drum.

operate as a single unit. Typical of all such brakes is the Bendix single-anchor, single-cylinder, double-piston brake. That's quite a mouthful for one set of brakes. With the exception of disc brakes, this type brake has been used on all American-made cars since 1961. However, there was a time when the Bendix servo brake was known as a "General Motors" brake.

The word "servo" means that the braking effort is multiplied to some extent—without the aid of any outside mechanism such as power brakes. Unlike the shoes of the Lockheed brakes, which act independently of each other, the Bendix brake shoes are linked together to operate as a single unit. They are allowed to "float" on the backing plate. That is, the hardware holding the brakes has enough give to allow a considerable counterclockwise or clockwise twisting action. The upper ends of the shoes are linked to the wheel cylinder and the lower ends to each other by a threaded device which serves to adjust the brakes as they wear. Unlike the Lockheed brakes, there are no cams behind the shoes for adjustments.

Operation is beautifully simple. When the brake pedal is depressed, the shoes expand outward. As the forward shoe contacts the revolving drum, it tends to turn along with it. To some extent it does, pushing the rear shoe against the drum. Now the whole assembly wants to wrap itself around with the drum. With the addition of hydraulic pressure, the brakes grip the drums ever more tightly, multiplying braking effort. During normal operation, the rear shoe tends to wear faster than the forward one, due to the wrapping action. To compensate, the lining on the forward shoe is softer and has high coefficient of friction. The rear shoe is much harder.

Consequently, it has lower friction qualities but wears fast. The result is that both shoes will wear at about the same rate.

Adjusters and Self-adjusters. The adjusting mechanism for the Bendix servo brakes is a very simple device. It consists of a screw and a threaded sleeve. At the head of the screw is a large notched disc called a starwheel. When the brake lining is new, the screw is set deeply into the sleeve. Therefore, the overall length of the adjusting assembly is quite short. The starwheel is lined up with a small window in the backing plate.

As the lining wears, the brake pedal travel increases before the lining makes contact with the drum. At a certain point, operating the car becomes unsafe due to the excessive brake travel. Then a brake adjustment is necessary. The technician raises the car and, with a special tool

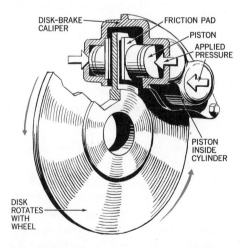

Typical disc brake. The tire and wheel are mounted to the disc. When the brakes are applied, the friction pads are forced against the disc, causing the stop. Many such brakes today use only one pad.

called a brake spoon, reaches into the backing plate window and turns the starwheel so that the assembly adjusting it becomes longer. In this manner the shoes are brought outward, toward the drum. When this is done on all four wheels, the brake pedal travels only a little before brake contact.

A newer innovation is a mechanism called a self-adjuster. It first appeared, believe it or not, on the 1957 Edsel. The self-adjuster consists of a set of small springs, a cable or lever, and a claw for contacting the teeth on the starwheel. The setup is placed on the rear shoe and is designed to operate only when the car is moving in reverse.

When no adjustment is necessary and the car is stopped in reverse, the secondary shoe will contact the lining and pull slightly on the claw. Because the distance to the drum is not great, nothing happens. However, when lining wear makes the shoe travel a greater distance to the drum, the claw will move far enough to turn the starwheel one notch. When the lining gets very thin, the self-adjusters stop working.

DISCS

Rising in popularity is the disc brake. The concept behind this design is totally different from the one behind drum brakes.

To help you imagine how disc brakes work, pick up a piece of paper with your thumb and index finger. With your other hand move the paper around while the fingers grasp the paper. Now, slowly clamp the fingers tighter together and notice the paper's resistance to movement. Finally, clamp the paper very tightly; the paper cannot move.

If we translate the elements of this illustration to parts of the disc brake, your fingers are the caliper. Your fingertips holding the paper contain the friction pads. The paper is the disc. Disc brakes do not have drums. Instead, they have a steel disc which revolves on the same axis as the wheel. When the brake pedal is applied, small friction pads on both sides of the disc clamp the disc and retard the circular motion. These pads are pushed by a hydraulic force, much like the pistons of the wheel cylinders.

One of the great advantages is the fact that the pads contact a very small surface of the disc, leaving the remaining area open to the atmosphere for cooling. Because of this, these stoppers are quite efficient and last a long time.

DRIFTING AWAY

This brings us to one of the bugs in braking—*"brake fade."* You may have had the experience of braking down a long hill, applying the brake pedal all the way down. If you did, you can probably recall that at the bottom of the hill the brake pedal had almost reached the floorboard. This fading of the brake pedal is caused by a number of factors. First, under conditions of extreme heat, such as when you ride the pedal down a hill, the coefficient of friction in the lining changes—to your disadvantage. Second, ultrahigh heat may cause some vaporization of the brake fluid allowing the pedal to drop somewhat as it compresses the vapor. Third, when the drums do not have the opportunity to cool, the heat buildup causes them to expand away from the drum. This makes the pedal sink lower "chasing" the shoes after the drum.

This is one great advantage of the discs. If prolonged braking is necessary, the steel disc will expand. However, the expansion will make the disc bigger, or fatter. Therefore, the expansion will be toward the brake pads, rather than away from them.

Another peculiarity about braking is the effects of weight shift when the car stops. When the car is cruising or stopped, the distribution of the car's weight is fairly even. Of course, due to engine location, the front section of a Ford will weigh more than its rear; the rear part of a Volkswagen will weigh more than its front. However, this is negligible under cruising or standstill modes. But, when the brakes are hit, the car's forward momentum and the retarding force of the brakes cause, in effect, a weight shift. This increases the traction at the front wheels and decreases the traction at the back. The result is that the brakes in the front wheels do more than half the braking. For this reason many of the front-wheel brakes are heavier than those in the rear. On some cars, to compensate, the rear wheel cylinders are slightly smaller than the fronts, allowing the fronts a greater hydraulic boost.

POWER BRAKES

Back in the days when a car weighed under 1,000 pounds and top speed was less than 60 mph, stopping the car was no great problem. Even with the primitive brakes operated by cables and levers, moderate brake pedal force could overcome vehicle momentum. Today we have high-speed engines, faster cruising speeds, heavier cars, and more stop-and-go situations—all factors requiring not only better brake design but more braking effort for

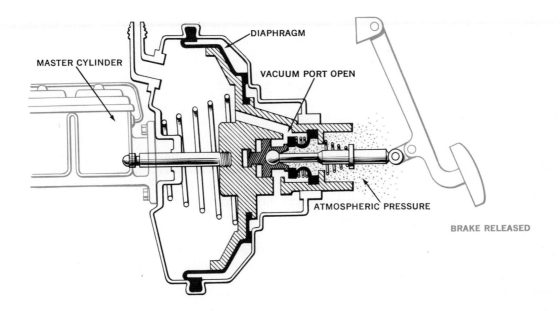

MASTER CYLINDER

DIAPHRAGM

VACUUM PORT OPEN

ATMOSPHERIC PRESSURE

BRAKE RELEASED

Typical power brake booster. Action is from vacuum supplied by the engine. When the brakes are released, the diaphragm is relaxed because the vacuum port is open. Applying the brakes closes the port. Vacuum then pushes the diaphragm against the rod going into the master cylinder.

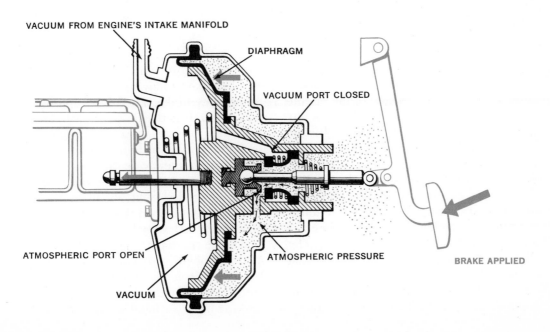

VACUUM FROM ENGINE'S INTAKE MANIFOLD

DIAPHRAGM

VACUUM PORT CLOSED

ATMOSPHERIC PORT OPEN

ATMOSPHERIC PRESSURE

BRAKE APPLIED

VACUUM

safer car operation. Add to this the touch of indolence we are all prone to, and we come up with the need for a power-assisted brake. Here, the effort applied to the brake pedal is multiplied for a greater stopping force.

Where does the power come from? From the atmosphere, from plus and minus air pressures. Assisting in brake operation are atmospheric pressure and the vacuum created by engine operation. As a team, atmospheric pressure and vacuum provide an extra foot pressing down on the brake pedal.

To illustrate, when you suck on a drinking straw, you do not really "pull" soda out of that bottle. Rather, atmospheric air pushes it. In principle, you are lowering the pressure of the air inside the straw. Then the atmospheric pressure (14.7 pounds per square inch) bears down on the surface of the soda and pushes the soda toward the reduced air pressure in the straw.

Keeping this in mind, let's look at two types of brake power units on a car. The first is called the *atmosphere-suspended vacuum brake system.* It uses atmospheric pressure around the engine vacuum that is created by the displacement of the engine pistons. The setup looks like this: On one side there is a metal chamber. Inside, dividing the chamber in two is a stretched skin called a diaphragm. One section of the system has a valve and a tube leading to the engine's intake manifold, where the suction is strongest. Also in this section is a metal rod which leads from the diaphragm to the master-cylinder piston. The other section merely has an opening that leads to the atmosphere.

When the driver hits the brake pedal, a valve is opened which permits atmos-

pheric air in the first chamber to fill the engine vacuum. This is like sucking on the soda straw. As a consequence, the air pressure in the second section pushes the diaphragm toward the area with the lesser air pressure. As the diaphragm moves, so does the push rod; and the hydraulic action commences at the master cylinder. With the diaphragm being pushed from one side, the force of the driver's foot is now, in effect, pushing many times harder on the hydraulic system.

A second type of power unit for passenger cars is called the *vacuum-suspended power brake system.* In this case a vacuum exists on *both* sides of the diaphragm. When the brake pedal is depressed, a valve opens one section to the atmosphere, causing the push-pull situation as in the atmosphere-suspended design. In both cases, when the brakes are released, a large return spring puts the diaphragm back into neutral position.

HAND BRAKES

The final subsystem in the brakes is the hand brake, today often misnamed an emergency brake. The term "emergency" was created in the days when hydraulics was new on cars and the mechanically operated brake was touted as a brake to be used in emergency in the event the hydraulic system failed. In these days of high-powered cars, it would be a serious error to rely fully on the hand brake in an emergency. At very low speeds the hand brake can, perhaps, cause a safe stop. But at high speeds, put your faith in the foot brakes or in a Greater Power. So, to be correct, you should use the correct names: parking brake or hand brake.

The earliest designs for hand brakes had a friction band poised around the drive shaft. When the lever was pulled, a cable tightened the band and locked the shaft. In this situation, the car could not move forward or back. Chrysler cars used this external contracting band on their cars until 1955. Then they switched to internal expanding shoes, again at the drive shaft. When Chrysler cars went from the Lockheed to the Bendix servo in the 1960s, they also switched hand brake design to that used by General Motors since the late 1920s. Drive shaft hand brakes are used today on many trucks.

Presently the universal style for the parking brake uses a pair of cables that lock the rear wheels by mechanically applying the brake shoes. Starting at the top, there is a control lever which is actuated by the driver's left foot. Attached to the lever is a cable which goes through the firewall and loops around under the car to about midway between the front and rear wheels. The cable goes to a pivot arm which is anchored at the chassis. Secured to the arm is a U-shaped bracket which has cables running from each leg of the U to the rear wheels.

When the pedal is depressed, it pulls the control cable toward the front of the car. As the cable moves, it pulls the pivoted arm, in turn, the U-shaped bracket is moved forward, pulling on both cables. Inside the drums, the cables are attached to the brake shoes in such a way that the shoes expand against the drums on forward movement of cables.

The purpose of the pivot bracket under the center of the car is to assure an even pull on both cables whenever the brake pedal is applied.

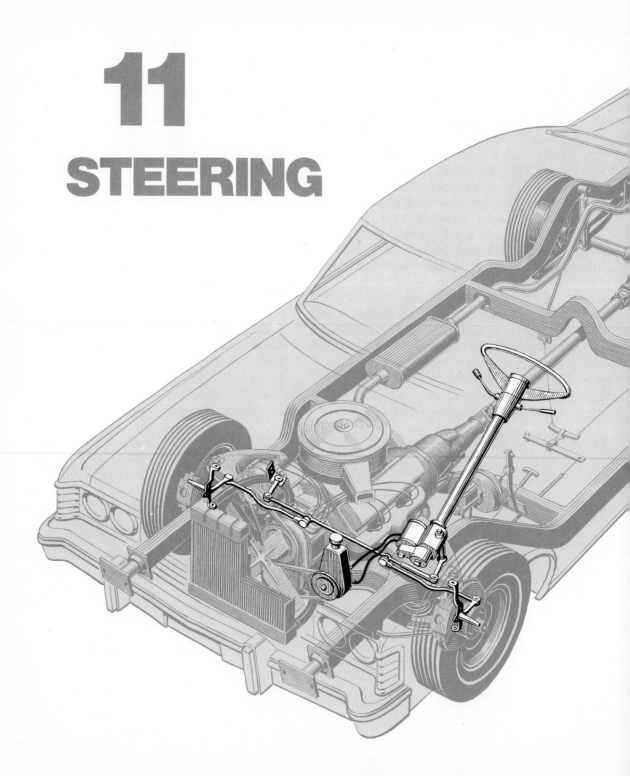

11
STEERING

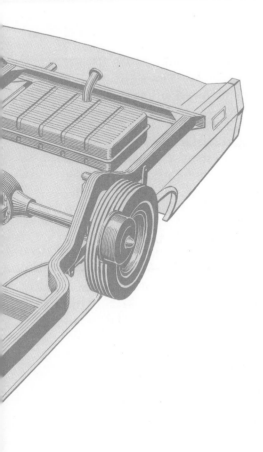

If the most important invention was the wheel, then the second-most important development was steering. At first thought, you might nominate braking as more important. But try driving a car for some distance without using the brake, and then drive the same route without touching the steering wheel. Steering will win.

On the most primitive of vehicles, a platform moved over log rollers. Steering was done by resetting the angle of the logs in the direction of the turn and giving the platform a healthy shove to the side.

Later came the rickshaw-like cart. But this system had its problems in that the load had to be placed directly over the single axle if the rails were to be light enough for steering. Despite these drawbacks the two-wheeled trailer or wagon is still in use today.

At about the tenth century came the system that endured until the development of steering for automobiles in 1890.

The idea was to eliminate the fixed front axle and replace it with one that would swing left and right. This new axle employed an iron bar pivot point in the center, called a *king pin.* Children who build their own push-scooters made from baby carriage parts and wooden boxes are quite familiar with this system.

With this king pin arrangement, the entire axle can swing, and the front wheels lead the vehicle around a turn. But the turning axle was only briefly used in the automobile because it had a basic flaw. The front wheels hitting a bump or a stone, impeded the forward motion of the axle. With the opposite wheel free to turn, the entire axle would swing and the vehicle would change direction. Given the unpaved roads of those days, the driver had to correct the steering constantly.

Only the very early cars employed the king-pin steering system. In this case, the driver aimed the car with the help of a tiller, much like those found in sailboats. The tiller arm entered the driving compartment while the opposite end connected to the axle for simple pivoting.

A breakthrough in steering occurred in 1901, when the Electric Vehicle Company switched to a front axle designed by Sterling Elliot that eliminated the central king pin. Instead, each front wheel pivoted on an independent hinge. This allowed the wheel to swing to the left and right like a door with the pivot point being the steel pin running through each hinge. The importance of this development for the steering was that the pivot points were moved away from the center, toward the outside, close to the wheel. This eliminated the leverage imposed on the front axle when one wheel was impeded. Thus, steering became better stabilized.

UNITING THE WHEELS

With the Elliot front axle, both front wheels are independent and can swivel in either direction. Obviously, the driver can't control the car unless both wheels point the same way. The answer is to unite the wheels by installing a solid bar that ties the wheels together. This bar is called a *tie rod.* Naturally, the tie rod cannot be attached to the wheel itself, since the wheel must rotate. Therefore, the rod is attached to the non-rotating part of the front wheel assembly, the backing plate. This is the same plate which is used as the base for the brake shoes.

Working from one side to the other, the lineup of components under the car consists of the following: the spindle and the backing plate, the tire, wheel and drum — mounted on the spindle. Bolted to the backing plate is a *steering arm.* The tie rod is attached to this steering arm. The tie rod runs to the opposite front wheel where a matching set of components exists. With this construction, moving the tie rod to the left side of the car will push the left steering arm and pull the right steering arm to angle the wheels for a right turn.

Over the years there has been very little evolution in steering gear linkage. While it is true that many different designs have been used, no one configuration has been considered superior to any other. In almost all cases, the shape of the linkage depends on space requirements.

In the steering system shown here, rods and arms are employed in a parallelogram arrangement. In this four-sided figure, opposite sides are of equal length. With ball joints, this figure can swing from a rectangle to nearly flat angles — opposite sides always remaining parallel.

Within the parallelogram arrangement,

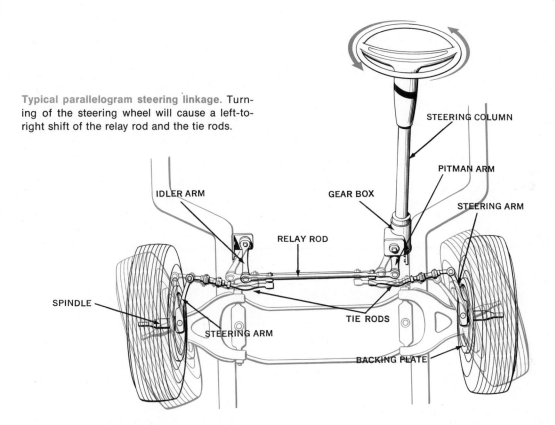

Typical parallelogram steering linkage. Turning of the steering wheel will cause a left-to-right shift of the relay rod and the tie rods.

STEERING COLUMN

PITMAN ARM

STEERING ARM

GEAR BOX

IDLER ARM

RELAY ROD

SPINDLE

TIE RODS

STEERING ARM

BACKING PLATE

from the backing plate to the center, each wheel has a short tie rod, which is just a simple bar. Both ends of each rod are fitted with ball and socket joints. To visualize the joint, make a fist with your left hand and cover the fist with the palm and fingers of your right hand. Given the proper dimensions and quality of steel, such a joint is quite strong and flexible. Here these ball joints are called *tie-rod ends*. They cut friction and increase mobility. In addition to the sophisticated ends, each tie rod's length is adjustable by means of threaded holes in the ends of the rod. One side the tie-rod end is screwed in with a conventional, right-hand thread. The other side is screwed in with a left-hand thread, sometimes called a reverse thread. With these opposing threads, it is possible to shorten or increase the overall length of the rod by turning it, as you would a turnbuckle. This allows adjustment to correct front wheel alignment. Clamps are then placed around the threaded joints of the rod to hold the assembly in position.

The inner ends of both rods are attached to a *relay rod* that runs parallel and slightly to the rear of them. This rod relays the movement of the steering gear to the tie rods. Both ends of the relay rod are anchored. On the left side of the car (right side in illustration), the rod is attached to the *pitman arm,* which comes directly from the steering gear. On the other side of the car, the relay rod is attached to the *idler arm;* its only function is to support the relay rod. Within the parallelogram, the idler arm assumes the same angle as the pitman arm, regardless of the position of the front wheels.

In operation, when the wheels are turned to an extreme left or right position, the entire assembly of rods shifts left or right. However, the assembly remains at a right angle to the length of the car. Only the pitman arm and the idler arm change their angles in relation to the rest of the car. Parallelogram steering is certainly not the only kind, but it is the most popular. One of the reasons for its wide use is its ability to absorb road shock. Under driving conditions, the linkage can be jolted up and down without upsetting front-end alignment.

ROTARY TO LATERAL MOVEMENT

Now that we have the connections for making the wheels respond in unison, we need a means of supplying energy to the linkage. Nowadays, steering energy comes in two packages—muscle power and hydraulic power. In some cases manual steering and power steering are similar; in others they are quite different. But both convert the rotary movement of the steering wheel into a lateral movement of the tie rods.

Manual Steering. Before the use of the Elliot front axle, the steering system didn't give the driver a mechanical advantage in steering the car. Linkage from the tiller to the tie rod was quite direct. By 1901 all cars had switched to the steering wheel and gear system which changed rotary to lateral motion.

The *steering wheel* is attached to a long shaft by means of a set of matching splines and is secured to the shaft with a nut. The shaft is usually concealed within a tube called the *steering column* and travels through the engine firewall where it enters a steel gear box bolted to the left chassis member in the engine compartment. The steering wheel has been on the left side in U.S. cars since the 1908 Knight.

Inside the box, two gears provide the driver with a mechanical advantage and change the direction of torque. The amount of gear reduction must be very high in order to overcome the heavy weight borne by the front section of the car as well as overcome the friction within the steering mechanism and the friction between the front tires and the ground. All this resistance must be overcome with a 14-inch steering wheel which, when turned, acts as a 7-inch lever. The secret is the use of ratios from 15:1 all the way to 24:1. The driver must turn the steering wheel four to six complete revolutions to carry the front wheels from one extreme position to the other.

Manual Styles. Not all cars use the same type of steering gears. Engineers are concerned both with giving the proper gear reduction and providing gears that will wear. In this regard they have done a creditable job. Given the proper adjustment and lubrication, steering gear parts usually last the life of the car.

All steering gear boxes have within them a driving gear and a driven gear. The driven gear is not a gear in the usual sense. It is a section of gear which is turned by the driving gear for less than a quarter turn. The driving gear is always part of the steering shaft. The most popular styles in use are as follows:

Worm and Sector. This is the simplest of all steering gears. The worm gear is so called because its wide spiral thread resembles a coiled worm. The sector is a five-tooth "slice of pie" section of a round gear. The pieces mesh at right angles to each other. Integral with the sector gear is the sector shaft which protrudes from the

bottom of the steering box and is linked with the pitman arm. When the driver turns the steering wheel, the shaft and the worm gear turn the same amount since the parts are pressed together. As a result the sector gear and shaft are turned about $\frac{1}{15}$ or $\frac{1}{20}$ of a circle, depending on gear ratios. As small as this amount may seem, the movement is reflected in the steering linkage and the front wheels.

Worm and Roller. This is a similar design to the worm and sector. The difference is that the driven gear does not have teeth. Instead it is a small wheel with worm-like threads cut into it. But the steering action is the same.

Recirculating Ball. In recent years this

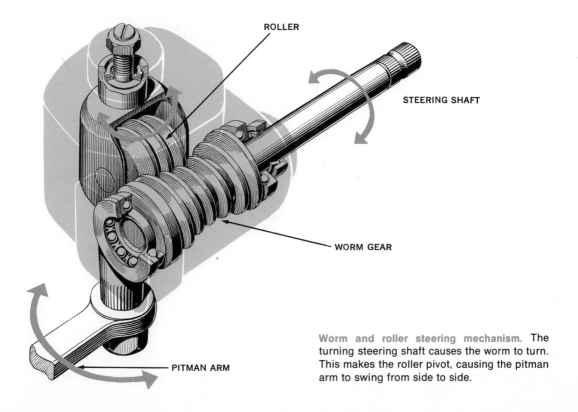

ROLLER

STEERING SHAFT

WORM GEAR

PITMAN ARM

Worm and roller steering mechanism. The turning steering shaft causes the worm to turn. This makes the roller pivot, causing the pitman arm to swing from side to side.

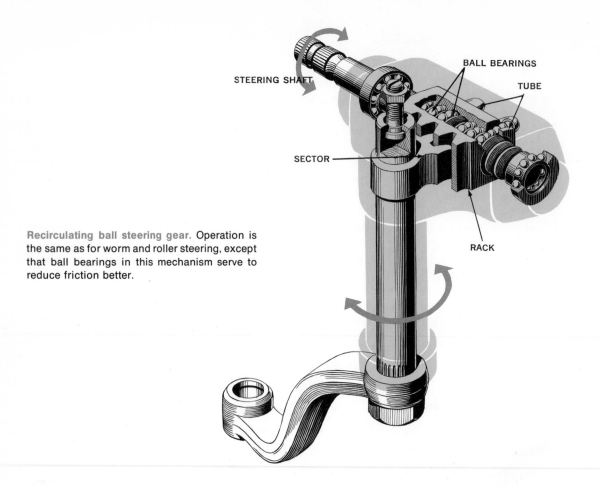

STEERING SHAFT

BALL BEARINGS

TUBE

SECTOR

RACK

Recirculating ball steering gear. Operation is the same as for worm and roller steering, except that ball bearings in this mechanism serve to reduce friction better.

type of gearing has gained popularity and is considered very efficient. Instead of a worm gear, the driven unit is a straight rectangular piece with teeth cut on one edge. This is called a rack. Meshed in the rack's teeth is a sector. The rack travels up and down the steering shaft when the steering wheel and shaft turn. The assembly is very much like a big bolt and nut with the nut riding up and down the threads as the bolt is turned. To reduce the friction, the bolt and nut threads serve as channels for steel ball bearings. Since rolling friction is less than sliding friction, the ball bearings considerably reduce the effort required to turn the shaft. To keep

these bearings from piling up, a small tube connects both ends of the rack. Then as the shaft turns, the ball bearings flow through the thread channels, drop into the tube, and re-enter at the opposite end to start all over again.

Rack and Pinion. This style is found mostly on foreign cars. It consists of a pinion gear inside a steering box. Running through the box along the width of the car is a straight rack with teeth. The rack is connected to the tie rods. Turning the steering gear makes the pinion turn and causes the rack to shift left or right.

Aside from the huge gear ratios, the

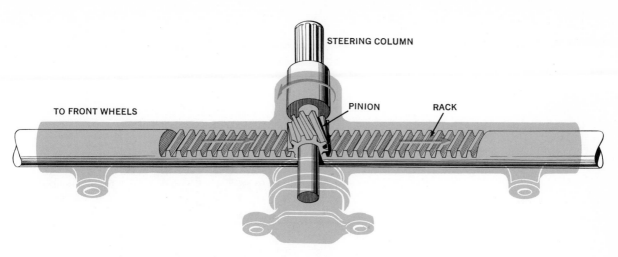

Rack and pinion steering. The turning of the shaft and pinion gear will make the rack shift from side to side. This type is found mostly on imported cars.

steering gear box mechanism is also equipped with a variety of bearings, bushings and filled with a thick oil for the reduction of friction. In addition the tie rod ends are packed with grease for further ease of movement.

POWER STEERING

Almost any steering system that reduces effort is called *power steering*. Though its popularity on passenger cars has steadily increased since the 1950s, power steering goes much further back in automotive history, particularly on commercial vehicles. In the development of power steering, a number of energy sources were tried, including compressed air, electricity and oil pressure. Today, only oil pressure is used.

Power-steering design falls into two main types—*integral* and *linkage*. In the integral type, the power operating assembly is part of the steering gear box. In the linkage type, the power operating assembly is part of the steering linkage. Though both types employ the hydraulic

power differently, they have basic parts in common. These are the pump, the reservoir hoses, the control valves, the power cylinder and the pressure relief valve.

Pump. The pump keeps the fluid in the power steering system under a constant pressure by using the power supplied by the engine. In most cases, the pump is mounted at the side of the engine such that a simple belt attached to the engine fan pulley can drive it. There was a time when the pump was mounted directly behind the generator and driven by the generator shaft. All power steering pumps are classified as *positive displacement pumps*. This simply means that a fixed volume of fluid is pumped within a certain time span, regardless of engine speed, and assures that the driver gets a full power assist whether the engine is idling or at a high rpm. Of the designs used to push fluid through the system, the most popular today is the vane type which is, essentially, a small paddle wheel. The center of the wheel is called a rotor and is connected to a shaft which is driven by the fan pulley. Attached to the rotor are flat vanes. As the

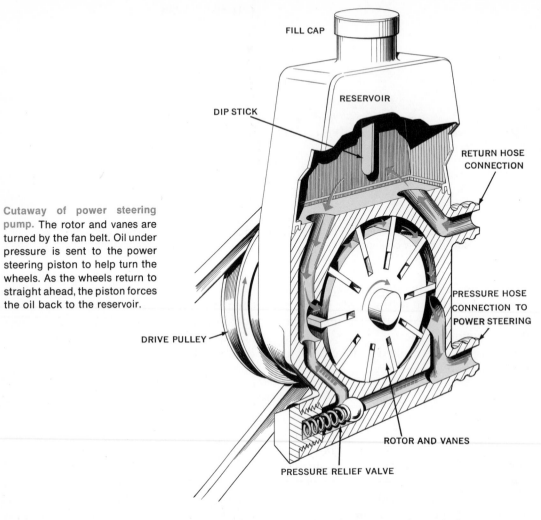

FILL CAP

RESERVOIR

DIP STICK

RETURN HOSE
CONNECTION

Cutaway of power steering pump. The rotor and vanes are turned by the fan belt. Oil under pressure is sent to the power steering piston to help turn the wheels. As the wheels return to straight ahead, the piston forces the oil back to the reservoir.

PRESSURE HOSE
CONNECTION TO
POWER STEERING

DRIVE PULLEY

ROTOR AND VANES

PRESSURE RELIEF VALVE

rotor turns it sucks in fluid through an inlet port, traps it and whips it around to the opposite side of the chamber where the oil is forced through the outlet port.

Reservoir. The small steel tank immediately over the pump holds an ample supply of automatic transmission fluid. A passageway from the reservoir to the pumping chamber feeds the rotor. The cover of the reservoir is either a simple screw-type or it fastens with a spring clamp. All fluid is added to the system through the reservoir.

Hoses. There are two main hoses in the power steering system. The first is the pressure hose which carries high pressure oil from the pump to the power cylinder; here pressures often go as high as 1500 psi. A second hose returns oil to the reservoir; pressures are considerably less in the second hose.

Control Valve. The function of the control valve is to direct the flow of fluid from the pump to the proper chamber in the power cylinder. Since the system operates under three basic conditions – straight ahead, left turn and right turn – each condition requires that the fluid travel a different route. The most commonly used valve for most systems is called a *spool valve*. In appearance it looks like three small sewing thread spools mounted on a pencil and held in place. The valve is situated so that it can slide forward and back, covering or uncovering ports that allow proper flow.

Power Cylinder. The function of the power cylinder is to receive the hydraulic pressure and apply it mechanically. Basically the construction consists of a piston within a cylinder. For a left turn, pressure will enter one end of the cylinder and force the piston in one direction; for a right turn the fluid will enter the other side of the cylinder and force the piston the other way. When the steering wheel is in the straight-ahead position, pressures on both sides of the piston are equal.

Pressure Relief Valve. Because the pump is a positive displacement type and keeps the system pressurized when the engine is operating, a severe buildup of pressure can occur. The pressure relief valve "blows" this pressure before any damage occurs to the system. In construction, the valve is a small metal cylinder with a calibrated spring and a steel ball inside. When pressure in the system drops below a certain limit, the spring-driven steel ball covers this escape route. When the hydraulic pressure becomes greater than spring pressure, it forces the ball off its seat and holds the pressure-relief route open. As soon as spring pressure gets greater than hydraulic pressure, the spring

forces the ball onto its seat, and the valve closes.

Thus these six components, existing on all types of power steering units work together to give the driver the needed boost for making a turn. Now, let's look at the two basic power steering designs.

Integral-type Power Steering. There are many integral-type power steering designs used on cars today. Each of them has distinguishing features. But there are enough similarities among the different designs to allow a general description of the integral type.

It is comforting to know that any car with power steering can be safely guided should any part of the power system fail. This is possible because the core of the power system contains all the essential elements of a mechanical steering system – in most cases, the recirculating-ball type. In the power system, just as in the mechanical system, are a worm gear at the bottom of the steering shaft and a recirculating ball rack, its teeth meshed with a sector shaft.

To make the assembly work with a power booster, some modifications are made. But these changes do not alter the basic mechanical steering structure. Rather than being in a simple case at the bottom of the steering shaft, the gear assembly is contained in a large oil-filled chamber. Enveloping the ball rack and sector is the *power piston,* sometimes called the *rack piston.* Just above the chamber (on the right in the three illustrations) are the parts which determine which way the pressurized fluid flows. These parts include the spool control valve and its actuator plus the fluid inlet and outlet.

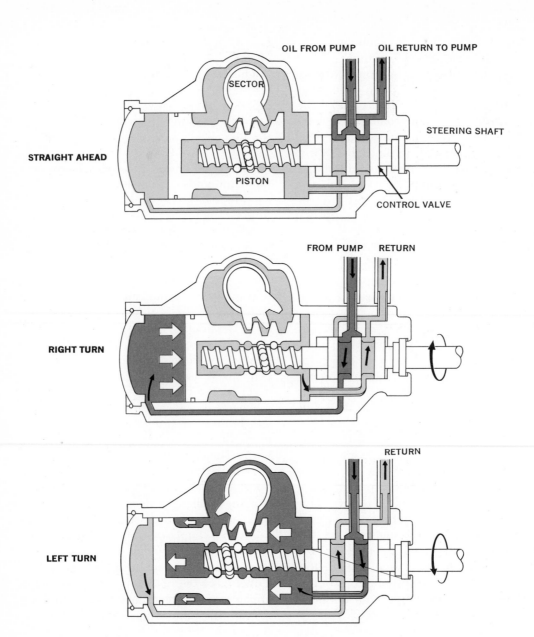

STRAIGHT AHEAD

OIL FROM PUMP   OIL RETURN TO PUMP

SECTOR

STEERING SHAFT

PISTON

CONTROL VALVE

RIGHT TURN

FROM PUMP   RETURN

LEFT TURN

RETURN

Operation of one type of power steering. Turning the steering shaft will reposition the control valve and allow pressurized oil to move the steering gear.

214

When the steering wheel is in straight-ahead position, the spool valve is said to be in neutral. Oil coming down from the pump is directed equally to both sides of the power piston. Oil is also forced to make a U turn in the area of the spool valve and return to the reservoir. Thus no pressure affects any of the mechanical parts in the system. When the driver pulls up to a parallel parking space, his first action is to turn the steering wheel all the way to the right and back the car into the parking space. As the wheel is turned, the power piston responds to the movement of the worm shaft. This small piston movement sets off the spool valve actuator which shifts the valve. The bypass passages close

as the valve shifts and new routes open. Now the pressurized oil flow is directed to the chamber holding the power piston face. Here the oil pushes on the face, helping with the right-turn movement of the steering gear and linkage.

After the car is backed in at an angle from the curb, the driver must turn the steering wheel to the left. Here the sensors and the actuator shift the spool valve. Oil pressure then increases at the base of the piston and aids the gear and linkage in making the left-hand turn. During turns in both directions, piston movement pushes on the rack, which turns the sector. And this, in turn, shifts the linkage, mechanically.

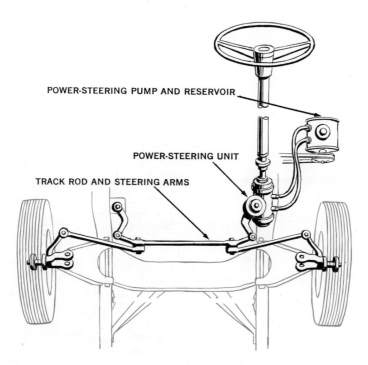

POWER-STEERING PUMP AND RESERVOIR

POWER-STEERING UNIT

TRACK ROD AND STEERING ARMS

Coaxial power steering. The power assist takes place in the steering unit at the bottom of the steering shaft.

Linkage-type Power Steering. A much simpler steering booster system is found in the popular linkage-type design. Physically, the setup uses the conventional manual gearbox. The steering shaft and gear mechanically turn the sector gear and shaft, causing the pitman arm to pivot. But here the arm is not attached directly to the steering linkage; it is attached to a control valve.

The valve is located in the circuit between the pump and the power cylinder. In effect, the valve tells the power cylinder and piston what to do. One end of the cylinder is anchored to the car frame or the crossmember; the piston moves in and out of the cylinder and

pushes or pulls the steering linkage. It is important to recognize that the piston movement is actually left and right in relation to the car. On some cars the piston is secured to the frame and the cylinder is attached to the linkage. However, the effects are the same.

The power cylinder resembles a large shock absorber with two hoses connected to it. Both lines lead from the control valve. One hose provides presure for a right turn by carrying the fluid to one side of the piston; the other hose provides left-turn pressure by carrying the fluid to the other side of the piston. When fluid under pressure is coursing through one hose making the piston move, the displaced

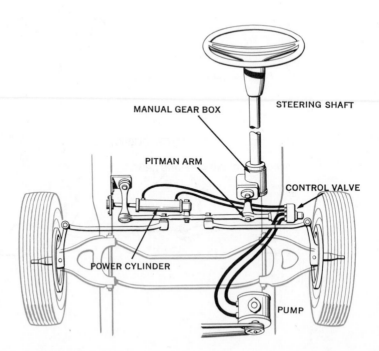

MANUAL GEAR BOX

STEERING SHAFT

PITMAN ARM

CONTROL VALVE

POWER CYLINDER

PUMP

Linkage-type power steering. Mechanical linkage is almost the same as for cars without power steering. The assist is afforded by pressurized oil entering the power cylinder when the steering shaft is turned.

fluid on the other side of the piston will flow through the opposite hose back to the control valve and then to the pump reservoir.

Basic internal operation here is similar to that in the integral type. When the steering wheel is in straight-ahead position, the pitman arm places the spool valve in neutral position. Fluid from the pump flows through the pressure line, into the control valve and back to the reservoir via the return line. When the driver turns the steering wheel, the gears in the steering box move and cause the pitman arm to shift. This shifts the spool inside the control valve and opens a passageway for the pressurized fluid to enter the right side of the cylinder and push the piston to the car's left. Since the piston is connected to the steering rods, they also shift to the car's left to produce a right turn.

A left turn of the steering wheel sets off another chain of events in the opposite direction. The shifting spool permits the fluid to enter the left side of the cylinder, pushing the piston to the right, pulling the linkage to the right—producing a left turn.

Within this system is an interesting control device. When steering motion stops, whether the front wheels are in straight-ahead or a turned position, power assist stops. Boosting will resume only when the steering wheel is turned. This is deter-mined by a spring within the control valve. As soon as the spring senses that there is no turning motion of the wheel, it moves to center the spool, putting it into a neutral position. Thus there is no steering push unless needed.

SAFETY FEATURES

Since 1969 a safety steering column has been required on all cars. The column is designed to give, or telescope when subject to severe impact. This feature minimizes the danger of the steering column's piercing the driver in the event of an auto mishap.

The modern steering column and shaft that is strong enough to withstand the rigors of use, while conforming to safety requirements, is indeed a remarkable piece of engineering. In one popular design, the steering column is made of steel strands woven into a lacework. The steering shaft is two-piece. The lower section is hollow and has a slightly larger diameter than the solid upper section. Both sections are held in place with a metal pin which is designed to shear at a set impact level. Thus, in the event of a crash, the upper section of the shaft will drop into the lower one as the lacework of the column folds.

12
AIRCONDITIONING

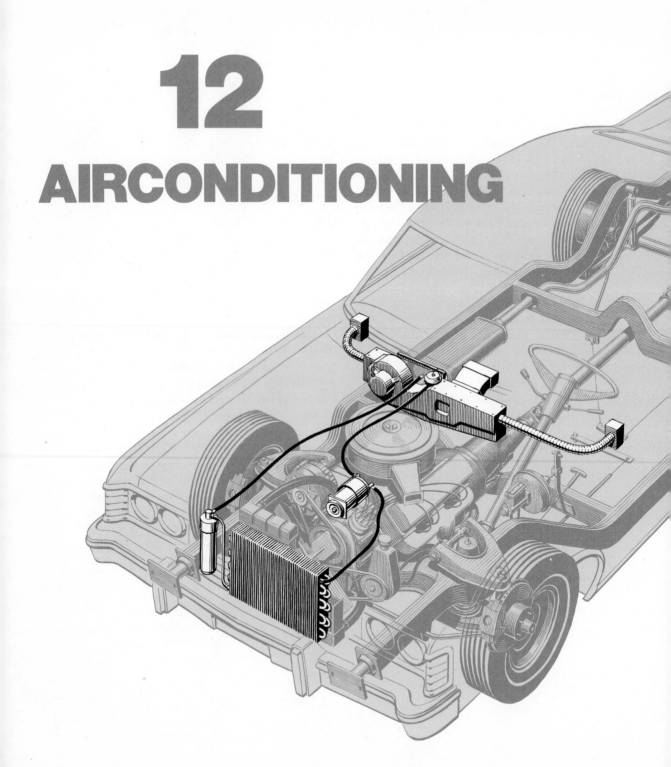

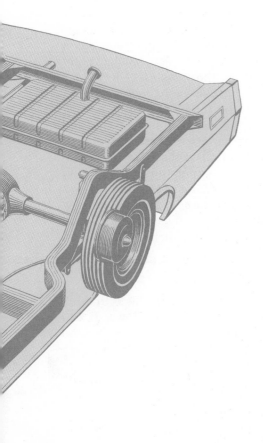

Airconditioning is probably the most pleasant innovation for the car since the cushioned seat.

Contrary to popular belief, an airconditioner does not *cool* the passenger compartment. Cooling is really the *effect* of airconditioning. The process, what the airconditioner actually does, is to *remove heat*. (For a review of some of the basic principles of heat removal, please turn to the beginning of Chapter 5, "Cooling System.")

"Heat" is everything. "Cool" is only an auxiliary word which indicates that heat has been reduced to a low level.

What Heat Is. We feel heat when it is abundant (hot). We sense it when it is scarce (cold). It has neither weight nor substance, yet all matter on this planet contains heat. Heat is energy, the first cousin to light, electricity, sound and magnetism. Heat is the energy generated by the friction of molecules racing around and colliding within all matter. How much heat is generated depends on how agitated the mole-

219

cules are at a given moment. In many cases we can control this.

Putting a flame under a pan of water will speed up the molecules to such an extent that they will fly off into space. That's boiling. Placing the pan in a freezer withdraws heat, and the molecules huddle together and slow down to such an extent that they form a lattice-like structure chemists call crystal—or ice.

But don't be fooled. Ice still contains some heat, because its molecules continue to move. Scientists have theorized that activity will cease and all heat will be absent only at minus 460 degrees Fahrenheit. This temperature is known as Absolute Zero and, so far, has not been reached.

It is vital that we regard heat quantity and heat intensity as separate factors. Heat intensity describes how hot a substance is. It does not say how much heat this substance has. A tea cup full of boiling water has a greater heat intensity than a bath tub full of 80-degree water; the tea is hotter. However, the bath water has more heat. The thermometer measures only heat *intensity*. Measurement of heat *quantity* is somewhat less familiar to most people. The BTU (British Thermal Unit) is often used to rate the capacity of the airconditioner. Technically, a BTU is the *amount* of heat (not intensity) required to raise one degree the temperature of a pound of water at 39.2 degrees Fahrenheit. Keep in mind that the BTU is a unit of heat. The unit can be of great intensity (very hot) and applied for a short duration, or it can be less hot and applied longer.

Moving Heat. Like other forms of energy, heat can be moved or transferred from one place to another. However, heat is rather particular about the direction it will move. It flows down the temperature scale— never up. Heat flows only from a higher temperature to a lower one, from a hot object to a cooler one. This law has nothing to do with the *amount* of heat in a body—only with *intensity,* technically referred to as the temperature differential.

Suppose you heat an iron cherry red and quench it in a tub of water. Heat will flow from the iron to the water very rapidly, until the temperature equalizes. If you then heated the iron until it was merely hot, the same direction of flow would take place, but at a slower rate. *The greater the heat differential between two bodies, the faster the heat will flow from hot to cold.* This principle is essential to the airconditioning process.

A good way to remember this is to think of a slope on which water flows. It can only go in one direction. The steeper the slope, the faster the water will flow.

Kinds of Heat Transfer. This "downhill" ride heat takes can occur in three ways. These modes of transfer can be demonstrated by use of a pan of water several inches above a flame.

Radiation. Though the flame is placed several inches below the pan, not in direct contact with it, heat is transferred by waves through air. This "broadcasting" is very much like radio or water waves which fan out from a source.

Conduction. As heat waves hit the metal pan, the molecules of the metal at the bottom of the vessel absorb some of the heat and pass it to the molecules further in, like a bucket brigade. In time the heat affects all the molecules in the pan and is conducted to the molecules of water.

Convection. The water in the bottom of

the pan will be heated first since it is closer to the source of heat. As the water gets warmer, it will rise. Cold water will rush in; it too gets warm and rises. Soon there is a circulation. Water heated at the bottom will always rise, making room for cooler water. This circulation flow generates what are known as convection currents.

Hot to Cool. We are not quite ready to get into the function of the many components in the airconditioning system unless we see how the nature of heat gives us cooling comfort. Let us take all the aspects of heat—intensity, quantity measurement, and movement—and see what happens when we carry it a step closer to the airconditioning process.

All matter, everything we contact, is in one of three states—solid, liquid or gas. But it is heat which determines the state in which matter exists. A pan of water placed in an environment between 32 and 212 degrees will surrender or absorb very little heat. Thus it will remain a liquid. When placed in a freezer it will give up its heat and convert to a solid. Placed over a flame the liquid water will absorb heat until it boils to a vapor.

Every change of state produces a substantial exchange of heat. As the substance goes up the scale from a solid to a liquid or from a liquid to a gas, it absorbs heat. As the substance goes down the scale from a gas, to a liquid, to a solid, it surrenders heat. These axioms are the essence of the refrigeration process, which is what airconditioning is all about.

People living in the primitive cultures of the Pacific have utilized this heat-exchange concept since ancient times for cooling their drinking water. This in spite of the fact that they didn't see ice until modern times. These people placed fresh water in porous jars. The small amounts of moisture seeping through the crockery evaporated. In changing state from liquid to vapor, the water supply lost heat. Warm water minus heat equals cool water.

Where does the lost heat go? Technically the phenomenon is called: *Latent (hidden) Heat of Fusion* or *Latent Heat of Vaporization.* Both are amazing occurrences and take place at opposite ends of the temperature scale.

The solid part of a melting block of ice always remains at 32 degrees. Further, a temperature check of the melt water shows it to be, perhaps, 33 degrees. However, after the ice is gone, the temperature of the water starts to climb.

Let's say this same block of ice had been in a picnic food cooler. Heat left the food. Yet with all this heat liberated, the ice remained at 32 degrees. And the temperature of the ice melt hardly rose until all ice melted. What became of the heat given up by the food? The lost heat is written off as *latent* heat of fusion and cannot be recorded on a thermometer. This latent heat represents the energy that was used to convert the ice to a liquid.

On the other end of the temperature scale, a similar "mystery" occurs. If you set a kettle of water over a 500-degree flame and insert a thermometer into the liquid, the temperature gradually rises. At 212 degrees the water will boil. Regardless of how much hotter you make the flame, regardless how long you allow the kettle to boil, the temperature of the water will not rise over 212 degrees. Surely, the heat pumped into the water from the flame must go someplace. It does. This hidden heat is called *latent heat of vaporization.*

Combining these two concepts, we can declare the following: *Due to the latent heat of fusion, frozen substance can continue to soak up heat without getting warmer. Due to the latent heat of vaporization, a boiling substance can soak up large amounts of heat without getting hotter.*

Drawing the Line. When you boiled water last time, did you stop to think that at the precise moment before the water bubbled and vaporized, the temperature of the water was 212 degrees? Yet, in one moment it was liquid and in the next it became a vapor. Similarly, as the temperature of the water lowers for freezing, the water is 32 degrees just before it becomes a solid. In other words, though there is a critical moment when the substance changes state, the temperatures before and after the change, are the same. Of importance here is the critical moment of change, rather than the temperatures on either side of the moment.

Think of this tiny period of time, the moment when the change of state occurs, as a huge wall on wheels. The wall is located on a giant football field with each yardline marked off in degrees of temperature. On one side of the wall there is liquid; on the other, vapor. Under atmospheric conditions at sea level, the "boiling" wall will be located on the 212 yardline. However, if we enclosed the entire stadium and heated the water so as to create a pressure, the wall will have to be shifted up the field. That is, for every pound of pressure created, the point at which the water will boil will be advanced three degrees.

Suppose we allow a buildup of a pressure of five pounds per square inch over normal atmosphere. This means that the water will not start boiling until it reaches 212 plus (5 × 3) or 227 degrees. If this pressure was maintained, then a new norm is established. Water will boil at 227 degrees and the vapor under this pressure will condense at 227 degrees.

Pressure has another ability. It can raise temperatures without the use of additional heat. That is, if any substance is subjected to pressure, the heat in that substance is concentrated and squeezed so the heat intensity is highly localized. You will soon see that this concept is absolutely essential to the airconditioning process.

This gives us three additional airconditioning principles to remember: (1) *The greater the pressure exerted on a fluid, the higher the boiling point.* (2) *All fluids will condense at the same temperature at which they will boil.* (3) *Pressure produces heat.*

So far, the only substance mentioned in discussing the peculiarities of heat, freezing and boiling was the familiar substance, water. Suppose we follow through and use water in the airconditioning system of the car to remove heat.

Keep in mind that to remove large amounts of heat you must have a temperature differential which will cause a substantial hot-to-cold flow. And you will need a boiling substance that will absorb heat by the phenomenon of latent heat of vaporization. If boiling water were pumped through the system, heat would then flow *into* the passenger compartment, rather than from it. Since the boiling water is hotter than the temperature inside the car, the temperature differential will work, but not in your favor, unless you wanted to convert the car into a rolling sauna.

What about using cold water? It would take solid ice melting to water, employing the principle of latent heat of fusion, to draw necessary amounts from the passenger compartment. Even so, how would the water be cooled again after it absorbed heat?

The basic solution is to use a substance which will boil readily so large amounts of heat are absorbed. This substance must also return to its original liquid state readily so that it can surrender this heat and be reused again. To accomplish all of these tasks, the substance must be quite volatile. That is, it must boil at a temperature much lower than that of the air in the passenger compartment.

Rubbing alcohol is a good example of a liquid with high volatility used for cooling. When placed as a liquid on a warm body, the alcohol evaporates very quickly, drawing the heat from the body and providing a cool sensation. Water will provide the same effect, but at a much slower rate. On the other hand, ether will provide the fastest cooling because it is very volatile.

In the history of modern refrigeration, various substances of high volatility were used. Among them was sulphur dioxide and ammonia. But these had basic drawbacks. Namely, they were poisonous. Modern airconditioning systems use a substance called Refrigerant-12. There are many trade names for this product such as Genetron-12, Isotron-12 or Prestone-12. However, the most widely-known name is Freon-12, a product of DuPont. So established is this product that its name is generally substituted for the word "refrigerant." Therefore, when the term Freon is used here, it is interchangeable with the terms refrigerant or R-12. Freon is colorless, odorless, nontoxic, nonflammable and chemically stable. It is such a benign substance that it is also used as a propellant in spray containers.

The most important feature of Freon is that it boils at 22 *degrees below zero* under normal atmospheric pressure. At room temperature, it boils so rapidly that it quickly absorbs vast amounts of heat. This is the key to success of the airconditioning process. The refrigerant draws heat from the passenger compartment by boiling to a vapor. The heat within the vapor is then dumped into the outside air, thus condensing the refrigerant to a liquid, enabling it to repeat the process. Freon is a refrigerant, but so is ice for it too absorbs heat. Freon can be recycled. Ice is a one-shot deal.

Review of Underlying Principles. We are just about ready to trace the cooling cycle. Here is a review of the principles and physical laws underlying airconditioning:

"Hot" and "cold" are relative terms. An object at a higher temperature than its surroundings can be called hot. An object at a lower temperature than its surroundings can be called cold.

Heat will flow only from a hotter object to a colder one—never the other way.

Heat can be transferred. The three forms of movement are radiation, conduction and convection.

There are two measurements for heat. Heat intensity is measured in degrees of temperature. Heat quantity is measured in BTUs.

Temperature determines state. Whether matter is a solid, liquid or a gas at any given moment depends on its heat intensity.

Large amounts of heat are absorbed or released by a change of state.

Increasing the pressure of a boiling substance raises its boiling point. Every pound of pressure increase raises the boiling point three degrees.

Pressure applied to a substance raises its temperature. This is how to raise temperatures without adding heat.

THE AIRCONDITIONING PROCESS

Airconditioning is refrigeration with a blast. However, there is a distinct difference between an airconditioner and a refrigerator. To fully appreciate this, it is necessary to ask this question: Why is it impossible to cool off a room by leaving the refrigerator door open? Don't be tempted to answer that the unit in the refrigerator is no match for an entire room. The same question would be valid if the refrigerator were the size of a box car. The answer is that trying to cool a room with a refrigerator is like walking up a down escalator. The very same heat absorbed by the freezing unit in the refrigerator is dumped into the room. The airconditioner, on the other hand, takes the heat from the air in the room or passenger compartment and releases it somewhere else—outside the area being cooled.

Within the Car. The airconditioner in today's car is not just a simple magic box, which merely blows cold air. The car airconditioner has a system of parts and components designed to implement the refrigeration cycle. The results are not only the withdrawal of heat but the lowering of humidity and the cleansing of pollen from entering air. In a word, the air you get is *conditioned.*

A good way to learn about the workings of an airconditioner is to imagine that we are building one from scratch. Let's say we are in a huge warehouse with an infinite number and variety of parts available.

All we have to do is wheel a shopping cart down the aisles and pull out the parts we need for construction.

Receiver-dryer. A good place to start discussing the cycle is at the storage unit where the refrigerant is held to assure a steady supply to the system. This unit will have to be a container strong enough to squeeze into a crowded engine compartment. In addition to storing the Freon, the unit must have provisions for "cleaning" it before it enters the system. The unit must also be designed so that the Freon leaving it is 100 percent liquid.

The unit meeting these specs is called the *receiver-dryer,* which is a metal cylinder, often the size of a small fire extinguisher. On the outside, a solid fitting serves as refrigerant inlet while a metal fitting with a glass tube serves as the outlet. The glass is for viewing the Freon during maintenance checks. Inside the cylinder there are two filter pads for removing any dirt or debris finding its way into the system. Below the first filter is a quantity of silica gel, a chemical drying agent called a desiccant. The silica gel attracts and holds moisture, but in the receiver-dryer it is inaccessible for drying out. When the gel becomes saturated, the entire receiver-dryer must be replaced. How can a technician determine when a moisture saturation point is reached? The answer is, moisture allowed to roam free in the system will soon turn to ice. This will clog openings and interrupt the free flow of Freon. Hence, no cooling. Since moisture is such an enemy of the refrigeration cycle, engineers have rigged the system to make sure that the Freon is filtered and "dried" with each cycle.

The desiccant in the receiver-dryer can

only hold about 100 drops of water at a temperature of 150 degrees. Capacity decreases as temperature increases. This is why the receiver-dryer must be mounted away from concentrated heat and is therefore placed in the front of the engine compartment where it receives the benefit of ram air hitting the car.

Below the desiccant inside the can is another filter pad. The remaining space at the bottom is used as a reservoir for the liquid Freon. Through the center of the entire canister is a "drinking straw" called a quill which extends from the reservoir below to the outlet fitting above. The quill nozzle draws up only liquid refrigerant.

The Freon then passes the sight glass before leaving the outlet fitting. If the system is functioning normally, the glass will appear clear since Freon is normally a colorless liquid. When the car is first started, or when it must travel in a severe stop-and-go situation, a few bubbles may appear in the glass — but for a short while only. However, if leaks in the system cause a shortage of Freon, bubbles will appear in a steady stream.

TXV and Evaporator. Having secured the proper type reservoir for holding an adequate supply of Freon, we are ready to shop for parts for the cooling process.

What we need now is a unit that will suck the heat from the air. Therefore, it must be located in the warm passenger compartment. Let's place the unit under or behind the dash, since this puts it out of the way of passengers yet quite close to the engine compartment.

This unit must serve the same function as the so-called freezing unit found in today's refrigerators. We need a series of

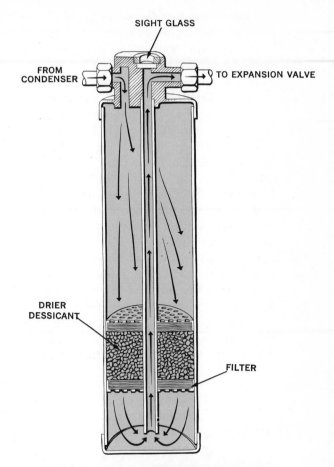

SIGHT GLASS

FROM CONDENSER

TO EXPANSION VALVE

DRIER DESSICANT

FILTER

Cutaway of receiver-dryer. Liquid Freon entering the canister is filtered and forced through a chemical drying agent (desiccant) which removes moisture in the Freon. Then the Freon is allowed to flow to the expansion valve.

tubes exposed to the warm air so that the Freon flowing through can boil readily, to evaporate and absorb heat. Since the basic process here is evaporation, let's call this unit the *evaporator*.

The evaporator's main function is to cool, dry and clean the air that will circulate around the passenger compartment. When stripped of its plastic case and air ducts, the evaporator resembles a cooling system radiator or heater core. But its job is the reverse. The heater core gives off heat, the evaporator absorbs it.

The evaporator has a series of tubes with fins bristling from the exterior surface. It also has inlet and outlet pipes leading to and from the tubes. Refrigerant flows from the inlet pipe, through the tubes and exits at the outlet, called the *tailpipe*. But the flow of Freon must be regulated to provide maximum evaporation under varying conditions. The entire airconditioning system is really a network of plumbing.

In the system, we are now at the junction between where high-pressure liquid is stored in the receiver-dryer and where low pressure liquid is required at the evaporator for rapid boiling. Remember the principle that high pressure results in a high boiling point. And, without boiling

there is little heat absorption. Therefore we need some way of lowering the pressure.

What we need is a control device which will determine the rate of refrigerant flow. The device must be able to sense temperature conditions at the evaporator and respond by opening or shutting the gate to refrigerant flow. In this case a thermostatic device can automatically set valves and switches through the expand-shrink effects of heat and cooling.

In the operation of the thermostat, a drop in refrigerant pressure results from the rapid expansion of Freon as it goes from the small opening inside the valve to the relatively larger tubes of the evaporator. Now, if we combine the method of operation (thermostatic) and the function (to drop pressure by allowing a rapid

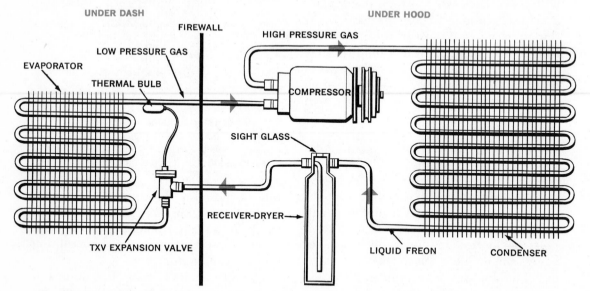

Schematic of typical airconditioning system. Starting at the receiver-dryer, high-pressure liquid Freon flows to the expansion valve where it becomes low-pressure liquid. As the Freon flows through the evaporator under the dashboard, it absorbs heat and becomes a low-pressure gas, until it reaches the compressor. There the Freon is converted to a high-pressure gas which flows to the condenser in front of the car's radiator where the gas is condensed to a liquid and stored in the receiver-dryer. This process repeats.

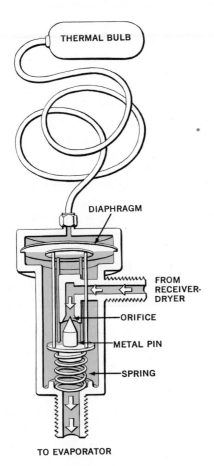

THERMAL BULB

DIAPHRAGM

FROM RECEIVER-DRYER

ORIFICE

METAL PIN

SPRING

TO EVAPORATOR

Cutaway of one type expansion valve. Its function is to meter the precise amount of Freon entering the evaporator. The thermal bulb sends the signals to the diaphragm, allowing the needle to regulate the size of the orifice.

expansion) we can give this unit a significant name: *thermostatic expansion valve.* For short, it's called a *TXV.*

The major parts of the TXV are a body and a power element which controls the valve opening. In the body there is a tiny orifice and a metal pin which dictates the size of the orifice. Assisting the operation is a spring which tries to hold the orifice wide open and a diaphragm which oper-

ates in conjunction with the power unit to compress the spring and close the orifice. Included in this setup is a screen filter to make certain that the orifice never gets clogged. The power element consists of a metal heat-sensing bulb and a very fine conduit called a capillary tube. Both are filled with a volatile fluid which expands easily when heated and condenses just as easily when cooled.

When installed in the car, the system is arranged like this: The evaporator is inside the passenger compartment. If the airconditioner is factory-installed it is most likely behind the dashboard. Should the system be installed after the sale of the car, chances are that the evaporator is secured to the lower edge of the dash. In the trade this is called a "hang-on" unit.

The TXV body is secured to the inlet pipe of the evaporator in such a manner that the Freon coming from the receiver-dryer must pass through it in order to get to the evaporator. The heat-sensing bulb, however, is strapped to the evaporator tailpipe and sends its messages to the valve body via the capillary tube.

Cooling. Here's how the evaporator and the TXV work together to give you a refreshing breeze. During normal operation, Freon enters the TXV as a medium-temperature, high-pressure liquid. As it passes through the valve orifice it changes to a low-temperature, low-pressure liquid, which is then fed to the evaporator.

Behind the evaporator coils is an electric fan which passes warm air over the tubes of the evaporator. High temperatures conducted to the low-pressure liquid cause the refrigerant to boil, then vaporize. This is the point when the heat of the air in the car is soaked up. As a result the passengers receive a stream of air minus the heat—cool air.

As the air inside the compartment gets cooler, its ability to hold moisture decreases. As a result, the excess moisture in the air condenses on the evaporator tubes and drains off.

While the passengers are languishing in the cool breezes, the TXV is alerted for action. If there was no control and the Freon is permitted to flow through the evaporator tubes at a maximum rate, the result will be extreme cooling of the tubes and fins. This will lead to ice formation on the evaporator. Then warm air will be blocked from flowing through the evaporator and, oddly enough, the ice will stop the cooling process.

Because the air passing over the evaporator coils becomes cooler and affects refrigerant boiling and the efficiency of the cooling process, there is need to periodically cut down refrigerant flow. Now, with the power element receiving temperature messages from the evaporator tailpipe, the see-saw effect begins. In the center is the valve diaphragm and the linkage to the pin controlling the size of the orifice. Pushing to close the orifice is the spring. Opposing this force is the pressure of the liquid in the sensing bulb and capillary which pushes against the diaphragm to open the orifice.

When the airconditioner is first started, the temperature of the vapor leaving the tailpipe is relatively high. When the temperature of the vapor becomes 15 degrees higher than the boiling liquid Freon, the liquid inside the sensing bulb will boil and begin to expand. This exerts a pressure against the diaphragm and enlarges the orifice for an increased flow of Freon.

As the temperature at the tailpipe lowers such that there is more than 15 degrees difference between the escaping vapors and the boiling liquid refrigerant, the material inside the sensing bulb stops boiling and starts contracting. Thus pressure against the diaphragm is relieved. This puts the valve spring in a stronger position and the size of the orifice decreases. With a reduced flow of refrigerant through the evaporator, tailpipe temperatures start to rise and the control cycle is repeated. This on-and-off action is continuous while the airconditioner is in operation.

The Compressor. Let's continue shopping for parts. So far we have a reservoir and a means of making cool air by rapid vaporization, with controls to assure a steady flow of cool air. The cooling portion of the system is assembled. Now we must dump the heat and reverse the vaporization process in order to reuse the refrigerant.

At this moment we have a low-pressure vapor. Though the vapor has absorbed much heat, its temperature is quite low to the touch. Vapor condenses to a liquid by cooling. But, if we were to employ "cool" we just made to draw off the heat in the vapor, it would be like trying to cool off a room by leaving the refrigerator door open. In short, it just cannot be done.

The only way to cool the vapor is to play the relativity game. The vapors are hot, yet the outside air is much hotter. Therefore, we cannot expect the heat from the vapors to gravitate to the outside air, since heat flow is always down the temperature scale. The only practical solution now is to make the vapors much hotter than the outside air so that all the heat will flow from the vapors and cause condensation.

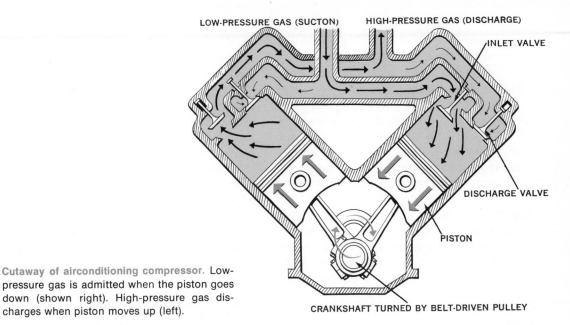

LOW-PRESSURE GAS (SUCTON)   HIGH-PRESSURE GAS (DISCHARGE)

INLET VALVE

DISCHARGE VALVE

PISTON

CRANKSHAFT TURNED BY BELT-DRIVEN PULLEY

Cutaway of airconditioning compressor. Low-pressure gas is admitted when the piston goes down (shown right). High-pressure gas discharges when piston moves up (left).

How can the vapors be made hotter? Certainly it is impractical to have a small boiler or other cumbersome equipment. However, it is practical to squeeze them into a small space where they will be concentrated. Thus they can be made hotter without our adding any outside heat. What is needed is a pump-like pressure machine which can draw in quantities of Freon vapor and compress it. What we need is a *compressor*.

The compressor used on airconditioning systems functions almost like a small automotive engine. It has a crankshaft, valves and pistons. Most airconditioning systems use a compressor with two cylinders, while some cars use a five or six-cylinder compressor.

The compressor is located in the front of the engine compartment, positioned parallel to the engine. Belts run from the pulley on the compressor to the engine

crankshaft pulley. When the compressor is operating (it does not always function while the engine is operating), it sucks the low-pressure refrigerant vapor through one of the inlet valves into the cylinder. When the piston is at the bottom of the cylinder, the valve closes and traps the vapor. Then the piston rises and squeezes the vapor. At once, a great deal of temperature is concentrated; thus the temperature of the compressed vapor rises sharply. In most cases temperatures go up to 200 degrees; pressures are from 50 to 300 pounds per square inch. After the pressure buildup, an exhaust valve opens and the compressed vapors flow out.

The compressor does more than squeeze the Freon vapors. In the crankcase of the unit is a special oil which provides lubrication for the seals of moving parts and for the gaskets. This oil mixes with the Freon but has no effect on its cooling properties.

Because the compressor is situated between the low- and the high-pressure sides of the system, it is ideal for fittings that provide pressure checks in the system. Though the configuration may vary, the compressor is equipped with threaded ports on which a technician may screw a set of gauges. By observing the high and low pressure readings, he can determine what is happening inside the system.

The Condenser. At this stage we are left with a high-pressure, high-temperature vapor, just ready for conversion to a liquid. Now we can condense with cooling, since the vapors are much hotter than the immediate surroundings. These vapors are so hot now that they would readily surrender heat to the relatively cooler air. The next piece of equipment required for the system we are building must be able to accept the hot, high-pressure vapor and convert it to a liquid. Since the process is condensation, let's call this unit the *condenser.*

The function of the condenser is exactly like the function of a steam radiator in a home. In the home radiator, steam comes up from the boiler and courses through a series of pipes. Heat is then conducted from the steam through the cast iron pipes and radiated into the room. As the steam loses heat, it condenses into water, which is then allowed to drain back into the boiler. The condenser in the airconditioner also consists of tubes and fins which conduct the heat of the Freon vapor to the outside. This time, however, the object is not to heat up the atmosphere but to draw the heat from the vapor for condensation.

The condenser must be located so that it gets first crack at the onrushing air,

which is the coolest available. Thus the condenser is mounted in front of the car's radiator. Now as the system functions, the compressor pumps the hot vapor to the top of the condenser where the vapor starts its downward plunge through the tubing, giving up heat as it falls. This is the same heat that was absorbed in the passenger compartment at the evaporator.

When the refrigerant reaches the bottom of the condenser, it is a liquid, still under high pressure. As such it enters the reservoir of the receiver-dryer ready to start its odyssey again. Cycle time for one drop of refrigerant around the entire system is about 60 seconds.

Auxiliary Equipment. There are still quite a number of items required to complete the system. To link all the components we just outlined, we must have a network of tubing and hoses. In those areas where the refrigerant is under high pressure, steel tubing is used. In other areas, heavy rubber hoses are sufficient. In many joints, rubber "O" rings are used as seals to prevent leakage. These resemble small washers and are usually made of neoprene. Every bend and turn in the tubing or hoses must be gradual. Kinks or sharp bends would impede refrigerant flow.

To accommodate an airconditioner, the car's engine cooling system must be altered slightly. A radiator cap with a pressure rating of 16 pounds per square inch is usually employed to raise the boiling point of the radiator coolant to 244 degrees. This special cap is needed because the radiator must perform its primary job of cooling the engine while heat from the airconditioner's condenser pours on it. On the other hand, antifreeze is a must in airconditioned cars year-round to prevent freeze-ups at the heater core. Thus, we begin to note the close association between the airconditioner and the heating system. A larger radiator fan, or one with more blades, provides more air-drawing for the condenser and radiator. The fan is usually accompanied by a shroud to increase pulling efficiency.

Probably the most expensive modification for airconditioned cars is the installation of tinted windshield and window glass, to keep out many of the heat-producing rays from the sun. But the amount of tint must be limited. True, the darker the glass, the greater it will shield the sun's rays. However, too much tint can dangerously limit vision, especially during night driving. In the near future there will be increased use of a glass which grows darker as it is exposed to greater amounts of light. Then the glass becomes clear when not subject to light.

Special Features. We just assembled an auto airconditioner with the basic and auxiliary components. But alas, the system is not that simple; mainly because our needs are not that simple.

Everyone enjoys comfort as well as convenience. For convenience the consumer wants automatic controls.

Earlier in this chapter we noted that the compressor does not pump Freon every moment the engine is in operation. This applies even though the compressor is powered by a belt attached to the engine crankshaft. The compressor pulley travels continuously with the engine. But this pulley is separate from the compressor crankshaft and can travel without causing a pumping action that compresses Freon vapor.

The link between the compressor pulley and the shaft is an electromagnetic clutch which is powered by the car's electrical system and designed to operate on signals from a special switch that controls the flow of current to the electromagnet at the clutch. Two styles are in popular use today. One is a bimetal type as found on many household thermostats. Another is a heat-sensing bulb and capillary tube similar to the setup in the TXV. In both types, current to the electromagnetic coil is interrupted when the evaporator is sufficiently cold. Therefore, the compressor clutch disengages, separating the pulley from the shaft. Pumping stops.

This cycle keeps repeating itself over and over again, maintaining an average desired air temperature. Further control of the airconditioning output is given to the driver and passengers who may adjust the temperature manually. Most cars have a selector knob which actually adjusts spring tension on the switch contacts for opening at any stage before maximum cooling is achieved.

Another Design. With four major corporations producing airconditioners for their cars and a large number of independent firms offering "hang-on" units, we can expect more than one way to handle certain problems.

Take the temperature control. On home airconditioners it is a simple matter to get the desired amount of cooling by using a thermostat arrangement that operates a valve which controls the amount of refrigerant entering the evaporator. The thermostat is concerned only with the temperature of outflowing air. When the temperature gets too low, the unit stops cooling for a while and resumes cooling when the room temperature rises. Power to the unit is as constant as the voltage coming out of the wall.

Power to push and pull the Freon through the car's system comes from an engine-driven compressor. Since a steady engine speed is a rarity in the average driving trip, variable compressor load makes accurate temperature control an uncertainty, some engineers feel.

Some major car makers such as General Motors and Chrysler do not use a magnetic clutch for temperature control. They control the temperature output with a pressure-sensitive device. On their systems, the compressor is always pumping when the airconditioner is on. The compressor continues functioning as long as the engine is running and the switch is on.

Temperature is regulated by controlling the pressure of the gas leaving the evaporator. This is done with a special valve, known by many names. One such design is called the Evaporator Pressure Regulator (EPR); another is the Suction Throttling Valve (STV); still another is the Pilot Operated Absolute (POA).

The STV is probably the most accurate name for these valves, since the process is actually a throttling (closing) of the feed side (suction side) of the compressor.

The valve is placed in the stream of gas leaving the evaporator. When the airconditioner is first turned on, the valve is wide open. As operation progresses, refrigerant gas leaving the evaporator becomes colder. This signals the valve to shut down somewhat. As a result a pressure buildup occurs in the evaporator. Higher pressure means higher temperature. As a result, the airconditioner is operating at less than total efficiency. Temperature control is achieved by main-

taining evaporator pressure at a predetermined setting.

Some of the more sophisticated units have provisions for diverting the cold discharge air through the heater core as an additional means of temperature control. In these cases, the throttling valve is calibrated to produce maximum cold at about 30 degrees. This is an advantage for the greatest amount of moisture is extracted from the air at this temperature. Then to prevent frostbite among the car's occupants, the cold air is sent through the heater core before final discharge. The extent to which the cold air is warmed depends on the setting fixed by the driver. Now you may see why antifreeze is necessary in the cooling system of airconditioned cars.

Air Regulators. To completely assemble the airconditioner, we need a final group of parts to handle the air distribution system. This consists mainly of ducts for channeling the flow of cool air, doors for regulating the volume of air, and an electric blower. Many airconditioners have levers or buttons marked with "RECIRCULATE" and "FRESH AIR" or other such identifications. These controls determine the amount of outside air allowed to flow over the evaporator coils. For rapid cooling, the fresh air door is shut, the air inside the car is passed over the evaporator coils, cooled, circulated, and then passed over the coils again. The only drawback to this is that the air gets stale after a short while and opening the fresh air intake helps in changing the air. However, under extreme conditions this setup is useful only until the initial heat is gone.

A system of ducts ensures that the cooled air is properly distributed throughout the passenger compartment. The ducts usually terminate at louvered openings which can be adjusted to direct the air stream.

Another essential piece of auxiliary equipment is the blower motor. On most factory-equipped airconditioned cars, this is usually the same blower motor used in the heating process. The "hang-on" units usually contain their own motor. Forced air distribution is made possible by the attachment of a large "squirrel-cage" drum to the shaft of the motor. Do not underestimate the importance of this small motor. The rate at which air is discharged into the passenger compartment is governed by the speed of the motor. Most have three-position switches which provide varying amounts of blowing. On the heater-air-conditioner combinations the three speeds for cooling are usually faster than the three for heating.

In recent years airconditioners have become very sophisticated. However the basic principles in the refrigeration cycle remain the same.

Ratings. If we understand ratings, we can figure, in comparative terms, how much heat the unit can remove in a given time.

Not too long ago, airconditioners were rated in "tons." Though this system has been discarded by the refrigeration industry, it does refer to the present BTU system. Here's how: In the early days refrigeration was measured by the amount of heat ice would absorb as it melted. It was arbitrarily decided that a ton of refrigeration was the same as the number of BTUs absorbed by one ton of ice in 24 hours. Since it takes 144 BTUs of heat to change one pound of pure ice to water at a temperature of 32 degrees, it will take 280,000 BTUs to melt 2000 pounds of ice. This figure was divided by 24, representing the hours in a full day. As a result, a ton of refrigeration is equal to the removal of 12,000 BTUs of heat per hour.

Many car airconditioners are rated at $1\frac{1}{2}$ tons. This equals a BTU rating of 18,000. These units are more than twice the size of many room airconditioners. But bear in mind that a house is far better insulated than a car. In addition the engine radiates much heat, and large glass areas allow heat waves to enter and to be absorbed by upholstery and passengers.

13
BODY AND
GLASS

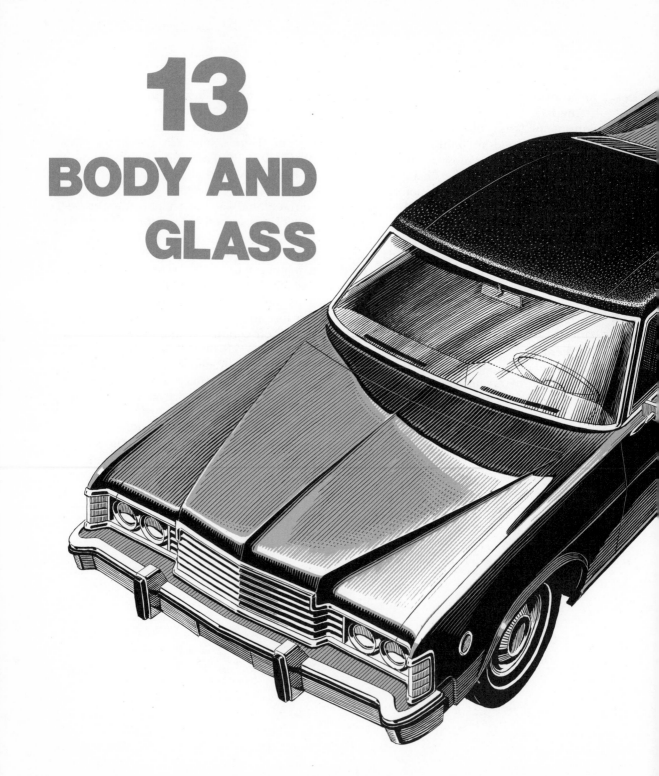

No other part of the car receives more attention than the body. Indeed, within the hierarchy of any auto maker, the stylist's whisper carries more weight than the mechanical designer's shouts.

The body is more than skin deep. True, the body's surface metal gives the car its distinctive sweep, its special look which sets it apart from other vehicles. However, there is much below the body surface which is vital to the basic outer structure. In other words, the present-day car body consists of more than a few doors and fenders hung on to a shell. It is a system which can be divided into seven basic units. Let's look at them individually.

BODY SHELL

The body shell is a rather complex assortment of large sections of steel which have been stamped into a definite shape.

At the bottom of the assembly is the *floor pan*. This is the foundation, stamped with bulges and curves to conform to the

235

space requirements of the engine, transmission and rear axle. The stamping must also consider the ultimate size and shape of the passenger compartment. If the car has a separate frame, the floor pan is bolted to the side rails, but kept from actual contact by large rubber cushions. If the car is of unitized construction, without a frame, the floor pan is attached to various metal pieces which make up the center section of the chassis. Most cars have two floor pans. One is for the passenger compartment; the other extends rearward to make up the floor of the trunk.

The next piece is the *cowl assembly.* This part is often called the firewall because it separates the passenger and engine compartments. The cowl is a flat piece of steel punched with appropriate curves. In addition, it has a number of openings and notches to allow various wires, tubes and levers to come through for car operation. The cowl assembly does not stop at the height of the instrument panel. It continues up both sides of the dashboard and stops when it meets at the roof panel. These pillars, which also provide the frame for the windshield, are called "A" pillars.

On the opposite end of the cowl assembly is the *rear quarter panel.* This assembly runs from the rearmost part of the rear door edge, around the back and to the rear door on the other side. On a number of cars, the rear quarter panel is integral with the rear fenders. A major difference between this and other panels is its inner construction. Unlike the floor pan or the cowl assembly, the rear quarter panel is made up of an outer skin and inner panels which serve as reinforcements for the rear passenger compartment, the trunk and the wheel housings. Most of the inner panels

are not readily visible. But without them, the vibration in the rear section of the car would be quite severe, and construction would be weak.

The next piece in the puzzle is the *center body pillar,* called the "B" pillar. The "B" describes the piece quite accurately. All cars have a center body pillar, regardless of whether they are 2-door or 4-door vehicles. Made of heavy stock and formed for strength, the pillar extends from the floor pan straight upward. On a 4-door sedan, the pillar reaches up to the roof and is welded to it. On a 4-door hardtop, the pillar rises only as high as door level. On a 2-door hardtop the pillar is incorporated into the rear quarter panel. Aside from providing strength, the pillar serves as a foundation for locks and hinges of the front and rear doors.

We are now ready to top off the system with the *roof assembly.* This unit is the largest and the simplest in construction. Its actual shape is determined by the style of the car. In some cases it extends below the actual roof line at the windshield or the rear window.

With the basic skeleton assembled, let's add the *doors* along with *deck lids.* The latter are the hinged covers of the engine and the luggage compartments. A station wagon has a tailgate assembly.

The door is made up of an outer and inner panel. The inner panel provides strength; the outer panel is a mere metal sheet. The inner panel must have a variety of holes and offsets for the attachment of window mechanisms and door locks. The upper section of the door is for the glass, which rides in a channel on two sides of the door frame.

The deck lids are really another type of door. These too consist of an outer

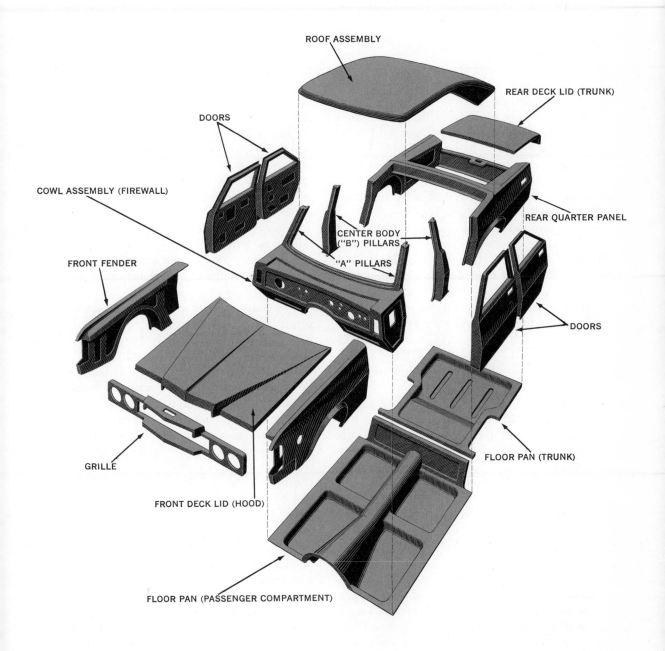

ROOF ASSEMBLY

REAR DECK LID (TRUNK)

DOORS

COWL ASSEMBLY (FIREWALL)

REAR QUARTER PANEL

CENTER BODY
("B") PILLARS

"A" PILLARS

FRONT FENDER

DOORS

GRILLE

FLOOR PAN (TRUNK)

FRONT DECK LID (HOOD)

FLOOR PAN (PASSENGER COMPARTMENT)

Exploded view of basic body components. These are the parts most subject to changes in style.

panel, the "skin," with crossbars on the inner panel, supported for strength.

GLASS

The concept of fenestration didn't enter into car design until about 1908. Even then, the only piece of visible glass was a very flat windshield which was sold as an optional item. The windshield finally became standard equipment on the Owen in 1910. Door glass wasn't employed until around 1917, and even then it appeared only on the more expensive cars.

In engineering language a glass is a "light." Expressions such as "sidelight" and "backlight" are used to describe a door glass and a rear window. Automotive glass is somewhat different from ordinary house glass. Car glass must be strong enough to withstand severe bouncing, vibration and weather. And when it breaks it must do so "gracefully," without inflicting damage with splinters and pointed shards.

The first move toward "safety" glass came in 1926 when two cars offered it. The Stutz had a windshield with lengths of wire running horizontally across every seven inches. The wire gave the glass some coherence when it was struck very hard. The Rickenbacker car offered a windshield that was a sandwich of clear celluloid between two pieces of clear glass. This was the first laminated auto windshield.

Today there are three major types of glass found on all cars. *Laminated safety sheet glass* is the sandwich type used on door glass and vent windows before 1960. Though its safety aspects rate high, it is considered of poor optical quality and is not used on windshields and backlights.

The successor to the pre-1960 glass is called *laminated safety plate glass*. This too is a sandwich of glass and clear plastic. However, its optical quality makes it far better for windshields and backlights. A major improvement in this glass occurred in 1966 and has been used on most vehicles since. This glass is made with less adhesion between the plastic center and the sheet glass. In addition, the thickness of the plastic center is raised from .015 inch to .030 inch. The thicker plastic acts as a softer, protective barrier when it is struck by a passenger during a collision. The low adhesion allows the glass to fall away when the windshield is struck from within; the heavier plastic prevents penetration by the victim, thus minimizing injury.

The latest development is *tempered safety glass*. It has two interesting qualities. First, it is unusually hard and has many times the impact resistance of the other types of glass of the same thickness. When it does finally give way and break, it forms small granular fragments, glass crumbs which have no sharp corners. Since this glass is so hard and since a sharp blow will make it optically useless, it is not used in windshields. Its great strength is the result of its surface being placed in a high-compression state by rapid heating and rapid cooling at the factory. Some motorists have returned to their parked cars only to find the backlight has become crumbs. This is often due to a manufacturing defect or to the weakening of the outer skin by the impact of a small flying stone.

In addition, the various types of glass are available in tints. By adding a color to the batch of molten glass it is possible to create a sheet which will filter out the sun's rays. Tinted glass is usually found on cars which are equipped with factory-installed airconditioning. Thus, with reduced heat and glare, driving is made much more comfortable. While tinted glass has advantages for daytime driving, it does present hazards at night in that it filters out light and impairs visibility.

Moving and Stationary Glass. Various methods are used to hold glass in place, depending on where the glass is used. Some car windows are stationary while others can be moved.

Windshields and backlights now belong to the stationary class. This was not always the case. Many cars up to 1935 had a hinged windshield which could be opened or laid flat on top of the engine hood. Today, the windshield is fixed in place by a rubber weatherstrip. The strip is made with a groove on its inside and outside lips. The inside lip holds the glass while the outside grips the metal rim around the windshield opening. In late-model cars, the glass "floats" in a plastic sealant which is spread out between the edge of the glass and the windshield frame.

Door glass is installed in a *window regulator* which permits it to be raised and lowered inside the door. The regulator consists of a metal strip which is affixed to the lower edge of the glass, two small arms, a large pie-shaped gear, and a small round gear. The handle which is used to raise and lower the glass is attached to a short shaft which is part of the small gear. Turning the smaller gear causes the larger gear to turn. In so doing, it shifts position and changes the angle of the two small arms. Since the arms are attached to the lower edge of the glass, the shifting of the arms raises or lowers the window.

In 1946 power windows were introduced. The basic mechanism remains the same. The change is the installation of a small electric motor inside the door which is attached to the small gear. When the switch is activated, the electric motor merely does the job of cranking.

MOLDINGS

For the most part, moldings on the car are nonfunctional. Only in some cases do the moldings hide a seam or cover a rough edge. Lavish use of moldings didn't begin until about 1938, even though cars began sporting brightwork such as bumpers, grilles and door handles in 1915.

In the very early days, the brightwork was nickel-plated. In the 1920s came chrome plating. Though most of the moldings today are made of aluminum and stainless steel, the trim is still popularly known as chrome.

Though on the late model cars ornamental moldings have diminished, moldings are far from archaic. The most popular names for moldings still in use are: *rocker* molding, running along the lower rim of sheet metal just below the doors; *drip* molding, at the side edges of the roof; *lip* molding, which keeps water away from windows; *garnish* molding, the metal rim around the windshield or backlight; *lip* molding, applied to the edge around the wheel opening.

SEATS AND UPHOLSTERY

Today, the common names for seat configurations are either bench seats or bucket seats. The former is a continuous cushion and backrest running the width of the car interior. The bucket seats are individual units with a separation between the left and right seats. But bucket seats are not new. The 1915 Packard featured what was called the "sociable" body. Packard advertised the fact that there was an aisle between the seats so the passengers could change places easily.

The earliest seats were little more than a leather cushion placed on top of a wooden bench. As the cruising range of the car increased, the seats became more comfortable. There were some luxury models in the early 1920s which had seats that put some elegant drawing rooms to shame. These seats had genuine leather with heavy brass trim. Others boasted plush velvet.

In the 1930s and 1940s most sedans settled on mohair covered seats, while convertibles sported leather. Then, after the war, the plastic revolution took over. First, plastic was used extensively for seat covers. Later, vinyl was used as basic long-wearing upholstery.

As far as seat springs were concerned, the early cars used the bulky coil springs found in furniture. The coils, plus the cotton padding, plus the heavy upholstery, made the seats quite bulky. In the early 1950s the flatspring appeared. The flatspring is a piece of spring wire bent into a zigzag pattern. Both ends of the wire are anchored to the seat frame. Additional lengths are attached about every six inches. Using the foam padding and vinyl upholstery, the total bulk of the seat is substantially reduced.

The rear seat is stationary. The backrest attaches to the partition between the passenger and luggage compartments. The seat cushion actually rests upon the floor pan and is secured so that it does not shift.

The front seat is set on a rail which, in turn, is bolted to the floor pan. The rail allows forward or backward adjustment of the seat to suit the driver. The seat-adjustment handle near the driver is attached to a latch which fits into teeth along the rail. Movement of the handle releases the latch and frees the seat. At any point in the travel, the release of the handle causes the latch to engage one of the teeth. Often, there is a pull-spring which draws the unoccupied seat forward when the latch is released.

Upholstery. In addition to seats, other sections of the interior are covered with decorative vinyl. In most cases, the covering is made of the same material used on the seats. The covering for the ceiling is called the *headlining*. In addition, all inside door panels and arm rests are covered. Often the instrument panel is covered. Finally, there is a floor mat or a rug which covers the floor pan.

HARDWARE

Parts which come under the heading of auto hardware are almost the same as house hardware. These include door handles, window handles, locks and latches.

The door handle is used both as a grasp and as a means to release the door latch. The latch, or striker plate, is mounted on the door pillar. It is designed to mate with a toothed wheel at the side panel of the door. This wheel is called a rotor. When the door is closed, one of the teeth contacts the striker and causes the rotor to turn one tooth. When the door is closed properly, the rotor engages with the striker. The door cannot open because the rotor is locked. When the door button outside or the handle inside the door is moved, the rotor is allowed to rotate. Then the door opens.

Locking the door actually throws an interference between the outside button or inside handle and the rotor, rendering the rotor release ineffective. The interference can be released by inserting a key in the door lock or raising the inside lock button.

STYLING

From the very beginning, shaping a car has been a challenge to the imagination— a dynamic art. Early stylists had only the horse-drawn coach as a prototype. But that soon became tiresome, and the stylists began to create. To date, there have been nearly 1800 different makes produced in this country alone.

The stylist, as a professional, did not appear until around 1927. Before that time, styling was done either by old carriage makers or company presidents who knew little about styling, but knew what they liked.

Before the turn of the century all vehicles were built high off the ground because roads in those days were quite muddy and deeply rutted. Large-diameter wheels provided the necessary clearance. In addition, it was the vogue to place suspension springs over the axles. Thus, seats were often more than fifty inches off the ground.

A big change occurred around 1905 with the addition of rear seats and the lower carriage style. The trend swung to longer touring cars.

By 1912 the horseless carriage features had disappeared. The body became a big housing for parts such as the engine, steering wheel and levers. Folding tops became popular, replacing the surrey and open types. As car quality and roads improved, driving ranges extended and the style favored was the closed car.

By the middle 1920s the car was no longer a rich man's plaything, but a popular form of transportation. Styling still suffered from Henry Ford's maxim that it was engineering improvements that sold cars, not looks. This period saw few dynamic styling changes.

By the early 1930s the stylist began to gain in stature. The car took on a sweep that suggested motion. Ugly parts such as gas tanks and springs were covered by sheet metal. Windshields were tilted backward. Fender lines melted into the body. Streamlining came on strong.

By 1935 the car had been radically transformed from the horse-drawn coach prototype. The passenger compartment was lower. The spare tire was hidden with a newly created storage area—the trunk. The radiator began to disappear behind the engine hood. The steel top came into use, and the grille became a styling highlight.

In the late 1930s and early 1940s the Age of Deco design hit the car hard. Streamlining prevailed; all sharp corners became rounded. Grilles took on horizontal lines and began running the entire width of the front. The rear of the car body acquired a bullet shape. Running boards began to disappear. The key words for new models were *larger, lower* and *longer*.

After World War II, style moved; doors merged with fenders, and the body took on the look of a total unit. All glass curved and the two-door hardtop became very

STYLING

1908 Cadillac

1920 45-B Oldsmobile Pace Maker

1937 Buick Roadmaster

1947 Cadillac, Series "62"

242

popular. Emphasis shifted to creating strong corporate identity in car looks. A Ford product in no way was ever mistaken for a Chrysler product. New developments in paints brought brighter colors.

Today, corporate styling appears to be in a slump. The distinctive identity features are almost gone. Often it's hard to identify a car until you read the nameplate. Which way will styling go in the future? That is a difficult question to answer in light of today's emphasis on safety.

All photos courtesy of General Motors Corporation

1958 Chevrolet Impala

1967 Oldsmobile Cutlass Supreme

1974 Chevrolet Camaro

14
INSTRUMENTS
AND ACCESSORIES

The term "instrumentation" became a part of our language only with the coming of the space era. Yet, since the start of the mechanical era, machines have had their own gauges and other indicating devices.

Probably the most primitive "gauge" was the glass oil cup with the thin tube running to the bearing of a shaft. The person maintaining the machine could check oil level in the cup to be sure of sufficient lubrication. Compare this with the multitude of lights and gauges required by a

spacecraft. These indicate everything from ambient temperature to degrees of tilt.

The modern automobile instrument panel is an excellent example of everyday multi-instrument indication. The panel gives out information on conditions such as vehicle speed, miles driven, oil pressure in the engine lubricating system, charging rate of the alternator, temperature of the coolant, gasoline supply, and more.

Since gauges offer various types of information, they work on different princi-

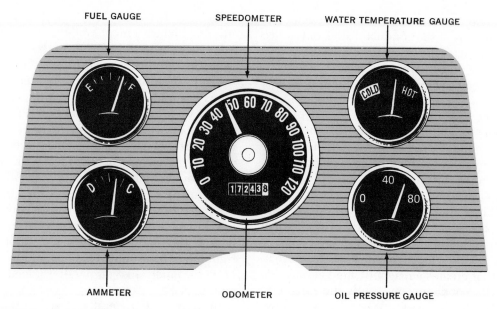

FUEL GAUGE   SPEEDOMETER   WATER TEMPERATURE GAUGE

AMMETER   ODOMETER   OIL PRESSURE GAUGE

View of the basic instrument panel. Only five basic gauges are used today to give information to the driver. These give data on the charging system, oil pressure, coolant temperature, fuel level and speed.

ples. In recent years, unfortunately, the move has been toward indicator lamps rather than gauges. Car makers claim that the lamps will more quickly attract the driver's attention and show a "go" or "no-go" condition. However, this may be just an excuse for installing a less expensive system. The problem with the lights is that they do not show quantity, but rather a "yes" or "no" situation. These are "idiot lamps."

They irk drivers who are responsible enough to glance at an instrument panel and realize what the readings have to say. Let's take a look at the indicators available.

AMMETER

The ammeter tells the driver whether the alternator or generator is charging the battery. More specifically, it measures the flow of electricity in amperes to or *from* the battery.

The parts of the gauge visible to the driver are a needle and a scale which say how much of a charge or discharge of the battery is taking place. When the alternator or generator produces an amperage greater than the amperage required to operate the car and its accessories, the needle of the gauge swings to the "charge" side. That is, the direction of current flow is toward the battery. When the engine is idling or off and current is applied, say for the lights or radio, the needle shows a "discharge." That is, the current flows from the battery.

The ammeter gauge consists of the needle and scale, a permanent magnet and a conductor. The magnet is so placed that the needle pivot is between its two poles. Both ends of the conductor stick out as two terminals at the rear of the gauge.

Since the instrument is an ammeter, it must be connected to the circuit in series. This means that the gauge must be in a direct line in the circuit. The wire runs from the battery, through the gauge conductor, out the other terminal, to the cutout relay of the voltage regulator. This is more fully explained in Chapter 2, "Electrical System."

When the ignition and accessories are off, the needle is balanced between equal magnetic forces and stays in the center of the scale. When current flows to the battery, it creates a magnetic field at one side of the conductor and pulls the needle to the "charge" side. When current flows from the battery, it creates a magnetic field at the other side of the conductor, pulling the needle to the "discharge" side.

On later model cars in which the charging regulator consists of only one unit—the voltage regulator—the ammeter is connected to the battery at one terminal and the "Bat" terminal of the alternator. But the magnetic pulling effects are the same as with older designs in that the current flowing to or from the battery must pass through the ammeter.

Discharge Lamp. This is used as a substitute for the ammeter. As mentioned, the lamp does not indicate how much charge or discharge is occurring; it only announces excessive discharges. It is usually mounted on the instrument panel and can glow red to catch the driver's attention. Unlike the ammeter, the lamp is not connected in series, but rather in parallel circuit.

Before going further, let's look at the difference between series and parallel circuits. Picture a main boulevard running from street A to street B. If the boulevard were the only way to get from street A to street B, then the boulevard (in electrical terms) would be in series. Suppose a detour were arranged so that both ends of the detour were connected to the main boulevard. Traffic could then choose whether to go up the boulevard or take the detour, which would involve making a right turn for one block, a left turn (running parallel to the boulevard), going a few blocks and making another left to get back to the boulevard, and taking another right to get back on it. This type of routing is very much like a parallel electrical circuit.

In a typical generator system in the automobile, the lamp is in parallel between the ignition switch and the "Gen" terminal of the voltage regulator. When the key is turned on before the engine has started, current flows from the battery, through the ignition switch, through the bulb and to the regulator. The lit lamp indicates a discharge. When the engine is started and the generator produces current greater than available from the battery, the current flow is reversed. It travels from the generator, to the current regulator, through the cutout relay and to the battery—bypassing the wire running to the bulb. The extinguished lamp indicates that the battery is charging.

In an alternator system with a lamp, the lamp is also connected in parallel. The only difference is that the lamp is between the ignition switch and the field relay of the regulator. Current flowing from the alternator, to the regulator, to the battery, bypasses the lamp. When battery current is greater, current flows through the lamp.

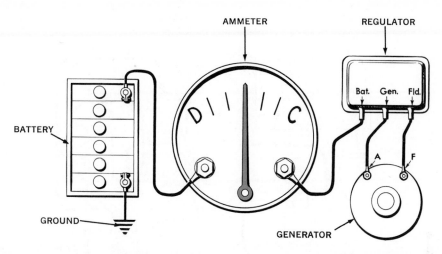

AMMETER   REGULATOR

Bat. Gen. Fld.

A   F

BATTERY

GROUND

GENERATOR

Ammeter for charging system indication. Inside the meter are two coils. When the battery current is greater than current from the charging unit, the needle will be pulled to the left, showing discharge. When current from the charging unit is greater than from the battery, the needle will swing to the right, showing charge.

OIL GAUGE

The oil gauge indicates only the pressure of the oil in the engine lubricating system. It is not a supply gauge which gives information on the amount of oil supply in the crankcase, unless the oil supply in the crankcase gets down to about one-half quart. In this case, the pressure will be so low that the gauge may not register a reading.

There are three different types of gauges used. One operates on direct pressure to the gauge; two operate on an electrical principle. (Then there is the oil light which glows when oil pressure drops below a certain point.)

Pressure Type. This gauge is probably one of the oldest in use on automobiles. It utilizes a direct reading of actual pressure in the oil passageways of the engine. A

small-diameter tube is attached to a threaded hole in the engine block. This hole is located precisely at an oil passage. The tube is sent through the engine firewall and is attached directly to the rear of the oil gauge.

The visible section of the gauge consists of a needle and a scale with numbers indicating pounds of pressure per square inch (psi). Not visible to the driver is the other end of the needle, which has a small gear attached to it. Meshed with the gear is a pie-shaped section of a larger gear. This sector has some linkage which is attached to the end of a flexible metal tube shaped like a question mark and sealed at the top end. This is called a Bourdon tube. When the line from the engine is attached to the gauge, it is fitted to the lower end of the Bourdon tube and traps the air within it.

When the engine is off, the oil pump

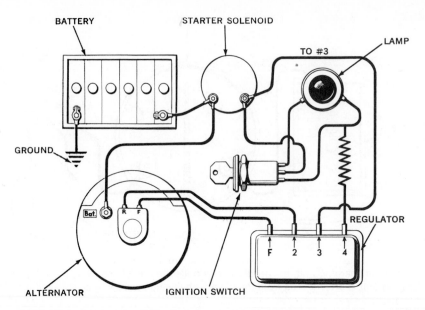

BATTERY   STARTER SOLENOID   TO #3   LAMP

GROUND

REGULATOR

Bat.   R   F

F   2   3   4

ALTERNATOR   IGNITION SWITCH

Discharge warning lamp. Current from the charging unit keeps the lamp contacts open. When current drops, the contacts close, allowing the lamp to glow.

does not operate. Therefore, there is no pressure in the oil passages; no pressure in the oil line; no pressure showing on the scale of the gauge. When the engine is started, pressure created in the oil line tries to push through into the Bourdon tube. But since the tube is sealed, the trapped air will not permit the oil to enter. The result is that a pressure builds up in the Bourdon tube and causes the curved tube to flex toward a straightened position. This moves the linkage, the sector gear and the small gear on the needle. Thus the needle moves to show a reading on the scale.

When the engine is turned off, oil pressure in the line falls off, and the tube resumes its curved shape with the needle pointing at zero.

Balancing-coil Type. This gauge uses electrical current to activate the needle. It is comprised of two separate components — the sending unit and the dash unit. The sending unit consists of a housing which is screwed into the engine block at an oil passage. Inside the housing is a metal diaphragm, an electrical resistor and a sliding contact. On the outside of the housing is an electrical terminal. A wire runs from this terminal to the dash unit.

Inside the gauge of the dash unit is a needle pointer and a scale. The pointer is located between two small electrical coils which are positioned in a V with the needle in the center. Electrically, the wiring for the gauge runs like this: One wire runs from the ignition switch and battery to the left-hand coil of the meter.

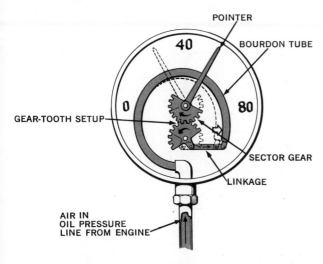

POINTER

BOURDON TUBE

40

0

80

GEAR-TOOTH SETUP

SECTOR GEAR

LINKAGE

AIR IN
OIL PRESSURE
LINE FROM ENGINE

Tube-type oil pressure gauge. Oil pressure from the engine pushes on the air trapped in the tube, forcing the tube to bend. This shifts the sector gear and causes the needle to move.

The circuit follows the windings around this coil and loops over to the right-hand coil, around the windings and then to ground. Thus there is a completed circuit. But, still the system is not complete. Attached to the loop between the two coils is the wire which comes from the sending unit at the engine block. This wire comes directly from the resistor in the sending unit. Resting against the resistor is the sliding contact which has its tail side attached to ground. Thus the amount of resistance in this line depends on the location of the sliding contact against the resistor.

With the engine off and the key on, there is no oil pressure to act against the diaphragm. Lack of pressure leaves the sliding contact at the zero end of the resistor. Current flows from the battery, through the ignition switch to the left-hand

coil. Then it has a choice. It can fight its way through the wires of the right-hand coil, or it can take the easy way and drift through the wire of the sending unit, through the sliding contact and then to ground. Naturally, it takes the easy way. This creates a magnetic field in the left-hand coil alone and pulls the needle to the left, or to "zero" pressure reading.

When the engine is started, oil pressure pushes on the diaphragm in the sending unit, which moves the sliding contact along the resistor. The greater the pressure, the farther the contact moves, and the greater the resistance in that part of the circuit. Let's assume that the engine we are talking about has an oil pressure within the normal limits. Then the diaphragm moves inward a certain distance. Now current flowing from the ignition switch goes through the left-hand coil *and* the right-hand coil, since the other circuit has so much resistance waiting for it. With the right-hand coil energized, the needle is attracted away from the zero point and indicates a normal pressure—at about the center of the scale. This is the result of equal magnetic pulls by both coils.

If the pressure gets abnormally high, the diaphragm is pushed in all the way. This makes the sliding contact rest on the far side of the resistor. With this high resistance in the line, almost all the current flows through the right-hand coil, and the needle is pulled all the way over to the right to indicate a high oil pressure on the scale.

Oil Indicator Lamp. This lights when the oil pressure drops to an unsafe level, usually around seven psi.

This system consists of a sending unit at the engine block, and wires leading to a

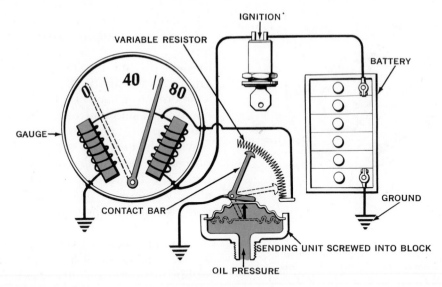

IGNITION

VARIABLE RESISTOR

BATTERY

40 80

0

GAUGE→

GROUND

CONTACT BAR

SENDING UNIT SCREWED INTO BLOCK

OIL PRESSURE

Electric oil-pressure indicator. The diaphragm in the sending unit will respond to the pressure in the engine, causing a contact to slide over a variable resistor. As a result, specific values are transmitted to the two coils in the gauge. The needle will reflect the magnetic pull of both coils.

bulb at the instrument panel. The sending unit is screwed into the block at an oil passage. Inside are a diaphragm and a set of contact points.

The wiring circuit is quite simple in that it is a continuous run of one line. Starting at the battery the wire runs through the ignition switch to the base of the bulb. The current follows through the lamp filament and out the bulb to the sending unit at the engine. Going inside the sending unit, the circuit comes to a stop at the lower electrical contact. The upper contact of the set is attached to the diaphragm on one side and to a spring on the other. The upper contact is the only link the entire unit has to a ground connection.

With the key on and the engine still off,

there is no oil pressure pushing on the diaphragm. Thus the spring forces the upper contact to touch the lower contact. The circuit is now complete and the bulb glows.

When the engine starts, oil pressure pushes against the diaphragm. In so doing, the upper contact is separated from the lower contact. Since the circuit is deprived of a ground connection, the bulb goes out. Should the pressure drop, the upper contact will be pulled by the spring to the lower contact, and the bulb will light.

The basic problem with the indicator light system is that it doesn't register when the oil pressure becomes abnormally high. To the engine, this situation may be as harmful as too low an oil pressure. But with the bulb indicator, the driver will never know a high-pressure situation exists. The bulb remains off just as long as there is seven or more pounds of pressure.

TEMPERATURE GAUGES

The temperature gauge tells the driver how hot or cold the engine coolant is. The scale on the gauge reads either in degrees of temperature or as "cold," "normal" or "hot." There are two popular types in use. One is based on a vapor pressure created by the temperature of the coolant; the other is based on electrical resistance.

Vapor-pressure Indicator. This type is a one-piece unit. The face of the gauge is marked with the appropriate indications; the needle is connected to a Bourdon tube — similar to the setup in the oil pressure gauge. Permanently connected to the Bourdon tube is a length of brass tubing which reaches through the firewall to the engine block. At the far end of the tubing is a brass capsule about the size of a rifle bullet. The design is such that a threaded collar is situated at the point where the capsule is soldered to the tubing. Inside the capsule is a liquid which evaporates at a fairly low temperature.

The capsule is inserted into the cylinder block or head directly into the water jacket. When the engine is first started, the coolant temperature is about the same as the surrounding air. The temperature is too low to have any effect on the capsule or the gauge. As the engine operates and the coolant temperature rises, the liquid within the capsule begins to boil and vaporize. The expansion of the vapors is conveyed through the tubing all the way up to the Bourdon tube. Just as in the oil

gauge, the air which is trapped inside the tube causes the Bourdon to bend. In so doing, the needle points to a section of the gauge scale which represents the degree that the Bourdon tube is bent, which is also an indication of the vapor pressure in the capsule and the temperature in the water jacket.

In this type of gauge the needle does not drop to zero when the engine is turned off. This is because there is no electricity involved in gauge operation. To get the needle to home base, the engine coolant must be allowed to disperse all of its heat.

Electric Heat Indicator. The electrical heat indicator uses a gauge which is identical to the one used for oil pressure, though the wiring is slightly different. However, the gauge does use two coils in a V shape with a needle in the center. Operation is based on magnetic attraction of the needle.

The sending unit, however, is slightly different from the one used in the oil gauge. Instead of having a variable resistor and a sliding contact, the sending unit has within it a solid-state material which changes its electrical resistance in response to temperature changes. Under cooler conditions, resistance is very high; under hotter conditions, resistance is very low. This sending unit is also inserted into the engine at the water jacket.

As noted before, the wiring of this gauge is slightly different from the wiring of the oil gauge. The oil gauge has the wire from the resistor connected between the left and right coils and the wire from the battery running to the left-hand coil. But the water temperature gauge has a variation. The wire from the temperature-sensitive sending unit is attached to the end of the right-hand coil, and the wire

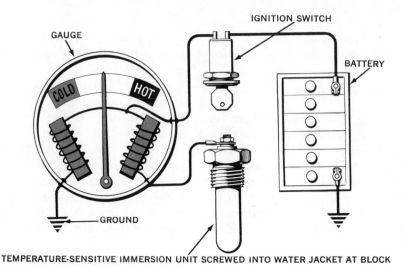

GAUGE

IGNITION SWITCH

BATTERY

COLD HOT

GROUND

TEMPERATURE-SENSITIVE IMMERSION UNIT SCREWED INTO WATER JACKET AT BLOCK

Electromagnetic temperature indicator. The immersion unit operates to offer less resistance as the coolant temperature rises. When temperature is low, the left-side coil will draw a greater current, pulling the needle to the left. When temperature is high, the right-side coil will attract the needle to the right.

from the battery is connected between the two coils.

When the engine starts, the coolant temperature is low. Hence the sending unit immersed in the water jacket has a very high electrical resistance. Current flowing from the battery goes through the ignition switch, through the left-hand coil and then to ground. It will not travel through the right hand coil because there is a very high resistance waiting for it at the other side of the coil. With the left-hand coil energized, the needle is attracted to the left side of the scale where the indication is "cold."

As the coolant gets hotter, the resistance at the sending unit diminishes. Finally, when the coolant reaches normal operating temperature, the resistance is very

low. With the lessened resistance, electricity flows to the right-hand coil as well as the left. With both coils energized, the needle is held in the center of the gauge by the equal magnetic attractions. Thus the gauge shows a "normal" condition.

If an abnormal situation should occur, such as a coolant leak which results in a very high temperature in the cooling system, the resistance at the sending unit will be almost zero. In this case, the right-hand coil receives most of the current, and the needle is pulled all the way to the right, indicating a "hot" condition.

FUEL GAUGES

The fuel gauge indicates the amount of gas in the tank. In almost all cases the

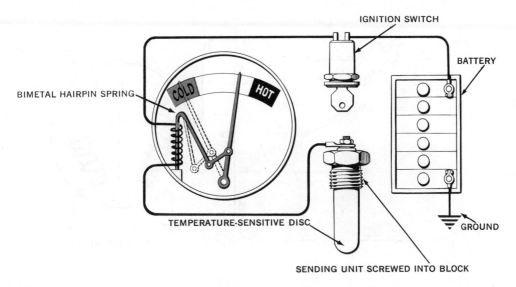

IGNITION SWITCH

BATTERY

BIMETAL HAIRPIN SPRING

COLD

HOT

TEMPERATURE-SENSITIVE DISC

GROUND

SENDING UNIT SCREWED INTO BLOCK

Bimetal type temperature indicator. When the coolant temperature is low, there is a high resistance at the disc in the sending unit; thus very little current reaches the bimetal hairpin spring. High coolant temperatures allow current flow to the bimetal, causing it to flex and move the needle indicator.

needle gives a comparative reading such as "full," "half-full" or "empty." Some do not give word indications but merely offer three small lines on the face of the gauge.

There are two types of systems used to make the gauge operate. Both depend on electrical current and both use a cork float in the tank as a sensing device.

Coil Type. The gauge here is almost identical to the one used for reading oil pressure. The difference lies in the design of the sending unit. Instead of having a diaphragm which responds to different oil pressures and causes a contact to slide along a variable resistor, this unit responds to a resistance set by the position of a float.

The float fits through an opening in the

top of the tank. It consists of a cork which is impregnated with a synthetic resin that seals its pores. Running from the cork is a stiff wire, usually about a foot long. The other end of the stiff wire goes into a small enclosed can, about the size and shape of a cupcake. Inside the can are a sliding contact and a resistor. An electrical wire is attached to the can and leads to the gauge. As mentioned, the dash unit is similar to the one used to show oil pressure.

When the tank is empty, the float is low. As a result, the sliding contact is at the lower end of the resistor. With the electrical wire at the upper end of the resistor bar, resistance in the circuit is at a maximum. As a result, the current which flows to the dash gauge will flow mainly through

253

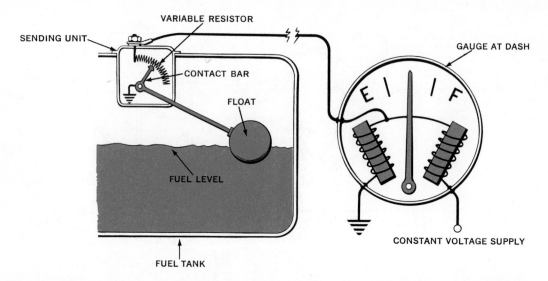

VARIABLE RESISTOR

SENDING UNIT

CONTACT BAR

FLOAT

FUEL LEVEL

FUEL TANK

GAUGE AT DASH

E | F

CONSTANT VOLTAGE SUPPLY

Electric coil-type fuel gauge. The position of the float in the fuel tank determines where the contact bar is located on the variable resistor. This determines how much current is allowed to the gauge on the dashboard. In turn, this determines which electromagnetic coil has the stronger field, influencing the shift of the needle.

the left-hand coil, the right-hand coil being a poor path since it has the resistance in the line. With the left-hand coil energized, there is a magnetic pull on the needle which swings it to the left, or "empty."

When the gas tank is full, the float rides high. As a result, the sliding contact is at the upper end, close to the electrical wire. Resistance in the circuit is now at a minimum. Current flowing to the gauge will flow from the left-hand coil to the right-hand coil and to the float unit for the ground. With the right-hand coil energized, the needle is pulled to the right to show "full."

When the tank is only half-full, current flows to both coils equally. Thus the needle is attracted equally to the right

and left and stays in the middle of the gauge, showing a half-full condition.

Bimetal Type. This design is somewhat simpler than that of the coil type. The float unit here is identical to the one for the coil type, but the receiving unit on the instrument panel is different. There are no coils used. Instead, the gauge has a thin strip shaped like a hairpin. This strip is made of two metals fused together. When it is heated a severe bending takes place as a result of the different rates of expansion of the metals. The hairpin is attached to the base of the indicating needle.

The wire from the tank unit leads to the bimetal strip and is wrapped around one leg of the hairpin. From there, the wire is attached to the ignition switch or to

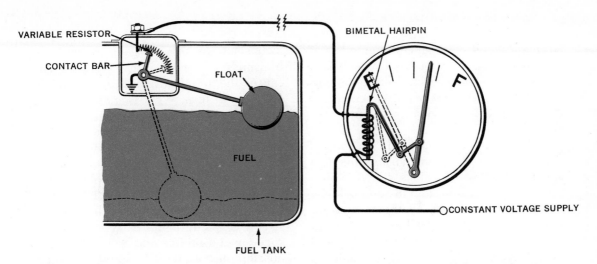

Bimetal-type fuel gauge. An empty fuel tank allows full flow of current to the bimetal hairpin, which flexes and pulls the needle toward "E." A full tank restricts current flow to the bimetal, pulling the needle to "F."

some other source of power.

When the tank is empty, the sliding contact is at the low end of the resistor bar. With a high resistance, voltage coming from the source cannot readily flow. As a result, the two ends of the hairpin are rather close together and the gauge reads all the way to the left—"empty."

When the tank is full, the sliding contact is at the high end of the resistor bar. This is a position of minimum resistance. Voltage flowing from the source entering the wire around the hairpin has some place to go to find a ground. The flow of electricity increases, heating up the hairpin. The heat affects the bimetal, and the legs of the hairpin spread apart. As a result, the needle shows a full tank.

SPEEDOMETER

The speedometer tells the driver the rate of speed traveled by the vehicle. The rate is measured in miles per hour (mph). Built into the speedometer is a special meter which records the total number of miles the car was driven. This gauge is called the odometer. In addition, certain cars are equipped with a trip odometer. This meter can be reset to zero at the beginning of every journey to determine the number of miles driven on a particular trip.

Speed itself? The face of the speedometer is usually rounded having numerals graduating upwards by fives or tens. A pointer is used as an indicator. On many cars the speedometer is a rectangular window with numbers and an indicator which appears to be a moving shaft, but is actually a rotating drum. We'll discuss this later.

To find out how fast the car is going, a reference point must be established. You might suggest referring to the speed of rear wheel or axle rotation. However, the rear wheels are much too far from the instrument panel. Though certain models of Oldsmobile cars use the front wheels as a take-off point, most cars today use the output shaft of the transmission—regardless of whether it is a manual or an automatic shift.

Slipped on and permanently attached to the output shaft of the transmission is a special gear which looks like a spiral ramp. This gear is located inside the housing on the same plane as the shaft, turning with it. Another small gear on a shaft is then placed in mesh with this spiral ramp gear at right angles to it. Called a pinion gear, it has a square hole in its

own shaft. As the car goes forward, the transmission output shaft turns. This causes the spiral gear and the small pinion gear to turn. What is most important is that the small square hole also turns.

These two gears at the transmission can be considered the "sending unit" for speed indication. Now the problem is to get this turning motion up to the speedometer gauge at the instrument panel. The answer is a flexible cable assembly. The unit consists of a casing which is screwed to the speedometer on one end and to the transmission on the other. Inside the casing is a small flexible cable which is made up

Dial-type speedometer. The cable is driven by a gear in the transmission and is attached to a permanent magnet behind the gauge. The whirling magnet creates a magnetic field. The speed cup creates an opposing field that is not strong enough to prevent the cup from turning. A delicate hairspring restrains the cup's turning and permits rotation that is directly proportional to the speed of the magnet. Since the cup is attached to the speed pointer, the pointer indicates car speed on the gauge.

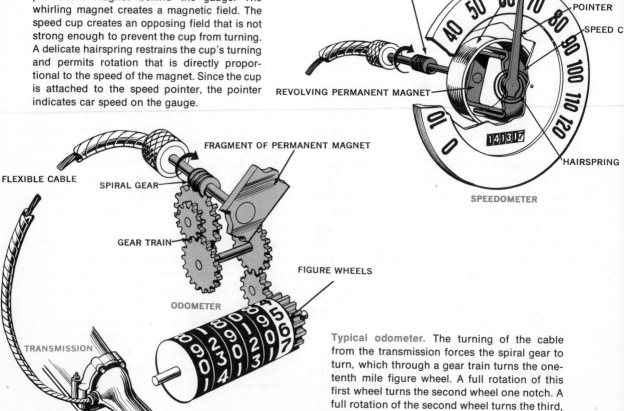

SPIRAL DRIVE FOR ODOMETER — FIELD PLATE — POINTER — SPEED C — REVOLVING PERMANENT MAGNET — HAIRSPRING

SPEEDOMETER

FLEXIBLE CABLE — SPIRAL GEAR — FRAGMENT OF PERMANENT MAGNET — GEAR TRAIN — FIGURE WHEELS — ODOMETER — TRANSMISSION

Typical odometer. The turning of the cable from the transmission forces the spiral gear to turn, which through a gear train turns the one-tenth mile figure wheel. A full rotation of this first wheel turns the second wheel one notch. A full rotation of the second wheel turns the third, and so on.

of many stiff wires tightly wound around each other. The cable is round but its ends are squared. One of the squares fits into the shaft of the small pinion gear at the transmission; the other end fits into a small square hole at the rear of the speedometer. Because the casing and the cable are flexible, the turning force is transmitted from one end to the other regardless of how many bends and turns are necessary to reach from the lower point to the upper. Oldsmobile cars have a similar setup from the right-front wheel to the instrument panel.

The speedometer itself works on a magnetic principle. Its basic parts are a revolving permanent magnet which is driven by the flexible shaft; a stationary field plate is situated around the permanent magnet. On some speedometers, the field plate revolves and the magnet is stationary. Between the magnet and the field plate is a moveable speed cup which gets its name from its shape. In the center of the cup is a small staff. On the end of this staff is the speedometer pointer. The magnet is situated inside the speed cup. As the action of the cable causes the magnet to revolve, a rotating magnetic field develops within the cup. The faster the rotation of the magnet, the stronger the field. The field sets up a magnetic pull or drag on the cup and causes the cup to rotate slightly in the same direction as the magnet. Movement of the cup is slightly retarded and held steady by a small hairspring attached to the staff of the speed cup. The speed cup (and the pointer) comes to rest at a point where the magnetic pull is just balanced by the retarding force created by the hairspring. Thus the speed is shown at the speedometer window by the position of the pointer.

When the car comes to a stop, the hairspring pulls the needle back to zero. There is no mechanical connection between the revolving magnet and the cup. The strength of the magnetic field is based strictly on the speed of rotation of the permanent magnet by the flexible shaft. The amount that the speed cup is pulled around is at all times proportional to the speed at which the magnet revolves. The one critical point is the ratios of the various gears. Engineers, in designing a speedometer system, translate the movements of the transmission shaft and the spiral gear, the pinion gear, the cable, the permanent magnet and the speed cup into the correct miles per hour of travel.

As we noted earlier, there are some speedometers that are rectangular, with an indicator which looks like a sliding shaft. In these cases, the movements of the permanent magnet are picked up by a long rotating drum, rather than by a speed cup. Painted on the black drum is a triangular wedge, usually a bright fluorescent color. As the magnet spins, it starts the drum turning in magnetic pull, in the same way that it turns the speed cup. In this case, however, the painted wedge slowly rotates and appears to be moving sideways as the drum turns. When car speed increases, the wedge appears to be moving from left to right; in deceleration, the wedge will appear to be moving from right to left. Many years ago cars had a "digital" speedometer system. That is, the face of the speedometer was a small window with a revolving numbered drum. As car speed varied, one number at a time showed in the window.

Odometer. This device consists of a series of five or six turning figure wheels which are geared to indicate the total distance travelled by the car.

Each of the small wheels is about the size of a round candy drop. They stand on edge and are linked to each other by gear teeth. The teeth are arranged in such a manner that it takes a full revolution of one wheel to make its neighbor to the left move one-tenth of a turn. Most odometers show a limit of 99,999 miles; after that all the figures show zero. Most odometers have a sixth wheel which indicates tenths of a mile.

The process of moving the figure wheels is complex, but the distances involved are much shorter than the action which moves the speedometer pointer. The starting point for odometer operation is the speedometer gauge itself. On the same shaft which holds the spinning permanent magnet is a small spiral gear, which is connected to the figure wheels by a series of spur gears. The final gear is linked only to the first figure wheel—none other.

This arrangement is an involved, but necessary one. The gear teeth are designed to produce a turning of the figure wheels which is equal to the distance covered by the vehicle itself. Remember, even if the car is driven at one mile per hour, the odometer will register mileage. While no speedometer will show one mph readily, the transmission shaft still turns at that speed, the flexible cable still turns, the permanent magnet still turns. Hence, the gears will turn and mileage will register.

Trip Odometer. Many cars are equipped with a *trip odometer* which can be set to zero at the beginning of a trip. It registers the number of miles driven until it is reset to zero again. Cars with this device

have the conventional odometer as well.

To make the trip odometer work, an additional gear is added to the gear train. This intermediate gear drives another row of figure wheels. However, this set has only three or four wheels. In addition, a small shaft is provided for the driver to reset the smaller assembly to zero. Therefore, the operation of the total-miles odometer is not disturbed. If the car has a total reading of 22,750 miles and the car travels 50 miles, the trip odometer will then read 50 while the total odometer will read 22,800.

TACHOMETER

The tachometer is an instrument which indicates the speed of the engine. Figures are given in revolutions per minute.

There are two basic types of tachometers—electrical and mechanical. As with the speedometer, a fixed point of reference is needed. Though the tachometer shows crankshaft rpm, it would be quite difficult to use the crankshaft itself as a means to activate the gauge. Far simpler is the use of a mechanism which reflects crankshaft rotation. The camshaft does this, but the difficulties of "tapping in" are just as formidable as with the crankshaft. The easiest method is to go to the distributor, which is affected by crank and camshaft movement. The fact that the distributor turns at one-half crankshaft speed is figured into the calibration of the gauge.

Mechanical Tachometer. The mechanical tachometer is not as popular as the electrical variety. But a fair number of foreign and race cars do have them. The setup is quite similar to that used to activate the speedometer. At the side of the distribu-

Tachometer and odometer.

tor is a threaded knurl. Inside is a small pinion gear in mesh with a spiral gear on the distributor shaft. Again there is a small square hole into which a flexible cable is fitted while the outside housing is screwed to the knurl.

The tachometer gauge is very much like the speedometer gauge. It has a permanent magnet, a speed cup, a needle and a hairspring. In operation, the distributor shaft rotates whenever the engine functions. Any motion of the shaft will turn the pinion gear and flexible cable. Thus, the magnet at the gauge will spin, and the speed cup will carry the needle around. The calibrated gauge will then indicate the number of revolutions made by the crankshaft per minute.

Electrical Tachometer. A much simpler design is the currently-popular electrical tachometer. Essentially, the instrument is a voltmeter with two small coils within it and some other modifications.

The sending unit, in this case, is the ignition contact set—the points. There is only one wire involved. This is attached to the electrical post at the side of the distributor. The wire is then fed to the tachometer which is grounded at the

instrument panel. This provides the basis for a complete circuit.

When the ignition is turned on, the system is ready to operate. If the instrument were an ordinary voltmeter, it would read zero when the points close and read all the way to the opposite side of the scale when the points open. If the meter is unmodified, the needle bounces from one side to the other when the engine is running. The modifications made to the meter drastically slow down this on-off situation and provide a steady voltage input to the gauge based on the speed at which the points open and close.

Modification is done with two wire coils, as used in the gasoline gauge. At low speeds, the magnetic action of the left-hand coil is greater, and the needle is attracted to the low end of the scale. As speed increases the right-hand coil acquires more energy and pulls the needle to the high end of the scale.

HORNS

It is interesting to note that the name "horn" is derived from the time when a musical horn was used to announce the arrival of a coach or to signal distress. We have come away from having to toot the horn whenever we arrive at a destination. Now, according to the laws of most states, the horn should be used only to warn of danger.

In the early days of the car, the driver was a very busy person. All of his hands and legs were moving to make sure the car did not stall, did not get too close to horses, did not end up in the ditch. It really would have been an imposition to place a wind instrument, say a trumpet, beside him and expect him to blow it to clear his path. To accommodate the driver, the squeeze-type horn was developed. This was a large brass trumpet with a rubber bulb at its end. When the driver squeezed the bulb, he forced air through the passageway that emitted a sound from the horn.

The first attempt to get away from this squeeze-type of horn was in 1905, when exhaust air pressure was used to operate the horn. In this case, the sound-making unit was screwed into an exhaust pipe, and a small valve opened the exhaust pressure into the unit. The valve was manually operated by the driver. These horns are still in use on fire-fighting vehicles. They are known for their loud, throaty sounds. The only drawback with the exhaust horn is that the engine must be operating to sound the horn.

The next advance in horns came in 1908 when the horns were connected to the engine through a small compressor which built up enough air pressure to operate the horn. Again, the drawback was that the engine had to be operating. In the 1920s the electric horn appeared on U.S. cars. Since that time there has been little change in horn operation.

The horn in use on an overwhelming majority of cars today is a vibrator-type. Its basic parts are the projector, a flared cylinder of metal which amplifies the sound; a back shell which is a small dome covering the operating mechanism; and the operating mechanism itself. This mechanism consists of a set of contact points, a small magnetic coil, a diaphragm and an adjusting nut. The wiring is such that the horn itself is not grounded. The "hot" wire does feed the small magnetic coil, but the circuit is grounded at the horn button on the steering wheel. So,

when the driver sounds the horn, he actually completes the circuit by grounding it.

The horn operates much like a common doorbell. That is, the operating mechanism is rigged in such a manner that the electrical circuit makes and breaks several times a second to cause the diaphragm to vibrate. The sequence of operation is like this:

When the horn is not in use, the contact points touch. The only reason electricity does not flow is that the total circuit lacks a ground. When the driver presses the horn button, he completes the circuit. This energizes the magnetic coil, which attracts the small metal diaphragm toward it. By going toward the coil, the diaphragm pulls the points open, breaking the circuit. Without electricity, the coil is no longer magnetic, and the diaphragm goes back to its original position. This action causes the points to close and starts the process all over again. Again, this happens several times a second. Every time the diaphragm makes a move, it also makes a small sound, which is amplified by the metal projector.

The note emitted by the horn is constant. To get a melodic sound, most cars use two horns. The only difference between the two is the length and shape of the projector. Generally, the horn that has a high-pitched sound has a short projector; a low-pitched horn has a long projector. Horns are adjustable by means of a special nut. However, the adjustment is for loudness and not for pitch.

FUSES AND CIRCUIT BREAKERS

A fuse is a protective device. Automotive fuses are no different. They are placed in a number of circuits to protect the appliances against overload. The automotive fuse is a glass cylinder with metal ends. Running through the cylinder is a wire of specified thickness. The wire is designed to melt at a predetermined temperature. The thickness of the wire depends on the capacity of the fuse. All fuses have a rating determined by the Society of Fuse Engineers (SFE). The number following the letters denotes the amps the fuse can safely tolerate. Fuses vary in size according to their rating. The fuse holders also vary in size. This is to foil any attempt to replace them with incorrect fuses.

It is important to understand that fuses are placed in the circuit in series. Should there be a short-circuit or an overload, the fuse will "blow."

Often certain circuits, such as for headlights, have a *circuit breaker.* This is a device with contact points on a bimetal arm. If an overload exists in the circuit, the bimetal strips heat and bend away from each other. With the points separated, the circuit is broken. In a few seconds, the bimetal strips cool and start bending toward each other. Momentarily, contact completes the circuit. However, if the abnormal condition still exists in the line, the heating effect will again cause the contacts to separate. Thus, some drivers have had the experience of driving at night with the headlights periodically going on and off, little realizing that the circuit breaker was trying to say that something in the circuit was amiss.

15
THE FUTURE

Probably no other consumer product in history has been the object of so many changes as the automobile. As soon as Unit One of the first production car was completed, engineers, designers and visionaries saw ways in which it could be modified. As cars were made better, more reliable, easier to drive, less costly to maintain, the compulsion for changes grew rather than diminished. Thus you may better appreciate our difficulty in trying to get sections of the composite car in this book to stand still long enough for us to examine them.

But now we are in a new phase. The car, once universally considered a blessing, is now the object of criticism by many and scorn by a few. Up until the 1970s so-called new mechanical improvements were not in a strict sense new. Power steering, automatic transmission and power brakes have been on the drawing boards and on the road since the early 1900s. Concepts in braking and in the use of gears for torque multiplication have been known for hundreds, if not thousands, of years. Essentially, whenever the new models were presented to us, the engineers were giving us up-to-date ways of solving old problems. Now, qualitatively different concepts are demanded because of changes in attitude toward the car. As an answer to the 55,000 highway deaths and 1.5 million injuries per year, the increased concern for our vanishing fresh air, the reluctance in giving up more of our countryside to the concrete ribbon, the strangulation of our urban arteries, and the continued need for private transportation, a totally new technology is at work. This concept attempts to reconcile all the positive aspects of having a car with the new concerns of society.

The answer to air pollution is sought not only in "cleaning" the basic internal combustion engine but also in new concepts of motive power. The answers to the accident question are sought not only through better driver training, but also in the use of sophisticated instrumentation, including radar and radio-controlled signals. The means for preventing injuries after the crash is sought not only in additional padding, but also in passive restraints which operate beyond the control of the driver and passenger.

It appears then that the concern for what the car is doing *to* our society in addition to the realization of what the car has done *for* our society is giving rise to some ultra-new technology. What the car will look like and what role it will play in twenty-five or one hundred years is not known. We can only speculate. However, there are some new and wonderful developments which have advanced past the drawing board. Before these developments become part of our ho-hum past, let's take a small dose of the future already perceived.

NO-FILL BATTERY

This battery is filled with electrolyte and water at the factory and is then sealed. After that it is unnecessary to add water during the battery's life. The advantage of such a design is that the battery can be located almost anywhere in the car, rather than restricted to the engine compartment. It may even return to a rack under the front seat.

The outside of the battery case has none of the familiar plastic filler caps; even the usual posts are missing on top. New type screw-on terminals are located on the side of the case for attaching the heavy cables. Inside, the lead grillwork is similar to that of the conventional battery. The big exception is that the lead paste has no antimony added to it. This element is used as a stiffener in a conventional battery. Instead calcium is used to support the lead paste. With calcium no electrolyte is lost through evaporation. Thus the unit never needs refilling. The No-Fill battery first appeared on Pontiac 1971 cars.

ANTI-SKID BRAKING SYSTEM

The function of this system is to control skidding by an automatic rapid pumping of the brakes during a panic stop. The pumping prevents wheel lockup by confining the friction to brake-drum-against-brake-shoe rather than to tire-against-road.

The system was first used by Chrysler on some of their 1970 vehicles. It consists of three components in addition to the

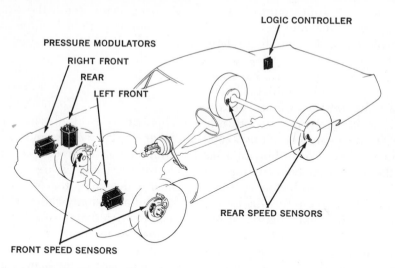

LOGIC CONTROLLER

PRESSURE MODULATORS

RIGHT FRONT

REAR

LEFT FRONT

REAR SPEED SENSORS

FRONT SPEED SENSORS

Anti-skid braking system by Chrysler. If any wheel spins faster than the others, the brakes will pulsate rapidly when the pedal is applied.

parts used in the normal braking system. *Sensors* measure the speed of each wheel. If all four wheels rotate at the same speed, the system remains inactive. A *control box* is actually a small computer which receives the readings from the sensors. The box is about the size of a cigar box and works on a logic system. Signals indicating a differential in wheel speed are sent to *modulators*. There are modulators on each car—one for both rear wheels and one for each front wheel. The modulator regulates the pressure between the master cylinder and the wheel cylinders. The modulator has been called a power brake in reverse since its job is to release the brakes in a rhythmic manner and thereby achieve a pumping effect. In certain situations, the brakes pump as often as six times per second.

AIRCONDITIONING: NO REFRIGERANT

The concept of providing cool air without the use of a refrigerant is contained in an invention of Thomas C. Edwards of Purdue University. The entire system consists of one moving part—a compressor which operates through spinning vanes, much like a paddle wheel. Also used is a heat exchanger, which is merely a network of tubing loops inside metal fins. Completing the system is the ductwork which carries the air to the passenger compartment. There is no refrigerant. There are no valves or blowers.

The heat exchange system operates on some very basic physical principles. As air is pulled in by the compressor vanes, it is highly compacted. As a result, it gets very hot. While under pressure the

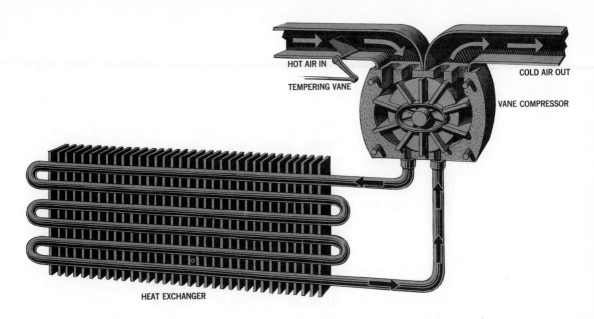

HOT AIR IN

TEMPERING VANE

COLD AIR OUT

VANE COMPRESSOR

HEAT EXCHANGER

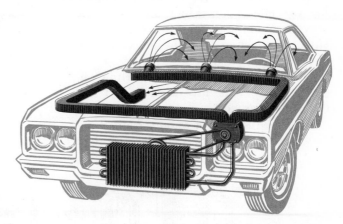

No-refrigerant airconditioner. This works with one moving apparatus, the compressor. Heat and pressure exchange produce cooling.

air flows to the heat exchanger, which is mounted in front of the radiator and resembles an airconditioning condenser. When the air leaves the exchanger it drops to about the same temperature as when it was first "captured." But the air is still under high pressure. Now the air is pulled to the discharge side of the compressor where it is then routed through the air ducts. Upon leaving the duct openings, the compacted air expands very rapidly. It is natural for expanding gases to absorb

heat. Thus this cools the passenger compartment. Though the device is not in production yet, it does hold the key to making the car's interior cooler in a more efficient and economical manner.

STIRLING-CYCLE STEAM ENGINE

Though this engine has been prominent on all recent lists of alternative power sources, it is by no means a new development. It was first conceived by a Scottish minister, Robert Stirling, around 1820. This engine has received renewed interest because it is one of the cleanest available.

Unlike the Otto-cycle engine found in today's cars, the Stirling engine thrives on external combustion. That is, consumption of the fuel takes place outside the chamber where the power impulses are born. Thus when a constant fire is going at a steady rate, pollutants are already drastically reduced. The Stirling engine is noiseless and vibration free. It has no carburetor since fuel is fed to a separate firebox. It has no valves since fuel is neither introduced nor removed from the piston area. It has no flywheel since the engine has two crankshafts which are turned by movement of the pistons. It has no muffler since combustion is silent and occurs in a separate chamber.

The principle behind the Stirling engine involves the use of expanded and contracted gas working on the pistons. The gas may be steam, or vapors from some exotic element. Each cylinder has two pistons, one above the other. Each cylinder also has a small pipe which runs from the top end of the cylinder to a point below the upper piston. When the lower

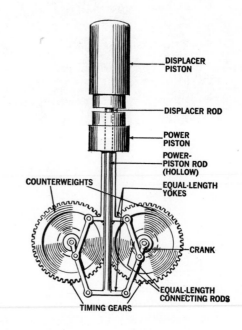

minister

DISPLACER PISTON
DISPLACER ROD
POWER PISTON
POWER-PISTON ROD (HOLLOW)
COUNTERWEIGHTS
EQUAL-LENGTH YOKES
CRANK
EQUAL-LENGTH CONNECTING RODS
TIMING GEARS

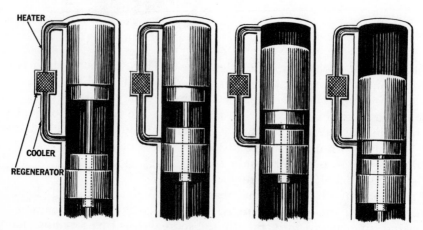

HEATER
COOLER
REGENERATOR

Four phases of Stirling-cycle steam engine. For details on operation, refer to the accompanying text.

piston, called the power piston, just completes a power stroke, it is in its lowest position in the cylinder. The upper piston, called the displacer is in its highest position in the cylinder. In the gap between the two pistons is a fixed volume of gas which is at a fairly low temperature. As the power piston starts to move upward some of the gas is forced into the small tube and is piped to the head of the displacer. There the gas is heated and, in expanding, forces the displacer downward. This forces more gas to the top of the displacer where it is heated and expanded. At a certain point the displacer blocks off the passageway to the small pipe, and whatever gas exists between the displacer and the power piston is trapped. As the displacer is forced further downward by the expanding gas, it pushes the power piston down to turn the crankshafts. The cycle then repeats. Note, there are no explosions driving the pistons. Rather, there is merely a fixed volume of gas which is heated and cooled.

A four-cylinder Stirling engine can pro-

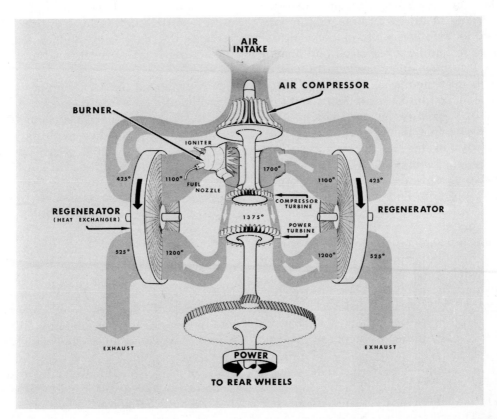

Diagram of Chrysler's twin regenerator gas turbine engine. Incoming air is compressed and then heated by the regenerator. With fuel supplied by the nozzle, the air is heated to 1,700 degrees. The hot gases pass through the compressor turbine and the power turbine, giving energy to the rear wheels. Heat recovered from the exhaust is used to heat more incoming air.

duce two-hundred horsepower with only fifty-seven cubic inches of displacement. It is efficient and does not pollute. Further refinements and then mass production seem likely.

GAS TURBINE ENGINE

The turbine is simply a spinning wheel which delivers energy. The problem is to get the wheel spinning through the use of some other form of energy. The turbo-generators at Niagara Falls use the force of falling water that spins wheels to create electricity. The gas turbine engine proposed for automotive use employs air that has been highly compressed and heated.

In a turbine engine combustion is internal, occurring as a constant "flame." Air is sucked into a compressor and then sent to a heat exchanger, which solves two problems at once. It warms incoming air by use of the hot exhaust gases which are piped through it, and it cools the exhaust gases before they are discharged. Both temperature inversions are necessary for a well-functioning engine. After the incoming air is warmed it is shipped to a combustion chamber where it is mixed with fuel and burned. The expanding gases are forced through small openings which are aimed at the blades of two turbines. After giving the blades a push, the gases are sent through the heat exchanger to cool and then they pass out the exhaust. One of the turbines drives the compressor and the engine accessories. The second turbine drives the output shaft.

This engine deals with large amounts of heat. Thus there have been some slow-downs in development owing to the search for suitable metals or ceramics for the turbine blades. However, advances are far enough along for us to assume that turbine engines will soon appear on trucks and buses, and on cars thereafter.

PROPANE GAS ENGINE

This is definitely not new. Many small engines have used propane gas for years. But the application of this gas to automotive power plants is new. There are no major modifications required for converting a gasoline engine to propane, called Liquid Petroleum Gas or LPG. Besides the plumbing from the tank bottles, the most important unit is the converter which reduces the very high tank pressure to low tolerable pressures the carburetor can handle.

Advantages of the LPG engine include a pollutant-free exhaust, longer oil life, longer spark plug life. Disadvantages are the many laws which bar the filling of propane tanks in populated areas; laws forbidding vehicles with bottled gas to pass through tunnels; and the large car storage space required to carry enough LPG for mileage equal to that from a full tank of gasoline.

OTHER ENGINES

In the search for alternative power sources, a number of inventors have developed totally new ideas. One inventor, Wallace Minto, developed an engine which runs on the refrigerant Freon. It uses the principle of expansion to drive the pistons. Another inventor team, Lindley Manning and Richard Schneider, are studying the use of liquid nitrogen as a fuel for an engine which emits only nitrogen gas as an exhaust. Though the liquid nitrogen will have to be stored in the vehicle at

5,500 psi, there is no danger of explosion because nitrogen is an inert gas.

When research people really get going on an idea, there is no way of knowing where it will lead them. Constantinos Vlachos of Grand Coulee, Washington, claims he has invented an engineless-automobile. The vehicle operates on liquid fluorocarbon which is used to drive a pump at each wheel. The liquid is vaporized by battery electricity, and the high pressure gas is applied to the pumps. After the gas leaves the pump, it is condensed to a liquid and returned to a reservoir to await vaporization again. Not only does the car lack an engine; it has no bearings, no differential, no radiator, no gears—not even brakes. The car stops by a reversing of the pump vanes.

Another weird development is by Sony of Japan. They use a zinc-air fuel battery system. Though the car is electric, it does not have to be recharged periodically. Electricity is generated by a continuous feeding of zinc fuel and electrolyte. The fuel must be replenished. However, the car is claimed to have all the advantages of an electric vehicle, in that it is free of pollution and noise; yet it does not need lengthy battery charges.

Electric vehicles are, by far, the most promising of the new developments in automotive power. As it stands now, the state of the art limits electric vehicles to local, low-speed operation. But since such operation is typical in crowded city driving, cities with poor air quality need such vehicles.

Right now, the biggest problem to overcome is the present lead-acid battery, which is heavy, bulky and has a limited life. To equal the energy stored in a 20-gallon tank of gasoline, the lead-acid battery system for one car would weigh 15,000 pounds, according to one engineer at GM. One of the key steps in using electric energy for vehicles is to get away from the present design of cars, and build a vehicle specifically for the battery propulsion system. Tires must be small diameter for minimum inertia and very narrow for minimum rolling resistance. All body and chassis parts must be light, with increased use of plastic and aluminum. In low-speed vehicles the attention to rolling resistance is more important than to aerodynamic drag. Already Fiat has a car, the X1/23, which weighs 1760 pounds and has a 40 mph top speed and a range of 65 miles.

Engineers feel that the electric car need not wait for new breakthroughs in battery technology before they can utilize the electric car. However, immediate production will be limited to cars with low-range operation. For longer range, a newer concept of batteries, such as the zinc-air type will have to be employed.

ROTARY HEAT EXCHANGER

Can you picture a car without a radiator and cooling fan? According to the engineers at Purdue University in Indiana and at the Donbar Development Corporation in New York, it is possible to keep the engine coolant at the proper operating temperature while doing away with the traditional cooling system components.

The method employs a rotary heat exchanger. This is a fancy name for a rather simple device which resembles a squirrel-cage type of blower. But instead of flat blades, the blades are hollow. The cage is attached to a belt and is driven by the engine crankshaft. Coolant flows through the hollow blades, and the heat is rapidly transferred to the outside air as the blades

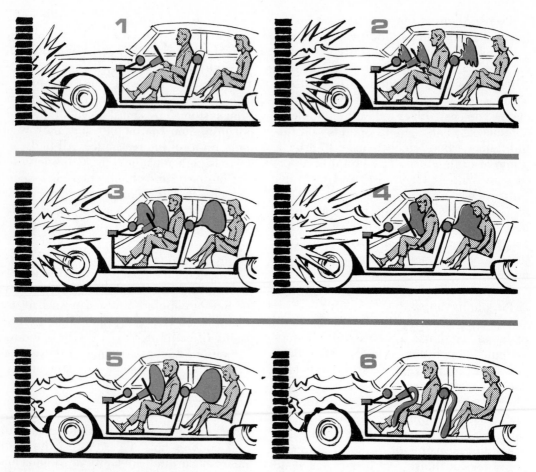

Sequence of operation for protective air bags. The bag inflates in 1/25 of a second after impact. Deflation is necessary to prevent suffocation of the car's occupants.

spin. When the fluid has traveled the length of the tube, it is reintroduced into the circulation system to pick up more heat. Heat exchangers will soon be seen as replacements for radiators and airconditioning condensers.

SAFETY SYSTEMS

In addition to the strictly mechanical improvements, new innovations have made the car's interior safer. The ultimate, for now, is the development of the Experimental Safety Vehicle (ESV). This is a vehicle which a number of car companies are experimenting with and must be built according to strict specifications of the U.S. Department of Transportation.

It must have an energy-absorbing frame and bumpers which will soak up much of the shock of a collision. Visibility must be improved for the driver, and the interior

REINFORCING
MEMBERS

BUMPERS

VOLUTE SPRINGS

An energy-absorbing bumper system. The bumper is made of high-integrity steel mounted on strong reinforcing members. Shock of impact is absorbed by the two springs which are spiral and operate in a rotary manner. These are known as volute springs.

must be built to protect the car's occupants during a 50-mph crash into a solid wall. The seats are fixed with adjustments made directly from the floor pedals. So far only a few of these prototypes have been built. However, starting in 1976 advanced safety features will be required on production cars.

The controversial *air bag* restraint system consists of a large plastic sack which is placed under the dashboard for the front passenger and in the hub of the steering wheel for the driver. The bags are con-

nected to tanks of inert gas. In the event of a crash of predetermined severity, a small percussion cap goes off, and the bag inflates. The bag fills up in $1/25$ of a *second*. This is faster than the car's occupants would be pitched forward against the dash or against the wheel. The bag interposes itself between the people and the dashboard and provides a cushion. After the bag is fully inflated, it starts to deflate under the pressure of the occupant's body.

Much of the opposition to the air bag is directed at the noise of the percussion caps going off in an enclosed car. In addition, some people are afraid that a mild collision or a bump may accidentally set off unnecessary inflation, much to the surprise of the driver.

In addition to the air bag and much more padding than we are accustomed to, the future will bring to cars the rear view mirror which enables drivers to see the total area behind them via a periscope going through the car roof.

Periscopic rear view mirror. This offers a greater field of view than the conventional mirror does and eliminates blind spots.

Dual-mode vehicles are for driver operation in the cities and can be switched to safe and effortless automatic operation on highways.

CHANGED TRANSPORTATION PROCESSES

In addition to the changes anticipated in the cars themselves, we can also expect different concepts in the transportation processes.

The typical city today has one or two major highways running through it, a bus line or two from the city's center to its edges, taxicabs working the shopping and commercial areas, an abundance of parking lots and traffic meters for private autos. As everyone knows, the normal city transportation systems are fraught with problems. The choking of streets and the inefficient transfer of people are but two of a long list of ills. To help solve some of these problems, a number of new concepts are being developed. Noteworthy are three which come from the Ford Motor Company.

Dial-A-Ride. This system offers door-to-door semiprivate transportation, using small buses dispatched by a computerized control center. A person needing a ride downtown calls the center and states his location and destination. The computer instantly determines which unit of a fleet of vehicles cruising the city can best fill that request. Then the driver of the correct unit is dispatched by radio to pick up the customer.

Activity Center Transportation. To solve the congestion problem in high density areas, small electric vehicles will operate driverless on a network of elevated guideways. People will get on and off at designated stops. Destinations will be selected from a button panel. Speeds of the small vehicles will reach thirty mph.

Dual Mode Vehicles. These cars will operate in a conventional manner on streets and highways. For longer trips, the cars will be automatically controlled by a computerized system, running on special guideways created along existing freeways. When the car leaves the guideway, the driver resumes full control.

These are but a few of the technological advances in store. Of course, there are more—either already proven, on the drawing boards or in the visions of creative people.

It is almost impossible to keep current on developments in the automotive field. And since we will always seek solutions to the pressing problems of getting from one place to another quickly, safely, and comfortably, we can probably count on continued developments, thick and fast, for decades to come.

INDEX